Student Solutions Manual
and Study Guide
to Accompany

Understanding Elementary Algebra

by
Arthur Goodman
and
Lewis Hirsch

Prepared by
Steven Kahan
Queens College
Flushing, New York

West Publishing Company
St. Paul   New York   Los Angeles   San Francisco

CONTENTS

PREFACE

This Student Solutions Manual and Study Guide is meant to afford you, the student, with an opportunity to see complete solutions to many of the exercises in the text. You'll find two more chapter tests for each chapter, one cumulative problem section and one cumulative review test for every three chapters, and a sample final exam. The answers to all of these supplementary questions appear in a separate section in the back of this book. Finally, an important element in the Student Solutions Manual and Study Guide is a complete set of answers for the Questions for Thought that are contained in the text. It is perfectly acceptable to answer these questions in your own words, as long as the true meaning of your response is in close agreement with what is presented here.

Of course, you should attempt to solve all the problems in the text on your own before seeking the help found in this book. All of its material is meant to emphasize the theme of your textbook: <u>understanding</u> algebra can only come from <u>doing</u> algebra, which means working out lots and lots of problems.

Chapter 1

THE INTEGERS

1.   True

3.   True

5.   True

7.   True

9.   True

11. $\{1,2,3,4,5,6,7\}$

13. $\{0,2,4,6,8,10,12,14,16,18\}$

15. $\{0,1,2,3,4,5,6\}$

17. $\{0,1,2,3,4,5\}$

19. $\{6,7,8,9,\ldots\}$

21. $\{7,8,9,10,\ldots\}$

23. $\{3,4,5\}$

25. $\{0,4,8,12,\ldots\}$

27. {0,12,24,36,...}

29. ∅

31. >

33. =

35. >

37. =

39. =

41. <, ≤, ≠

43. ≤, ≥, =

45. >, ≥, ≠

47. <, ≤, ≠

49. >, ≥, ≠

51. 2 · 7

53. 3 · 11

55. 2 · 3 · 5

57. Prime

59. 2 · 2 · 2 · 2 · 2 · 2

61. 2 · 2 · 2 · 2 · 2 · 3

63. 3 · 29

65. W contains the number 0; N does not.

66. In a sum, the numbers to be added are called terms; in a product, the numbers to be multiplied are called factors. In 2 + 5, 2 is a term; in 2 · 5, 2 is a factor.

67. A factor of n is a number which divides exactly into n; a multiple of n is a number which is exactly divisible by n. 3 is a factor of 12; 12 is a multiple of 3.

68. C is the set containing the first three multiples of 6.

69. C is the set containing the first three multiples of 12.

Exercises 1.2

 1. True (commutative law of addition)

 3. True (commutative law of addition)

 5. False

 7. False

 9. True (commutative law of multiplication)

11. True (commutative law of multiplication)

13. False

15. True (associative law of addition)

17. True (associative law of addition)

19. True (associative law of multiplication)

21. True (associative law of multiplication)

23. False

25. False

27. Associative law of addition

29. Associative law of multiplication

31. Commutative law of addition, followed by associative law of addition.

33. Commutative law of multiplication, followed by associative law of multiplication.

35. -4

37. +4

39. 4

41. 4

43. -4

45. -4

47. 5

49. 5

51. $7 + 3 \cdot 4 = 7 + 12 = 19$

53. $15 - 5 \cdot 3 = 15 - 15 = 0$

55. $6 + 4(3 + 2) = 6 + 4 \cdot 5 = 6 + 20 = 26$

57. $6 + (4 \cdot 3 + 2) = 6 + (12 + 2) = 6 + 14 = 20$

59. $6 + (4 \cdot 3) + 2 = 6 + 12 + 2 = 20$

61. $(6 + 4)(3 + 2) = 10 \cdot 5 = 50$

63. $\dfrac{15 + 2 \cdot 3}{3 + 2 \cdot 2} = \dfrac{15 + 6}{3 + 4} = \dfrac{21}{7} = 3$

65. $3 + 2[3 + 2(3 + 2)] = 3 + 2[3 + 2 \cdot 5] = 3 + 2[3 + 10]$
     $= 3 + 2 \cdot 13 = 3 + 26 = 29$

67. $9 - 4[6 - 2(3 - 1)] = 9 - 4[6 - 2 \cdot 2] = 9 - 4[6 - 4]$
     $= 9 - 4 \cdot 2 = 9 - 8 = 1$

69. $4 + [3 + 5[2 + 2(3 + 1)]] = 4 + [3 + 5[2 + 2 \cdot 4]]$
     $= 4 + [3 + 5[2 + 8]] = 4 + [3 + 5 \cdot 10]$
     $= 4 + [3 + 50] = 4 + 53 = 57$

71. $\dfrac{10 + 2(5 + 3)}{2 \cdot 5 + 3} = \dfrac{10 + 2 \cdot 8}{10 + 3} = \dfrac{10 + 16}{10 + 3}$
     $= \dfrac{26}{13} = 2$

Exercises 1.3

1. $+5 + (-7) = -(7 - 5) = -2$

3. $-9 + (-3) = -(9 + 3) = -12$

5. $-4 + (+11) = +(11 - 4) = +7$

7. $+8 + (-3) = +(8 - 3) = +5$

9. $+6 + (-2) = +(6 - 2) = +4$

11. $-6 + (-2) = -(6 + 2) = -8$

13. $-6 + (+2) = -(6 - 2) = -4$

15. $+6 + (+2) = 6 + 2 = 8$

17. $-7 + (-8) = -(7 + 8) = -15$

19. $10 + (-14) = -(14 - 10) = -4$

21. $8 + (-8) = 0$

23. $9 + (-16) = -(16 - 9) = -7$

25. $-30 + (-14) = -(30 + 14) = -44$

27. $-6 + 12 = +(12 - 6) = +6$

29. $-5 + (-4) + (-6) = -(5 + 4) + (-6)$
$$= -9 + (-6) = -(9 + 6) = -15$$

31. $5 + (-4) + (-6) = +(5 - 4) + (-6)$
$$= +1 + (-6) = -(6 - 1) = -5$$

33. $-5 + 4 + (-6) = -(5 - 4) + (-6)$
$$= -1 + (-6) = -(1 + 6) = -7$$

35. $-5 + (-4) + 6 = -(5 + 4) + 6$
$$= -9 + 6 = -(9 - 6) = -3$$

37. $16 + (-5) + (-7) + 2 = +(16 - 5) + (-7) + 2$
$$= +11 + (-7) + 2$$
$$= +(11 - 7) + 2$$
$$= +4 + 2$$
$$= 6$$

39. $-8 + 6 + (-5) + 1 = -(8 - 6) + (-5) + 1$
$$= -2 + (-5) + 1$$
$$= -(2 + 5) + 1$$
$$= -7 + 1$$
$$= -(7 - 1) = -6$$

41. $2 + (-9) + (-3) + (-1) + 6 = -(9 - 2) + (-3) + (-1) + 6$
$$= -7 + (-3) + (-1) + 6$$
$$= -(7 + 3) + (-1) + 6$$
$$= -10 + (-1) + 6$$
$$= -(10 + 1) + 6$$
$$= -11 + 6$$
$$= -(11 - 6) = -5$$

43. $27 + (-56) = -(56 - 27) = -29$

45. $-22 + (-45) = -(22 + 45) = -67$

47. $-31 + (-26) + 48 = -(31 + 26) + 48$
$$= -57 + 48$$
$$= -(57 - 48) = -9$$

49. $-5 + 7 + (-3) = -5 + +(7 - 3)$
$$= -5 + (+4)$$
$$= -(5 - 4) = -1$$

51. $-3 + 5 \cdot 2 + (-6) = -3 + 10 + (-6)$
$$= +(10 - 3) + (-6)$$
$$= +7 + (-6)$$
$$= +(7 - 6) = +1$$

53. $|2 + (-6)| + |2| + |-6| = |-(6 - 2)| + |2| + |-6|$
$$= |-4| + |2| + |-6|$$
$$= 4 + 2 + 6 = 12$$

55. $|-7| + (-7) = 7 + (-7) = 0$

57. $+48 + [(-18) + (-22) + (-15)] + (+50) + [(-28) + (-12)]$
$$+ (+20) + (-17) + (+27)$$
$$= +48 + (-55) + (+50) + (-40) + (+20) + (-17) + (+27)$$
$$= +33$$
So the final balance in Carla's checking account is $33.

59. $+25 + (+8) + (-14) + (-5) = +(25 + 8) + (-14) + (-5)$
$$= +33 + (-14) + (-5)$$
$$= +(33 - 14) + (-5)$$
$$= +19 + (-5)$$
$$= +(19 - 5) = +14$$

So on fourth down, the team is located on its own 14 yard line.

61. When we add an integer to its opposite, we get 0 as our result. This occurs because an integer and its opposite have the same absolute value.

62. If the sum of two integers is zero, the integers must be opposites. In all other cases, the sum of the integers would either be positive or negative.

63. $4 - 7 = -3$, because $-3 + 7 = 4$

64. $4 - (-7) = 11$, because $11 + (-7) = 4$

Exercises 1.4

1. $6 - (+10) = 6 + (-10) = -4$

3. $-7 - (+4) = -7 + (-4) = -11$

5. $3 - (-6) = 3 + (+6) = 9$

7. $-8 - (-2) = -8 + (+2) = -6$

9. $-5 + (+8) = 3$

11. $5 - (+8) = 5 + (-8) = -3$

13. $5 - (-8) = 5 + (+8) = 13$

15. $-5 - (+8) = -5 + (-8) = -13$

17. $-5 - (-8) = -5 + (+8) = 3$

19. $5 + (-8) = -3$

21. $-5 + (-8) = -13$

23. $6 - (-7) = 6 + (+7) = 13$

25. $-6 - (-7) = -6 + (+7) = 1$

27. $2 + (-6) - (+7) = 2 + (-6) + (-7) = -4 + (-7) = -11$

29. $2 - 6 - 7 = 2 + (-6) + (-7) = -4 + (-7) = -11$

31. $2 - (6 - 7) = 2 - (-1) = 2 + (+1) = 3$

33. $7 - 9 - 3 + 2 = 7 + (-9) + (-3) + 2 = -2 + (-3) + 2$
$$= -5 + 2 = -3$$

35. $11 - 5 + 4 - 7 = 11 + (-5) + 4 + (-7) = 6 + 4 + (-7)$
$$= 10 + (-7) = 3$$

37. $4 - 8 - 6 + 3 = 4 + (-8) + (-6) + 3 = -4 + (-6) + 3$
$$= -10 + 3 = -7$$

39. $4 - 8 - (6 + 3) = 4 - 8 - 9 = 4 + (-8) + (-9) = -4 + (-9) = -13$

41. $4 - (8 - 6) + 3 = 4 - 2 + 3 = 4 + (-2) + 3 = 2 + 3 = 5$

43. $4 - (8 - 6 + 3) = 4 - (8 + (-6) + 3) = 4 - (2 + 3)$
$$= 4 - 5 = 4 + (-5) = -1$$

45. $-8 + 8 = 0$

47. $-8 - 8 = -8 + (-8) = -16$

49. $-8 - (-8) = -8 + (+8) = 0$

51. $9 - 5 \cdot 4 - 2 = 9 - 20 - 2 = 9 + (-20) + (-2)$
$$= -11 + (-2) = -13$$

53. $9 - 5(4 - 2) = 9 - 5 \cdot 2 = 9 - 10$
$$= 9 + (-10) = -1$$

55. $9 - (5 \cdot 4 - 2) = 9 - (20 - 2) = 9 - 18$
$$= 9 + (-18) = -9$$

57. $|6 - 2| - |2 - 6| = |4| - |-4| = 4 - 4 = 0$

59. $|2 - 6| - (2 - 6) = |-4| - (-4) = 4 - (-4)$
$$= 4 + (+4)$$
$$= 8$$

61. |-4 - 3 + 2| -4 - 3 + 2 = |-4 + (-3) + 2| + (-4) + (-3) + 2
$$= |-7 + 2| + (-4) + (-3) + 2$$
$$= |-5| + (-4) + (-3) + 2$$
$$= 5 + (-4) + (-3) + 2$$
$$= 1 + (-3) + 2$$
$$= -2 + 2 = 0$$

63. The left side is equal to 4, while the right side is equal to -4. In general, the absolute value of a difference of two integers is not the same as the difference of the absolute values of those integers.

64. 4 times -3 should mean "add -3 four times," giving (-3) + (-3) + (-3) + (-3) = -12.

65. We can interpret -4 times 3 to mean "subtract 3 four times," giving -3 - 3 - 3 - 3 = -12. Similarly, we can interpret -4 times -3 to mean "subtract -3 four times," giving -(-3) - (-3) - (-3) - (-3) = +3 + 3 + 3 + 3 = +12.

Exercises 1.5

1. $(+5)(-3) = -(5 \cdot 3) = -15$

3. $(-5)(+3) = -(5 \cdot 3) = -15$

5. $(-5)(-3) = +(5 \cdot 3) = 15$

7. $-5 - 3 = -8$

9. $-(5 - 3) = -2$

11. $\frac{20}{-5} = -(\frac{20}{5}) = -4$

13. $\frac{-20}{5} = -(\frac{20}{5}) = -4$

15. $\frac{-20}{-5} = +(\frac{20}{5}) = 4$

17. $\frac{0}{7} = 0$

19. No answer (division by 0 is not allowed)

21. $4(-2) - 6 = -8 - 6 = -14$

23. $4 - 2 - 6 = 2 - 6 = -4$

25. $4 - (2 - 6) = 4 - (-4) = 8$

27. $4(-2 - 6) = 4(-8) = -32$

29. $-6(2)(-5)(-1) = -12(-5)(-1) = 60(-1) = -60$

31. $9 - 3(1 - 3) = 9 - 3(-2) = 9 + 6 = 15$

33. $8 - 3(2 - 5) = 8 - 3(-3) = 8 + 9 = 17$

35. $8 - 3 \cdot 2 - 5 = 8 - 6 - 5 = 2 - 5 = -3$

37. $8 - (3 \cdot 2 - 5) = 8 - (6 - 5) = 8 - 1 = 7$

39. $(8 - 3)(2 - 5) = (5)(-3) = -15$

41. $\dfrac{-12 - 3 + 1}{-7} = \dfrac{-15 + 1}{-7} = \dfrac{-14}{-7} = 2$

43. $\dfrac{-8 - 2 - 4}{-2} = \dfrac{-10 - 4}{-2} = \dfrac{-14}{-2} = 7$

45. $\dfrac{-8 - (2 - 4)}{-2} = \dfrac{-8 - (-2)}{-2} = \dfrac{-8 + 2}{-2} = \dfrac{-6}{-2} = 3$

47. $\dfrac{-8 - 2(-4)}{-2} = \dfrac{-8 + 8}{-2} = \dfrac{0}{-2} = 0$

49. $\dfrac{-4(-5)(-4)}{-4(-5) - 4} = \dfrac{20(-4)}{20 - 4} = \dfrac{-80}{16} = -5$

51. $\dfrac{3(-2) - 4}{-4 - 1} = \dfrac{-6 - 4}{-4 - 1} = \dfrac{-10}{-5} = 2$

53. $\dfrac{6 - 4}{4 - 4} = \dfrac{2}{0}$, which has no answer, since division by 0 is not allowed.

55. $-6[-3 - 2(5 - 3)] = -6[-3 - 2 \cdot 2] = -6[-3 - 4] = -6(-7) = 42$

57. $5 - 2[3 - (4 + 6)] = 5 - 2[3 - 10] = 5 - 2(-7) = 5 + 14 = 19$

59. $5 - \dfrac{3 - 5}{-2} = 5 - \dfrac{-2}{-2} = 5 - 1 = 4$

61. $6 - \dfrac{8 - 2(-3)}{-7} = 6 - \dfrac{8 + 6}{-7} = 6 - \dfrac{14}{-7}$

$$= 6 - (-2) = 6 + 2 = 8$$

63. Even though the symbols are the same in both examples, the parentheses lead to different results. Without the parentheses, we have a subtraction example: 5 - 2 = 3; with the parentheses, we have a multiplication example: 5(-2) = -10.

64. Again, the same symbols are used in both examples, but the location of the parentheses causes the difference this time. Our order of operations requires that we multiply before we subtract. Therefore, 6(-3) - 2 = -18 - 2 = -20, while 6 - 3(-2) = 6 + 6 = 12.

65. When we see -7 - 8, it must be interpreted as a subtraction, since no parentheses are present. Therefore, (a) and (b) are both wrong, since -7 - 8 = -15. (It would be correct to write -7(-8) = +56 or (-7)(-8) = +56.) Part (c) is wrong also. Since 2 - 4 = -2, it follows that -3 - (2 - 4) = -3 - (-2) = -3 + 2 = -1. In part (d), the order of operations has not been followed. Here, -4 - 2(5 - 6) = -4 - 2(-1) = -4 + 2 = -2. (-4 - 2 = -6 never legitimately enters into the calculation.)

66. The statement "two negatives make a positive" is accurate for multiplication and division but not for addition and subtraction. For instance, (-3) + (-2) = -5 and (-3) - (-2) = -1, and neither of these answers is positive.

Exercises 1.6

1. 4.2 + 5.9 = 10.1

3. 4(5.1) = 20.4

5. $\dfrac{12.8}{3.2} = 4$

7. $\dfrac{36.8}{1.5} = 24.533\overline{3}\ldots$

9. $\dfrac{8}{.2} + \dfrac{12}{.4} = 40 + 30 = 70$

11. -2 - 5.3 = -7.3

13. -2(5.3) = -10.6

15. -2(-5.3) = 10.6

17. $\dfrac{-8.4}{1.2} = -7$

19. $\dfrac{-6}{1.5} + \dfrac{21.6}{-1.2} = -4 - 18 = -22$

21. Between 4 and 5

23. Between 2 and 3

25. Between 7 and 8

27.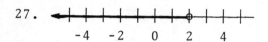

29.

31.

33.

35.

37. (a) Use the cummutative law of addition to rewrite the problem as 12.9 - 1.7 - 8.3.   Then this equals 12.9 - 10 = 2.9.

(b) Use the commutative law of multiplication to rewrite the problem as 7(10)(-2.3).   Then this becomes 7(-23) = -161.

(c) Use the associative law of multiplication to rewrite the problem as $-10\left(\dfrac{3.2}{-1.6}\right)$. Then this equals -10(-2) = 20.

(d) First, use the commutative law of multiplication to rewrite the problem as $-30(-10)\left(\dfrac{1.6}{3}\right)$, which becomes $300\left(\dfrac{1.6}{3}\right)$.   Then use the associative law of multiplication to write this as $\dfrac{300}{3}(1.6) = 100(1.6) = 160.$

38. Since (1)(1) = 1 and (2)(2) = 4, the square root of 3, to the nearest whole number, is 2.

Since (1.7)(1.7) = 2.89 and (1.8)(1.8) = 3.24, the square root of 3, to the nearest tenth, is 1.7.

Since (1.73)(1.73) = 2.9929 and (1.74)(1.74) = 30.276, the square root of 3, to the nearest hundredth, is 1.73.

Since (1.732)(1.732) = 2.999824 and (1.7333)(1.7333) = 3.003289, the square root of 3, to the nearest thousandth, is 1.732.

Chapter 1 Review Exercises

1. {2,4,6,8,10,12,14,16,18}

3. {2,3,5,7,11,13,17,19}

5. {23,29}

7. 2 · 3 · 5

9. Prime

11. 2 · 2 · 5 · 5

13. 3 - 7 = -4

15. -7 - 5 = -12

17. -2 - (-6) = -2 + 6 = 4

19. -4 - 5 - 6 = -9 - 6 = -15

21. -7 + 12 - 5 = +5 - 5 = 0

23. 7 - 4 + 3 - 9 = 3 + 3 - 9 = 6 - 9 = -3

25. 8 - 5 - 6 = 3 - 6 = -3

27. 8 - (5 - 6) = 8 - (-1) = 8 + 1 = 9

29. 8(5 - 6) = 8(-1) = -8

31. $8 - 3 - 6 = 5 - 6 = -1$

33. $8 - 3(-6) = 8 + 18 = 26$

35. $8 - (3 - 6) = 8 - (-3) = 8 + 3 = 11$

37. $8(-3)(-6) = -24(-6) = 144$

39. $9 - 4(3 - 7) = 9 - 4(-4) = 9 + 16 = 25$

41. $9 - 4 \cdot 3 - 7 = 9 - 12 - 7 = -3 - 7 = -10$

43. $9 - (4 \cdot 3 - 7) = 9 - (12 - 7) = 9 - 5 = 4$

45. $(9 - 4)(3 - 7) = 5(-4) = -20$

47. $|4 - 9| - |3 - 7| = |-5| - |-4| = 5 - 4 = 1$

49. $\dfrac{-7 - 3}{-2(-5)} = \dfrac{-10}{+10} = -1$

51. $\dfrac{-4(-2)(-8)}{-4(2) - 8} = \dfrac{8(-8)}{-8 - 8} = \dfrac{-64}{-16} = 4$

53. $\dfrac{6 - 4(3 - 1)}{-2(-3) - 4} = \dfrac{6 - 4(2)}{6 - 4} = \dfrac{6 - 8}{6 - 4} = \dfrac{-2}{2} = -1$

55. $8 + 2[3 - 4(1 - 6)] = 8 + 2[3 - 4(-5)]$
$$= 8 + 2[3 + 20]$$
$$= 8 + 2(23)$$
$$= 8 + 46 = 54$$

Chapter 1 Practice Test

1. (a) True
    (b) False
    (c) False
    (d) True (both have eight elements)
    (e) $C = \emptyset$

3. $|3 - 8| - |1 - 6| = |-5| - |-5| = 5 - 5 = 0$

5. $\dfrac{5(-4)(-3)}{1 - 7} = \dfrac{(-20)(-3)}{1 - 7} = \dfrac{+60}{1 - 7} = \dfrac{+60}{-6} = -10$

7. $8 - 5(4 - 7) = 8 - 5(-3) = 8 - (-15) = 8 + 15 = 23$

9. $-7[5 + 4(3 - 7) - 2] = -7[5 + 4(-4) - 2]$
    $= -7[5 - 16 - 2]$
    $= -7[-11 - 2]$
    $= -7(-13) = 91$

11. $2 \cdot 2 \cdot 3 \cdot 7$

Chapter 2

ALGEBRAIC EXPRESSIONS

1. $x \cdot x \cdot x \cdot x \cdot x \cdot x$

3. $(-x)(-x)(-x)(-x)$

5. $-(x \cdot x \cdot x \cdot x)$

7. $x \cdot x \cdot y \cdot y \cdot y$

9. $x \cdot x + y \cdot y \cdot y$

11. $x \cdot y \cdot y \cdot y$

13. a^4

15. $x^2 y^3$

17. $-r^2 s^3$

19. $-x^2 (-y)^3$

21. $x^3 x^5 = x^{3+5} = x^8$

23. $3^5 = 3 \cdot 3 \cdot 3 \cdot 3 \cdot 3 = 9 \cdot 3 \cdot 3 \cdot 3 = 27 \cdot 3 \cdot 3 = 81 \cdot 3 = 243$

25. $-2^3 = -(2 \cdot 2 \cdot 2) = -(4 \cdot 2) = -8$

27. $(-2)^4 = (-2)(-2)(-2)(-2) = 4(-2)(-2) = -8(-2) = 16$

29. $3^2 + 3^3 - 3^4 = 3 \cdot 3 + 3 \cdot 3 \cdot 3 - 3 \cdot 3 \cdot 3 \cdot 3$
$$= 9 + 27 - 81 = -45$$

31. $4 \cdot 3^2 - 2 \cdot 5^2 = 4 \cdot 3 \cdot 3 - 2 \cdot 5 \cdot 5 = 36 - 50 = -14$

33. $(3 - 7)^2 - (4 - 5)^3 = (-4)^2 - (-1)^3 = (-4)(-4) - (-1)(-1)(-1)$
$$= 16 - (-1) = 17$$

35. $3^2 4^3 = 3 \cdot 3 \cdot 4 \cdot 4 \cdot 4 = 576$

37. $3^2 3^3 = 3^{2+3} = 3^5 = 3 \cdot 3 \cdot 3 \cdot 3 \cdot 3 = 243$

39. $x^3 x^5 = x^{3+5} = x^8$

41. $a a^2 a^4 = a^{1+2+4} = a^7$

43. $(3x)(5x)(4x) = (3 \cdot 5 \cdot 4)(x \cdot x \cdot x) = 60x^3$

45. $(3r^2)(2r^3) = (3 \cdot 2)(r^2 r^3) = 6r^{2+3} = 6r^5$

47. $(-3x^3)(5x^2) = (-3 \cdot 5)(x^3 x^2) = -15x^{3+2} = -15x^5$

49. $(-c^4)(2^3)(-5c) = (-2^3(-5))(c^4 c) = 40c^{4+1} = 40c^5$

51. $(8x^3 y^2)(4xy^5) = (8 \cdot 4)(x^3 x)(y^2 y^5) = 32x^{3+1}y^{2+5} = 32x^4 y^7$

53. $(-2xy)(x^2 y^2)(-3xy) = (-2(-3))(xx^2 x)(yy^2 y)$
$$= 6x^{1+2+1}y^{1+2+1}$$
$$= 6x^4 y^4$$

55. $(3a^4)^2 = (3a^4)(3a^4) = (3 \cdot 3)(a^4 a^4) = 9a^{4+4} = 9a^8$

57. $(-4n^2)^3 = (-4n^2)(-4n^2)(-4n^2) = ((-4)(-4)(-4))(n^2 n^2 n^2)$
$$= -64n^{2+2+2}$$
$$= -64n^6$$

59. $(x^2)^3 (x^4)^2 = (x^2 x^2 x^2)(x^4 x^4) = x^{2+2+2+4+4} = x^{14}$

61. In $3 \cdot 2^4$, the exponent of 4 applies only to the 2, not to the 3; in $(3 \cdot 2)^4$, the exponent of 4 applies to both the 2 and the 3. Put another way, we compute $3 \cdot 2^4$ by first raising 2 to the fourth power and then multiplying the result by 3. We compute $(3 \cdot 2)^4$ by first multiplying 2 by 3 and then raising the result to the fourth power.

62. (a) The exponent of 2 applies only to the 2, not to the 3.

    (b) Only x should be raised to the fourth power.

    (c) 5^4 is not the same as $5 \cdot 4$.

    (d) When we square 3, we get 9, not 6. Addition is performed in the <u>exponents</u>.

    (e) -3^4 is the opposite of 3^4, so is equal to -81.

    (f) We add exponents when we multiply powers of x, not when we add powers of x.

    (g) When multiplying powers of x, we add exponents.
So $x^2 x^7 = x^{2+7} = x^9$.

    (h) Here, we do not add exponents, since
$(x^2)^4 = x^2 x^2 x^2 x^2 = x^{2+2+2+2} = x^8$.

Exercises 2.2

1. $-y = -(-3) = 3$

3. $-|y| = -|(-3)| = -3$

5. $x + y = (2) + (-3) = -1$

7. $x - y = (2) - (-3) = 5$

9. $|x - y| = |(2) - (-3)| = |5| = 5$

11. $|x| - y = |(2)| - (-3) = 2 + 3 = 5$

13. $|x| - |y| = |(2)| - |(-3)| = 2 - 3 = -1$

15. $x + y + z = (2) + (-3) + (-4) = -5$

17. $x + y - z = (2) + (-3) - (-4) = 3$

19. $xy - z = (2)(-3) - (-4) = -6 + 4 = -2$

21. $x(y - z) = (2)((-3) - (-4)) = 2(1) = 2$

23. $x - (y - z) = (2) - ((-3) - (-4)) = 2 - 1 = 1$

25. $xy^2 = (2)(-3)^2 = 2(9) = 18$

27. $x + y^2 = (2) + (-3)^2 = 2 + 9 = 11$

29. $x^2 + y^2 = (2)^2 + (-3)^2 = 4 + 9 = 13$

31. $(x + y + z)^2 = ((2) + (-3) + (-4))^2 = (-5)^2 = 25$

33. $xyz^2 = (2)(-3)(-4)^2 = -6(16) = -96$

35. $x(y - z)^2 = (2)((-3) - (-4))^2 = (2)(1)^2 = 2(1) = 2$

37. $xy^2 - (xy)^2 = (2)(-3)^2 - ((2)(-3))^2 = 2(9) - (-6)^2$
$$= 18 - 36 = -18$$

39. $(z - 3x)^2 = ((-4) - 3(2))^2 = (-4 - 6)^2 = (-10)^2 = 100$

41. $(5x + y)(3x - y) = (5(2) + (-3))(3(2) - (-3))$
$$= (10 - 3)(6 + 3) = (7)(9) = 63$$

43. $y^2 - 3y + 2 = (-3)^2 - 3(-3) + 2 = 9 + 9 + 2 = 20$

45. $3x^2 + 4x + 1 = 3(2)^2 + 4(2) + 1 = 3(4) + 4(2) + 1$
$$= 12 + 8 + 1 = 21$$

47. $x^2 + 3x^2y - 3xy^2 + y^3 = (2)^2 + 3(2)^2(-3) - 3(2)(-3)^2 + (-3)^3$
$$= 4 + 3(4)(-3) - 3(2)(9) + (-27)$$
$$= 4 - 36 - 54 - 27 = -113$$

49. $5x + 2[3 + 2(x + 1)] = 5(2) + 2[3 + 2((2) + 1)]$
$$= 10 + 2[3 + 2(3)]$$
$$= 10 + 2(9)$$
$$= 10 + 18 = 28$$

51. $3x - 4y$ has two terms. The first has a coefficient of 3 and a literal part of x; the second has a coefficient of -4 and a literal part of y.

53. $3x(-4y) = -12xy$ has one term, with a coefficient of -12 and a literal part of xy.

55. $3x(z - y)$ has one term, with a coefficient of 3 and a literal part of $x(z - y)$.

57. $4x^2 - 3x + 2$ has three terms. The first has a coefficient of 4 and a literal part of x^2; the second has a coefficient of -3 and a literal part of x; the third has no literal part -- it is just the constant 2.

59. $-x^2 + y - 13$ has three terms. The first has a coefficient of -1 and a literal part of x^2; the second has a coefficient of 1 and a literal part of y; the third has no literal part -- it is just the constant -13.

61. $3x(2x + 4y(5y) = 6x^2 + 20y^2$ has two terms. The first has a coefficient of 6 and a literal part of x^2; the second has a coefficient of 20 and a literal part of y^2.

63. A term is an algebraic expression which is connected by multiplication (and/or division). If a term is formed by multiplying two or more expressions, each is called a factor of that term.

64. $x + xy + xyz$ is one of many possible answers.

Exercises 2.3

1. Essential

3. Non-essential

5. Essential

7. Non-essential

9. Essential

11. Essential (both)

13. The first is non-essential; the second is essential.

15. x, $2x$: literal part is x, coefficients are 1 and 2.
    y, $3y$: literal part is y, coefficients are 1 and 3.

17. $2x^2$, $-x^2$: literal part is x^2, coefficients are 2 and -1
    $-3x$, x: literal part is x, coefficients are -3 and -1
    $4x^3$: literal part is x^3, coefficient is 4.

19. 4, 5: constant terms
    $4u$, $5u$: literal part is u, coefficients are 4 and 5
    $4u^2$: literal part is u^2, coefficient is 4.

21. $5x^2$: literal part is x^2, coefficient is 5
    $5x^2y$: literal part is x^2y, coefficient is 5
    $5y^2$: literal part is y^2, coefficient is 5
    $5xy^2$: literal part is xy^2, coefficient is 5.

23. $-x^2y$, $-2x^2y$: literal part is x^2y, coefficients are -1 and -2
    $2xy^2$, $3xy^2$: literal part is xy^2, coefficients are 2 and 3
    x^2y^2: literal part is x^2y^2, coefficient is 1.

25. $2x + 5x = (2 + 5)x = 7x$

27. $2x^2 + 5x^2 = (2 + 5)x^2 = 7x^2$

29. $3a - 8a + 2a = (3 - 8 + 2)a = -3a$

31. $-3y + y - 2y = (-3 + 1 - 2)y = -4y$

33. $-x - 2x - 3x = (-1 - 2 - 3)x = -6x$

35. $2x - 3y - 7x + 5y = 2x - 7x - 3y + 5y$
$$= (2 - 7)x + (-3 + 5)y$$
$$= -5x + 2y$$

37. $3x + 5y + 2z$ cannot be simplified

39. $3x^2 + 7x + x^2 + 3x = 3x^2 + x^2 + 7x + 3x$
$$= (3 + 1)x^2 + (7 + 3)x$$
$$= 4x^2 + 10x$$

41. $x^2 - 2x + x^2 - x = x^2 + x^2 - 2x - x$
$$= (1 + 1)x^2 + (-2 - 1)x$$
$$= 2x^2 - 3x$$

43. $5x^2y - 3x^2 + x^2y - x^2 = 5x^2y + x^2y - 3x^2 - x^2$
$$= (5 + 1)x^2y + (-3 - 1)x^2$$
$$= 6x^2y - 4x^2$$

45. $2x + 5x - 3y + y - 7x = 2x + 5x - 7x - 3y + y$
$$= (2 + 5 - 7)x + (-3 + 1)y$$
$$= 0x - 2y = -2y$$

47. $-5s^2 + 3st - s^2 + 6s^2 = -5s^2 - s^2 + 6s^2 + 3st$
$$= (-5 - 1 + 6)s^2 + 3st$$
$$= 0s^2 + 3st = 3st$$

49. $3a^2b + ab^2 - ab^2 - 2a^2b - ab^2 = 3a^2b - 2a^2b + ab^2 - ab^2 - ab^2$
$$= (3 - 2)a^2b + (1 - 1 - 1)ab^2$$
$$= 1a^2b - 1ab^2 = a^2b - ab^2$$

51. $2x + 10 = 2x + 2 \cdot 5 = 2(x + 5)$

53. $5y - 20 = 5y - 5 \cdot 4 = 5(y - 4)$

55. $9x + 3y - 6 = 3(3x) + 3y - 3 \cdot 2 = 3(3x + y - 2)$

57. $x^2 + xy = xx + xy = x(x + y)$

59. $3(x + 4) = 3x + 12$

61. $5(y - 2) = 5y - 10$

63. $-2(x + 7) = -2x - 14$

65. $3(5x + 2) = 15x + 6$

67. $-4(3x + 1) = -12x - 4$

69. $x(x + 3) = x^2 + 3x$

71. $x(x^2 + 3x) = x^3 + 3x^2$

73. $5x(2x - 4) = 10x^2 - 20x$

75. $3(x + y) + 4x - y = 3x + 3y + 4x - y$
$$= 3x + 4x + 3y - y$$
$$= (3 + 4)x + (3 - 1)y$$
$$= 7x + 2y$$

77. $3(x + y) + 4(x - y) = 3x + 3y + 4x - 4y$
$$= 3x + 4x + 3y - 4y$$
$$= (3 + 4)x + (3 - 4)y$$
$$= 7x + (-1)y$$
$$= 7x - y$$

79. $3(x + y) + 4x(-y) = 3x + 3y - 4xy$

81. $5x(x^2 + 3) + 2x(3 + x^2) = 5x^3 + 15x + 6x + 2x^3$
$$= 5x^3 + 2x^3 + 15x + 6x$$
$$= (5 + 2)x^3 + (15 + 6)x$$
$$= 7x^3 + 21x$$

83. $5x(x^2 + 3) + 2x(3x^2) = 5x^3 + 15x + 6x^3$
$$= 5x^3 + 6x^3 + 15x$$
$$= (5 + 6)x^3 + 15x$$
$$= 11x^3 + 15x$$

85. The distributive law allows us to combine like terms.

86. (a) Our order of operations requires that multiplication be done before addition. Therefore, we should never add 5 and 3.

(b) The distributive law requires that we multiply each term of x - 4 by 3.

(c) We cannot add 5 and 3x to get 8x, since these are not like terms.

(d) This is correct as written.

Exercises 2.4

1. $4x + y + 4(x + y) = 4x + y + 4x + 4y$
    $= 4x + 4x + y + 4y$
    $= 8x + 5y$

3. $5(m + 2b) + 3(m - n) = 5m + 10n + 3m - 3n$
    $= 5m + 3m + 10n - 3n$
    $= 8m + 7n$

5. $-2(x - 3y) + 5(y - x) = -2x + 6y + 5y - 5x$
    $= -2x - 5x + 6y + 5y$
    $= -7x + 11y$

7. $5 + 3(x - 2) = 5 + 3x - 6$
    $= 3x + 5 - 6$
    $= 3x - 1$

9. $5 - 3(x - 2) = 5 - 3x + 6$
    $= -3x + 5 + 6$
    $= -3x + 11$

11. $(5 - 3)(x - 2) = 2(x - 2)$
    $= 2x - 4$

13. $8 - (3x - 4) = 8 - 3x + 4$
    $= -3x + 8 + 4$
    $= -3x + 12$

15. $5y - (1 - 2y) = 5y - 1 + 2y$
    $= 5y + 2y - 1$
    $= 7y - 1$

17. $5(x - 3y) - x - 3y = 5x - 15y - x - 3y$
    $= 5x - x - 15y - 3y$
    $= 4x - 18y$

19. $5(x - 3y) - (x - 3y) = 5x - 15y - x + 3y$
    $= 5x - x - 15y + 3y$
    $= 4x - 12y$

21. $5(x - 3y) - x(-3y) = 5x - 15y + 3xy$

23. $5x(-3y) - x(-3y) = -15xy + 3xy$
$\qquad\qquad\qquad\quad = -12xy$

25. $5x(-3y)(-x)(-3y) = ((5)(-3)(-1)(-3))(x \cdot x)(y \cdot y)$
$\qquad\qquad\qquad\qquad = -45x^2y^2$

27. $2x^2(x - 2) + x(3x^2 - 4x) = 2x^3 - 4x^2 + 3x^3 - 4x^2$
$\qquad\qquad\qquad\qquad\qquad = 2x^3 + 3x^3 - 4x^2 - 4x^2$
$\qquad\qquad\qquad\qquad\qquad = 5x^3 - 8x^2$

29. $3a(4a - 1) - a(4 - a) = 12a^2 - 3a - 4a + a^2$
$\qquad\qquad\qquad\qquad = 12a^2 + a^2 - 3a - 4a$
$\qquad\qquad\qquad\qquad = 13a^2 - 7a$

31. $4(x^2 + 7x) - (x^2 + 7x) = 4x^2 + 28x - x^2 - 7x$
$\qquad\qquad\qquad\qquad = 4x^2 - x^2 + 28x - 7x$
$\qquad\qquad\qquad\qquad = 3x^2 + 21x$

33. $3a(a^2 + 3b) + 4b^2(a^2 - b) = 3a^3 + 9ab + 4a^2b^2 - 4b^3$

35. $3x^2 - 7x + 4 - 8x^2 - 3 - x = 3x^2 - 8x^2 - 7x - x + 4 - 3$
$\qquad\qquad\qquad\qquad\qquad = -5x^2 - 8x + 1$

37. $x^2y(xy - x) - 5xy(x^2y - x^2) = x^3y^2 - x^3y - 5x^3y^2 + 5x^3y$
$\qquad\qquad\qquad\qquad\qquad = x^3y^2 - 5x^3y^2 - x^3y + 5x^3y$
$\qquad\qquad\qquad\qquad\qquad = -4x^3y^2 + 4x^3y$

39. $4u^2v(u - v) - (uv^3 + u^2v^2) = 4u^3v - 4u^2v^2 - uv^3 - u^2v^2$
$\qquad\qquad\qquad\qquad\qquad = 4u^3v - 4u^2v^2 - u^2v^2 - uv^3$
$\qquad\qquad\qquad\qquad\qquad = 4u^3v - 5u^2v^2 - uv^3$

41. $4(x + 3y) + (4x + 3y) + 4x(3y) = 4x + 12y + 4x + 3y + 12xy$
$\qquad\qquad\qquad\qquad\qquad = 4x + 4x + 12y + 3y + 12xy$
$\qquad\qquad\qquad\qquad\qquad = 8x + 15y + 12xy$

43. $6(m - 2n) + (6m - 2n) + 6m(-2n) = 6m - 12n + 6m - 2n - 12mn$
$\qquad\qquad\qquad\qquad\qquad\qquad = 6m + 6m - 12n - 2n - 12mn$
$\qquad\qquad\qquad\qquad\qquad\qquad = 12m - 14n - 12mn$

45. $3t^3(t^4 - 4) - (t^5 + t^4) - 2t^3(3t)(-t^5)$
$\qquad\qquad = 3t^9 - 12t^5 - t^5 - t^4 + 6t^9$
$\qquad\qquad = 3t^9 + 6t^9 - 12t^5 - t^5 - t^4$
$\qquad\qquad = 9t^9 - 13t^5 - t^4$

47. $-3(-x + 2) + (8 - 5x) - (2 - 2x) = 3x - 6 + 8 - 5x - 2 + 2x$
$$= 3x - 5x + 2x - 6 + 8 - 2$$
$$= 0x + 0 = 0$$

49. $a - 2[a - 2(a - 2)] = a - 2[a - 2a + 4]$
$$= a - 2[-a + 4]$$
$$= a + 2a - 8$$
$$= 3a - 8$$

51. $x\{x - 4[x - (x - 4)]\} = x\{x - 4[x - x + 4]\}$
$$= x\{x - 4(4)\}$$
$$= x(x - 16)$$
$$= x^2 - 16x$$

53. $3(x + 2) + 4[x - 3(2 - x)] = 3(x + 2) + 4[x - 6 + 3x]$
$$= 3(x + 2) + 4(4x - 6)$$
$$= 3x + 6 + 16x - 24$$
$$= 3x + 16x + 6 - 24$$
$$= 19x - 18$$

55. $4(y - 3) - 2[3y - 5(y - 1)] = 4(y - 3) - 2[3y - 5y + 5]$
$$= 4(y - 3) - 2(-2y + 5)$$
$$= 4y - 12 + 4y - 10$$
$$= 8y - 22$$

57. (a) The solution is correct up to $3 + 2[5x + 12]$. At this point, it is wrong to add $3 + 2 = 5$. Instead, use the Distributive Law:
$$3 + 2[5x + 12] = 3 + 10x + 24$$
$$= 10x + 3 + 24$$
$$= 10x + 27$$

  (b) Within the brackets, we must add x and x + 3, not multiply them. As a result, we get
$$3x + 5[x + (x + 3)] = 3x + 5[2x + 3]$$
$$= 3x + 10x + 15$$
$$= 13x + 15$$

58. (a) Do not subtract 5 - 3; distribute -3 instead.

  (b) When -3 is distributed, it must multiply -4 as well as x.

  (c) When we multiply -3 by -4, we get 12, not -12.

  (d) This is done correctly.

Exercises 2.5

1. n + 4

3. n - 4

5. n - 4

7. 5n + 6

9. 2n - 9

11. n(n + 7)

13. (n + 2)(n - 6)

15. 2n - 8 = 14

17. 5n + 4 = n - 2

19. r + s = rs

21. 2(r + s) = rs - 3

23. x + (x + 1) = 2x + 1, where x = smaller integer

25. x + (x + 2) = 2x + 2, where x = smaller even integer

27. x(x + 2)(x + 4), where x = smallest of the odd integers

29. 8x = 7(x + 2) - 4, where x = smaller even integer

31. $x^2 + (x + 1)^2 + (x + 2)^2 = 5$, where x = smallest of the integers

33. (a) 8 nickels
     (b) 40¢ (= 8 x 5¢)
     (c) 12 dimes
     (d) 120¢ (= 12 x 10¢) or $1.20
     (e) 9 quarters
     (f) 225¢ (= 9 x 25¢) or $2.25
     (g) 29 coins
     (h) 40¢ + 120¢ + 225¢ = 385¢ or $3.85

35. (a) A reads 200 cards per minute
     (b) A reads cards for 15 minutes
     (c) A reads 3,000 cards (= 200 x 15)
     (d) B reads 160 cards per minute

(e) B reads cards for 20 minutes

(f) B reads 3,200 cards(= 160 x 20)

(g) A and B read 6,200 cards altogether (= 3,000 + 3,200)

37. (a) She walks at the rate of 100 meters per minute

(b) She walks for 25 minutes

(c) She walks 2,500 meters (= 100 x 25)

(d) She jogs at the rate of 220 meters per minute

(e) She jogs for 35 minutes

(f) She jogs 7,700 meters (= 220 x 35)

(g) She covers a distance of 10,200 meters altogether
(= 2,500 + 7,700)

Chapter 2 Review Exercises

1. $x \cdot y \cdot y \cdot y$

3. $-(x \cdot x \cdot x \cdot x)$

5. $3 \cdot x \cdot x$

7. $x^2 y^3$

9. $a^2 - b^3$

11. $-z^4 = -(-2)^4 = -(-2)(-2)(-2)(-2) = -16$

13. $xy^2 = (-3)(4)^2 = -3(16) = -48$

15. $xyz - (x + y + z) = (-3)(4)(-2) - ((-3) + (4) + (-2))$
$$= 24 - (-1) = 25$$

17. $|xy| + z - |z| = |(-3)(4)| + (-2) - |(-2)|$
$$= |-12| + (-2) - |-2|$$
$$= 12 - 2 - 2 = 8$$

19. $2x^2 - (x + y)^2 = 2(-3)^2 - ((-3) + (4))^2$
$$= 2(9) - (1)^2$$
$$= 18 - 1 = 17$$

21. $x^3 x^4 x = x^{3+4+1} = x^8$

23. $a^7 a^2 + a^3 a^6 = a^{7+2} + a^{3+6} = a^9 + a^9 = 2a^9$

25. $4x^3 x^2 + 3x^2 x^4 = 4x^{3+2} + 3x^{2+4} = 4x^5 + 3x^6$

27. $3x^2 - 7x + 7 - 5x^2 - x - 3 = 3x^2 - 5x^2 - 7x - x + 7 - 3$
$$= -2x^2 - 8x + 4$$

29. $2a^2b(3ab^4) = (2 \cdot 3)(a^2a)(bb^4)$
$$= 6a^{2+1}b^{1+4} = 6a^3b^5$$

31. $2a^2b(3a + b^4) = 2a^2b(3a) + 2a^2b(b^4)$
$$= 6a^3b + 2a^2b^5$$

33. $3x(2x + 4) + 5(x^2 - 3) = 6x^2 + 12x + 5x^2 - 15$
$$= 6x^2 + 5x^2 + 12x - 15$$
$$= 11x^2 + 12x - 15$$

35. $4y^2(y - 2) - y(y^2 - 5y) = 4y^3 - 8y^2 - y^3 + 5y^2$
$$= 4y^3 - y^3 - 8y^2 + 5y^2$$
$$= 3y^3 - 3y^2$$

37. $3xy(x^2 - 2y) + 4xy^2(y - x) = 3x^3y - 6xy^2 + 4xy^3 - 4x^2y^2$

39. $3(2x - 4y) - (x + 2y) - (x - 2y) = 6x - 12y - x - 2y - x + 2y$
$$= 6x - x - x - 12y - 2y + 2y$$
$$= 4x - 12y$$

41. $3x^4(x^3 - 2y^2) - 4x(x^2)(x^4) = 3x^7 - 6x^4y^2 - 4x^7$
$$= 3x^7 - 4x^7 - 6x^4y^2$$
$$= -x^7 - 6x^4y^2$$

43. $3 - [x - 3 - (x - 3)] = 3 - [x - 3 - x + 3]$
$$= 3 - [x - x - 3 + 3]$$
$$= 3 - 0 = 3$$

45. $5x^2 + 10 = 5x^2 + 5 \cdot 2 = 5(x^2 + 2)$

47. $3y - 6z + 9 = 3y - 3(2z) + 3(3) = 3(y - 2z + 3)$

49. $n + 7 = 3n - 4$

51. $n + (n + 2) = n - 5$

53. (a) He sells 12 newspaper subscriptions.

(b) He earns $2 for each newspaper subscription.

(c) He sells 9 magazine subscriptions.

(d) He earns $5 for each magazine subscription.

(e) He earns $24 (= 12 x 2) for the newspaper subscriptions.

(f) He earns $45 (= 9 x 5) for the magazine subscriptions.

(g) He earns $69 (= 24 + 45) altogether.

Chapter 2 Practice Test

1. $-3^4 = -(3 \cdot 3 \cdot 3 \cdot 3) = -81$

3. $(-3 - 4 + 6)^5 = (-7 + 6)^5 = (-1)^5$
    $= (-1)(-1)(-1)(-1)(-1) = -1$

5. $x - y - z = (-2) - (-3) - (-4)$
    $= -2 - 3 + 4 = -5 + 4 = -1$

7. $x^3 - z^2 = (-2)^3 - (-4)^2 = (-2)(-2)(-2) - (-4)(-4)$
    $= -8 - (+16) = -8 - 16 = -24$

9. $4x^2y - 5xy + y^2 - 3xy - 2y^2 - x^2y = 4x^2y - x^2y - 5xy - 3xy + y^2 - 2y^2$
    $= 3x^2y - 8xy - y^2$

11. $2x(x^2 - y) - 3(x - xy) - (2x^3 - 3x) = 2x^3 - 2xy - 3x + 3xy - 2x^3 + 3x$
    $= 2x^3 - 2x^3 - 2xy + 3xy - 3x + 3x$
    $= xy$

13. $4 - [x - 4(x - 4)] = 4 - [x - 4x + 16]$
    $= 4 - [-3x + 16]$
    $= 4 + 3x - 16$
    $= 3x - 12$

15. (a) $3

    (b) x

    (c) $2

    (d) 2x - 5

    (e) 3(2x - 5) dollars

    (f) 2x dollars

    (g) 2x + 3(2x - 5) = 2x + 6x - 15 = 8x - 15 dollars

Chapter 3

FIRST DEGREE EQUATIONS
AND INEQUALITIES

Exercises 3.1

1. $2(x - 3) = 2x - 6$
    $2x - 6 = 2x - 6$ identity

3. $5(x + 2) = 5x + 2$
    $5x + 10 = 5x + 2$
    $10 = 2$ contradiction

5. $2a + 4 + 3a = 6a + 4 - a$
    $5a + 4 = 5a + 4$ identity

7. $2z^2 + 3z - 2z^2 - z = z + z + 1$
    $2z^2 - 2z^2 + 3z - z = z + z + 1$
    $2z = 2z + 1$
    $0 = 1$ contradiction

9. $5u - 4(u - 1) - u = u - 4 - (u - 2)$
    $5u - 4u + 4 - 4 = u - 4 - u + 2$
    $5u - 4u - u + 4 = u - u - 4 + 2$
    $4 = -2$ contradiction

11. $7 - 3(y - 2) = y + 4(5 - y) - 7$
    $7 - 3y + 6 = y + 20 - 4y - 7$
    $7 + 6 - 3y = 20 - 7 + y - 4y$
    $13 - 3y = 13 - 3y$ identity

13. $w(w - 2) - w^2 + 2w = 3(w + 1) - (3w - 1)$
    $w^2 - 2w - w^2 + 2w = 3w + 3 - 3w + 1$
    $w^2 - w^2 - 2w + 2w = 3w - 3w + 3 + 1$
    $0 = 4$ contradiction

15. $2(x^2 - 3) - x(2x - 1) + x = 2 - x - (x + 8) + 4x$

$2x^2 - 6 - 2x^2 + x + x = 2 - x - x - 8 + 4x$

$2x^2 - 2x^2 + x + x - 6 = 4x - x - x + 2 - 8$

$2x - 6 = 2x - 6$ identity

17. Check x + 3: x + 5 = -2

$(-3) + 5 \overset{?}{=} -2$

$2 \neq -2$

Therefore x = -3 does not satisfy the equation.

Check x = -7:   x + 5 = -2

$(-7) + 5 \overset{?}{=} -2$

$-2 \overset{\checkmark}{=} -2$

Therefore x = -7 does satisfy the equation.

19. Check a = -5:   2 - a = 3

$2 - (-5) \overset{?}{=} 3$

$7 \neq 3$

Therefore a = -5 does not satisfy the equation.

Check a = 5:   2 - a = 3

$2 - (5) \overset{?}{=} 3$

$-3 \neq 3$

Therefore a = 5 does not satisfy the equation.

Check a = 1:   2 - a = 3

$2 - (1) \overset{?}{=} 3$

$1 \neq 3$

Therefore a = 1 does not satisfy the equation.

21.   Check $y = 2$: $3y + 7 = y - 3$

$$3(2) + 7 \overset{?}{=} (2) - 3$$

$$6 + 7 \overset{?}{=} 2 - 3$$

$$13 \neq -1$$

Therefore $y = 2$ does not satisfy the equation.

Check $y = -5$: $3y + 7 = y - 3$

$$3(-5) + 7 \overset{?}{=} (-5) = 3$$

$$-15 + 7 \overset{?}{=} -5 - 3$$

$$-8 \overset{\checkmark}{=} -8$$

Therefore $y = -5$ does satisfy the equation.

23.   Check $w = -4$: $6 - 2w = 10 - 3w$

$$6 - 2(-4) \overset{?}{=} 10 - 3(-4)$$

$$6 + 8 \overset{?}{=} 10 + 12$$

$$14 \neq 22$$

Therefore $w = -4$ does not satisfy the equation.

Check $w = 1$: $6 - 2w = 10 - 3w$

$$6 - 2(1) \overset{?}{=} 10 - 3(1)$$

$$6 - 2 \overset{?}{=} 10 - 3$$

$$4 \neq 7$$

Therefore $w = 1$ does not satisfy the equation.

25.   Check $x = 0$: $4(x - 7) - (x + 1) = 15 - x$

$$4((0) - 7) - ((0) + 1) \overset{?}{=} 15 - (0)$$

$$4(-7) - 1 \overset{?}{=} 15 - 0$$

$$-28 - 1 \overset{?}{=} 15 - 0$$

$$-29 \neq 15$$

Therefore $x = 0$ does not satisfy the equation.

Check x = 7: $4(x - 7) - (x + 1) = 15 - x$

$$4((7) - 7) - ((7) + 1) \overset{?}{=} 15 - (7)$$

$$4(0) - 8 \overset{?}{=} 15 - 7$$

$$0 - 8 \overset{?}{=} 15 - 7$$

$$-8 \neq 8$$

Therefore x = 7 does not satisfy the equation.

27.   Check z = -2: $3z + 2(z - 1) = 4(z + 2) - (z + 5)$

$$3(-2) + 2((-2) - 1) \overset{?}{=} 4((-2) + 2) - ((-2) + 5)$$

$$-6 + 2(-3) \overset{?}{=} 4(0) - 3$$

$$-6 - 6 \overset{?}{=} 0 - 3$$

$$-12 \neq -3$$

Therefore z = -2 does not satisfy the equation.

Check z = 1: $3z + 2(z - 1) = 4(z + 2) - (z + 5)$

$$3(1) + 2((1) - 1) \overset{?}{=} 4((1) + 2) - ((1) + 5)$$

$$3 + 2(0) \overset{?}{=} 4(3) - 6)$$

$$3 + 0 \overset{?}{=} 12 - 6$$

$$3 \neq 6$$

Therefore z = 1 does not satisfy the equation.

29.   Check x = -2: $x^2 - 3x = 2x - 6$

$$(-2)^2 - 3(-2) \overset{?}{=} 2(-2) - 6$$

$$4 + 6 \overset{?}{=} -4 - 6$$

$$10 \neq -10$$

Therefore x = -2 does not satisfy the equation.

Check x = 2: $x^2 - 3x = 2x - 6$

$$(2)^2 - 3(2) \overset{?}{=} 2(2) - 6$$

$$4 - 6 \overset{?}{=} 4 - 6$$

$$-2 \overset{\checkmark}{=} -2$$

Therefore x = 2 does satisfy the equation.

31.   Check a = -1: $a^2 - 4a = 4 - a$

$$(-1)^2 - 4(-1) \stackrel{?}{=} 4 - (-1)$$

$$1 + 4 \stackrel{?}{=} 4 + 1$$

$$5 \stackrel{\checkmark}{=} 5$$

Therefore a = -1 does satisfy the equation.

Check a = 4: $a^2 - 4a = 4 - a$

$$(4)^2 - 4(4) \stackrel{?}{=} 4 - (4)$$

$$16 - 16 \stackrel{?}{=} 4 - 4$$

$$0 \stackrel{\checkmark}{=} 0$$

Therefore a = 4 does satisfy the equation.

33.   Check y = -2: $y(y + 6) = (y + 2)^2$

$$-2((-2) + 6) \stackrel{?}{=} ((-2) + 2)^2$$

$$-2(4) \stackrel{?}{=} 0^2$$

$$-8 \neq 0$$

Therefore y = -2 does not satisfy the equation.

Check y = 2: $y(y + 6) = (y + 2)^2$

$$(2)((2) + 6) \stackrel{?}{=} ((2) + 2)^2$$

$$2(8) \stackrel{?}{=} 4^2$$

$$16 \stackrel{\checkmark}{=} 16$$

Therefore y = 2 does satisfy the equation.

35.   A value satisfies or it a solution to an equation if both
sides of the equation are equal when the value is substituted
for the variable.

36. An identity is an equation that is always true, no matter what value is chosen for the variable. A contradiction is an equation that is never true, no matter what value is chosen for the variable. A conditional equation is one that is true for some values of the variable and false for the others.

37. If two quantities are equal, then we will not disturb this equality if we change each quantity in exactly the same way.

38. Two equations are called equivalent if their solution sets are exactly the same.

39.
$$x + 1 = 16 \qquad\qquad x = -1 \qquad\qquad 2x = 18 \qquad 2x = 10$$
$$x - 3 = 12 \qquad x + 7 = 6 \qquad\quad x = 9 \qquad 5x = 25$$
$$x = 15 \qquad\qquad\qquad\qquad\quad x + 2 = 11$$
$$2x = 30 \qquad\qquad\qquad\qquad\quad x - 2 = 7$$

Exercises 3.2

1.
$$\begin{aligned} x + 3 &= 8 \\ -\ 3 &\ \ -3 \\ \hline x &= 5 \end{aligned}$$

   CHECK: x = 5 $5 + 3 \overset{?}{=} 8$

   $8 \overset{\checkmark}{=} 8$

3.
$$\begin{aligned} y - 4 &= 7 \\ +\ 4 &\ \ +4 \\ \hline y &= 11 \end{aligned}$$

   CHECK: y = 11 $11 - 4 \overset{?}{=} 7$

   $7 \overset{\checkmark}{=} 7$

5.
$$\begin{aligned} a + 3 &= 1 \\ -\ 3 &\ \ -3 \\ \hline a &= -2 \end{aligned}$$

   CHECK: a = -2 $-2 + 3 \overset{?}{=} 1$

   $1 \overset{\checkmark}{=} 1$

7.
$$\begin{aligned} a - 5 &= -8 \\ +\ 5 &\ \ +5 \\ \hline a &= -3 \end{aligned}$$

   CHECK: a = -3 $-3 - 5 \overset{?}{=} -8$

   $-8 \overset{\checkmark}{=} -8$

9.
$$3x = 21$$
$$\frac{\cancel{3}x}{\cancel{3}} = \frac{21}{3}$$
$$x = 7$$

   CHECK: x = 7 $3(7) \overset{?}{=} 21$

   $21 \overset{\checkmark}{=} 21$

11.
$$-4x = -12$$
$$\frac{\cancel{-4}x}{\cancel{-4}} = \frac{-12}{-4}$$
$$x = 3$$

   CHECK: x = 3 $-4(3) \overset{?}{=} -12$

   $-12 \overset{\checkmark}{=} -12$

13. $3x + x = 8 - 12$

$4x = -4$

$\dfrac{\cancel{4}x}{\cancel{4}} = \dfrac{-4}{4}$

$x = -1$

CHECK: $x = -1$

$3(-1) + (-1) \overset{?}{=} 8 - 12$

$-3 - 1 \overset{?}{=} 8 - 12$

$-4 \overset{\checkmark}{=} -4$

15. $4x - x = 2 - 8$

$3x = -6$

$\dfrac{\cancel{3}x}{\cancel{3}} = \dfrac{-6}{3}$

$x = -2$

CHECK: $x = -2$

$4(-2) - (-2) \overset{?}{=} 2 - 8$

$-8 + 2 \overset{?}{=} 2 - 8$

$-6 \overset{\checkmark}{=} -6$

17. $2z - 3z - 11z = -4(6)$

$-12z = -24$

$\dfrac{\cancel{-12}z}{\cancel{-12}} = \dfrac{-24}{-12}$

$z = 2$

CHECK: $z = 2$

$2(2) - 3(2) - 11(2) \overset{?}{=} -4(6)$

$4 - 6 - 22 \overset{?}{=} -24$

$-24 \overset{\checkmark}{=} -24$

19. $3w - 7w + 4w = 8 - 3$

$0w = 5$

$0 = 5$

contradiction

21. $2x + 1 = 7$

$\quad\ \ \underline{-1 \quad -1}$

$2x \quad\ = 6$

$\dfrac{\cancel{2}x}{\cancel{2}} = \dfrac{6}{2}$

$x = 3$

CHECK: $x = 3$

$2(3) + 1 \overset{?}{=} 7$

$6 + 1 \overset{?}{=} 7$

$7 \overset{\checkmark}{=} 7$

23. $2t = 3t + 5$

$\underline{-3t \quad -3t}$

$-t = \quad\ 5$

$\dfrac{-t}{-1} = \dfrac{5}{-1}$

$t = -5$

CHECK: $t = -5$

$2(-5) \overset{?}{=} 3(-5) + 5$

$-10 \overset{?}{=} -15 + 5$

$-10 \overset{\checkmark}{=} -10$

25. $9 = 6 - 3a$

$\underline{-6 \quad\ -6}$

$3 = -3a$

$\dfrac{3}{-3} = \dfrac{\cancel{-3}a}{\cancel{-3}}$

$-1 = a$

CHECK: $a = -1$

$9 \overset{?}{=} 6 - 3(-1)$

$9 \overset{?}{=} 6 + 3$

$9 \overset{\checkmark}{=} 9$

27. $20 = 3w - 1$
    $\underline{+1 \qquad\quad + 1}$
    $\overline{21 = 3w}$
    $\dfrac{21}{3} = \dfrac{\cancel{3}w}{\cancel{3}}$

    $7 = w$

CHECK: $w = 7$ $20 \overset{?}{=} 3(7) - 1$
                             $20 \overset{?}{=} 21 - 1$
                             $20 \overset{\checkmark}{=} 20$

29. $8y + 4 = 5y + 19$
    $\underline{-5y \qquad\quad -5y}$
    $3y + 4 = \qquad 19$
    $\underline{\quad - 4 \qquad\quad - 4}$
    $3y \qquad = \qquad 15$
    $\dfrac{\cancel{3}y}{\cancel{3}} \qquad = \qquad \dfrac{15}{3}$

    $y \qquad = \qquad 5$

CHECK: $y = 5$ $8(5) + 4 \overset{?}{=} 5(5) + 19$
                              $40 + 4 \overset{?}{=} 25 + 19$
                                    $44 \overset{\checkmark}{=} 44$

31. $2a + 5 = 4a + 13$
    $\underline{-2a \qquad\quad -2a}$
    $\qquad 5 = 2a + 13$
    $\underline{-13 \qquad\quad - 13}$
    $\qquad -8 = 2a$
    $\qquad \dfrac{-8}{2} = \dfrac{2\cancel{a}}{\cancel{2}}$

    $\qquad -4 = a$

CHECK: $a = -4$ $2(-4) + 5 \overset{?}{=} 4(-4) + 13$
                               $-8 + 5 \overset{?}{=} -16 + 13$
                                    $-3 \overset{\checkmark}{=} -3$

33. $5r - 8 = 3r - 20$
    $\underline{-3r \qquad\quad -3r}$
    $2r - 8 = \qquad -12$
    $\dfrac{\cancel{2}r}{\cancel{2}} \qquad = \qquad \dfrac{-12}{2}$

    $r \qquad = \qquad -6$

CHECK: $r = -6$ $5(-6) - 8 \overset{?}{=} 3(-6) - 20$
                               $-30 - 8 \overset{?}{=} -18 - 20$
                               $-38 \overset{\checkmark}{=} -38$

35. $10 - x = 4 - 3x$
    $\underline{\quad +3x \qquad + 3x}$
    $10 + 2x = \qquad 4$
    $\underline{-10 \qquad\quad -10}$
    $\qquad 2x = \qquad -6$
    $\qquad \dfrac{\cancel{2}x}{\cancel{2}} = \dfrac{-6}{2}$

    $\qquad x = -3$

CHECK: $x = -3$ $10 - (-3) \overset{?}{=} 4 - 3(-3)$
                                 $10 + 3 \overset{?}{=} 4 + 9$
                                    $13 \overset{\checkmark}{=} 13$

37.
$$
\begin{array}{rcl}
-4 - 3u &=& -2 - u \\
\underline{+ 3u} & & \underline{+ 3u} \\
-4 &=& -2 + 2u \\
\underline{+2} & & \underline{+2} \\
-2 &=& 2u \\
\dfrac{-2}{2} &=& \dfrac{2u}{2} \\
-1 &=& u
\end{array}
$$

CHECK: $u = -1$ $-4 - 3(-1) \overset{?}{=} -2 - (-1)$

$-4 + 3 \overset{?}{=} -2 + 1$

$-1 \overset{\checkmark}{=} -1$

39.
$$
\begin{array}{rcl}
x + 7 &=& 7 - x \\
\underline{+x} & & \underline{+ x} \\
2x + 7 &=& 7 \\
\underline{- 7} & & \underline{-7} \\
2x &=& 0 \\
\dfrac{2x}{2} &=& \dfrac{0}{2} \\
x &=& 0
\end{array}
$$

CHECK: $x = 0$ $0 + 7 \overset{?}{=} 7 - 0$

$7 \overset{\checkmark}{=} 7$

41.
$$
\begin{array}{rcl}
x + 7 &=& 7 + x \\
\underline{-x} & & \underline{- x} \\
7 &=& 7
\end{array}
$$

identity

43.
$$
\begin{array}{rcl}
x - 7 &=& 7 + x \\
\underline{-x} & & \underline{- x} \\
-7 &=& 7
\end{array}
$$

contradiction

45.
$$
\begin{array}{rcl}
x - 7 &=& 7 - x \\
\underline{+x} & & \underline{+ x} \\
2x - 7 &=& 7 \\
\underline{+ 7} & & \underline{+7} \\
2x &=& 14 \\
\dfrac{2x}{2} &=& \dfrac{14}{2} \\
x &=& 7
\end{array}
$$

CHECK: $x = 7$ $7 - 7 \overset{?}{=} 7 - 7$

$0 \overset{\checkmark}{=} 0$

47.
$$
\begin{array}{rcl}
2(t + 1) + 3t &=& 27 \\
2t + 2 + 3t &=& 27 \\
5t + 2 &=& 27 \\
\underline{-2} & & \underline{-2} \\
5t &=& 25 \\
\dfrac{5t}{5} &=& \dfrac{25}{5} \\
t &=& 5
\end{array}
$$

CHECK: $t = 5$ $2(5+1)+3(5) \overset{?}{=} 27$

$2(6)+3(5) \overset{?}{=} 27$

$12 + 15 \overset{?}{=} 27$

$27 \overset{\checkmark}{=} 27$

49. $2(y + 3) + 4(y - 2) = 22$ CHECK: $y = 4$ $2(4+3) + 4(4-2) \overset{?}{=} 22$

$$2y + 6 + 4y - 8 = 22$$
$$6y - 2 = 22$$
$$\underline{+\ 2+2}$$
$$6y = 24$$
$$\frac{\cancel{6}y}{\cancel{6}} = \frac{24}{6}$$

$$y = 4$$

$2(7) + 4(2) \overset{?}{=} 22$

$14 + 8 \overset{?}{=} 22$

$22 \overset{\checkmark}{=} 22$

51. $4 + 3(3y - 5) = 2y - 11 + y$ CHECK: $y = 0$ $4+3(3(0)-5) \overset{?}{=} 2(0)-11+0$

$$4 + 9y - 15 = 27 - 11 + y$$
$$9y - 11 = 3y - 11$$
$$\underline{-\ 3y -3y}$$
$$6y - 11 = -11$$
$$\underline{+\ 11 +11}$$
$$6y = 0$$
$$\frac{\cancel{6}y}{\cancel{6}} = \frac{0}{6}$$

$$y = 0$$

$4 + 3(0 - 5) \overset{?}{=} 0 - 11 + 0$

$4 + 3(-5) \overset{?}{=} -11$

$4 - 15 \overset{?}{=} -11$

$-11 \overset{\checkmark}{=} -11$

53. $3(a - 2) + 4(2 - a) = a + 2(a + 1)$ CHECK: $a = 0$ $3(0-2)+4(2-0) \overset{?}{=} 0+2(0+1)$

$$3a - 6 + 8 - 4a = a + 2a + 2$$
$$-a + 2 = 3a + 2$$
$$\underline{+a +a}$$
$$2 = 4a + 2$$
$$\underline{-2 -2}$$
$$0 = 4a$$
$$\frac{0}{4} = \frac{\cancel{4}a}{\cancel{4}}$$

$$0 = a$$

$3(-2) + 4(2) \overset{?}{=} 0 + 2(1)$

$-6 + 8 \overset{?}{=} 9 + 2$

$2 \overset{\cancel{=}}{} 2$

55. $8z - 3(z - 2) = -9$ CHECK: $z = -3$ $8(-3)-3(-3-2) \overset{?}{=} -9$

$$8z - 3z + 6 = -9$$
$$5z + 6 = -9$$
$$\underline{-\ 6 -6}$$
$$5z = -15$$
$$\frac{\cancel{5}z}{\cancel{5}} = \frac{-15}{5}$$

$$z = -3$$

$8(-3) - 3(5) \overset{?}{=} -9$

$-24 + 15 \overset{?}{=} -9$

$-9 \overset{\cancel{=}}{} -9$

57.

$$3t - 5(t - 1) = 23$$
$$3t - 5t + 5 = 23$$
$$-2t + 5 = 23$$
$$ - 5 \quad -5$$
$$\overline{ -2t = 18}$$
$$\frac{\cancel{-2}t}{\cancel{-2}} = \frac{18}{-2}$$
$$t \quad = -9$$

CHECK: $t = -9$ $\quad 3(-9)-5(-9-1) \overset{?}{=} 23$

$$3(-9) - 5(10) \overset{?}{=} 23$$
$$-27 + 50 \overset{?}{=} 23$$
$$23 \overset{\checkmark}{=} 23$$

59.

$$3 - 5(t - 1) = 23$$
$$3 - 5t + 5 = 23$$
$$-5t + 8 = 23$$
$$ - 8 \quad -8$$
$$\overline{ -5t = 15}$$
$$\frac{\cancel{-5}t}{\cancel{-5}} = \frac{15}{-5}$$
$$t \quad = -3$$

CHECK: $t = -3$ $\quad 3-5(-3-1) \overset{?}{=} 23$

$$3 - 5(-4) \overset{?}{=} 23$$
$$-27 + 50 \overset{?}{=} 23$$
$$23 \overset{\checkmark}{=} 23$$

61.

$$2(y-3) - 3(y-5) = 5y - 5(y-2)$$
$$2y - 6 - 3y + 15 = 5y - 5y + 10$$
$$-y + 9 = 10$$
$$ - 9 \quad -9$$
$$\overline{ -y = 1}$$
$$\frac{-y}{-1} = \frac{1}{-1}$$
$$y \quad = -1$$

CHECK: $y = -1$

$$2(-1-3) - 3(-1-5) \overset{?}{=} 5(-1) - 5(-1-2)$$
$$2(-4) - 3(-6) \overset{?}{=} 5(-1) - 5(-3)$$
$$-8 + 18 \overset{?}{=} -5 + 15$$
$$10 \overset{\checkmark}{=} 10$$

63.

$$4x - 3(x + 8) = 5x - 2(x - 12) - 2x$$
$$4x - 3x - 24 = 5x - 2x + 24 + 2x$$
$$x - 24 = x + 24$$
$$ -x \qquad -x$$
$$\overline{ -24 = \qquad 24}$$

contradiction

65.

$$a - (5-3a) = 7a - (a-3) - 8$$
$$a - 5 + 3a = 7a - a + 3 - 8$$
$$4a - 5 = 6a - 5$$
$$-4a \qquad -4a$$
$$\overline{ -5 = 2a - 5}$$
$$+5 \qquad + 5$$
$$\overline{ 0 = 2a}$$
$$\frac{0}{2} = \frac{\cancel{2}a}{\cancel{2}}$$
$$0 = a$$

CHECK: $a = 0$

$$0 - (5-3(0)) \overset{?}{=} 7(0) - (0-3) - 8$$
$$0 - (5 - 0) \overset{?}{=} 0 - (-3) - 8$$
$$0 - 5 \overset{?}{=} 0 + 3 - 8$$
$$-5 \overset{\checkmark}{=} -5$$

67. $x^2 + 3x - 7 = x^2 - 5x + 1$ CHECK: $x = 1$

$\underline{-x^2 \qquad\qquad -x^2}$

$$
\begin{array}{rcr}
3x - 7 &=& -5x + 1 \\
+5x && +5x \\
\hline
8x - 7 &=& 1 \\
+7 && +7 \\
\hline
8x &=& 8 \\
\frac{\not{8}x}{\not{8}} &=& \frac{8}{8} \\
\\
x &=& 1
\end{array}
$$

$(1)^2 + 3(1) - 7 \overset{?}{=} (1)^2 - 5(1) + 1$

$1 + 3 - 7 \overset{?}{=} 1 - 5 + 1$

$-3 \overset{\checkmark}{=} -3$

69. $x(x + 2) + 3x = x(x - 1) - 12$ CHECK: $x = -2$

$$
\begin{array}{rcr}
x^2 + 2x + 3x &=& x^2 - x - 12 \\
\hline
2x + 3x &=& -x - 12 \\
5x &=& -x - 12 \\
+x && +x \\
\hline
6x &=& -12 \\
\frac{\not{6}x}{\not{6}} &=& \frac{-12}{6} \\
\\
x &=& -2
\end{array}
$$

$-2(-2+2) + 3(-2) \overset{?}{=} (-2)(-2-1) - 12$

$-2(0) + 3(-2) \overset{?}{=} (-2)(-3) - 12$

$0 - 6 \overset{?}{=} 6 - 12$

$-6 \overset{\checkmark}{=} -6$

71. $2z(z+1) + 3(z+2) = 3z(z+2) - z^2$

$2z^2 + 2z + 3z + 6 = 3z^2 + 6z - z^2$

$2z^2 + 5z + 6 = 2z^2 + 6z$ CHECK: $z = 6$

$\underline{-2z^2 \qquad\qquad -2z^2}$

$$
\begin{array}{rcr}
5z + 6 &=& 6z \\
-5z && -5z \\
\hline
6 &=& z
\end{array}
$$

$2(6)(6+1) + 3(6+2) \overset{?}{=} 3(6)(6+2) - (6)^2$

$2(6)(7) + 3(8) \overset{?}{=} 3(6)(8) - 36$

$84 + 24 \overset{?}{=} 144 - 36$

$108 \overset{\checkmark}{=} 108$

73.   To check your answer after you have solved an equation, write your answer in place of the variable in the original equation. If the result is a true statement, then your answer satisfies the equation.

74.   (a) After subtracting 4 from both sides of the equation, we should get $2x = 4$, not $2x = 12$.

(b) Subtracting 3 from $3x$ will not give x. (These are not like terms.)

(c) When we divide both sides of the equation by 3, we must remember to divide both terms on the left. We would then get $x - 2 = 4$, not $x - 6 = 4$.

(d) We cannot divide both sides by x, since x might be equal to 0. (In this case, it is!)

(e) In the last step, we must divide both sides by the same amount. If we divide by -3, we get $\frac{-3x}{-3} = \frac{-6}{-3}$ which gives x = 2.

(f) We need to divide the final equation by -1 to obtain x = -2.

(g) This is correct as written.

Exercises 3.3

1.   Let x = one of the numbers
      3x + 4 = the other number

$$
\begin{array}{rl}
x + (3x + 4) &= 24 \\
4x + 4 &= 24 \\
- 4 & -4 \\
\hline
4x &= 20 \\
\frac{4x}{4} &= \frac{20}{4} \\
\\
x &= 5
\end{array}
$$

CHECK: 19 is 4 more than 3 times 5 and the sum of 5 and 19 is 24.

Then 3x + 4 = 3(5) + 4 = 19. Thus, the numbers are 5 and 19.

3.   Let x = one of the numbers
      4x - 5 = the other number

$$
\begin{array}{rl}
x + (4x - 5) &= 10 \\
5x - 5 &= 10 \\
+ 5 & +5 \\
\hline
5x &= 15 \\
\frac{5x}{5} &= \frac{15}{5} \\
\\
x &= 3
\end{array}
$$

CHECK: 7 is 5 less than 4 times 3 and the sum of 3 and 7 is 10.

Then 4x - 5 = 4(3) - 5 = 7. Thus, the numbers are 3 and 7.

5.   Let x = the number

$$x + (5x + 3) = 27$$
$$6x + 3 = 27$$
$$\underline{\quad -3 \qquad -3}$$
$$6x \qquad = 24$$
$$\frac{6x}{6} = \frac{24}{6}$$

$$x \qquad = 4$$

CHECK: 3 more than 5 times 4 is 23, and 4 + 23 = 27.

7.   Let x = the number

$$(2x + 4) - x = 12$$
$$x + 4 = 12$$
$$\underline{\quad - 4 \qquad -4}$$
$$x \qquad = 8$$

CHECK: 4 more than twice 8 is 20, and 20 - 8 = 12.

Thus, the number is 8.

9.   Let x = the smallest number
2x - 5 = the middle number
2x+10 = the largest number

$$x + (2x - 5) + (2x + 10) = 80$$
$$5x + 5 = 80$$
$$\underline{\qquad -5 \qquad -5}$$
$$5x \qquad = 75$$
$$\frac{5x}{5} = \frac{75}{5}$$

$$x \qquad = 15$$

CHECK: 25 is less than twice 15, and 40 is 10 more than twice 15. The sum of 15, 25, and 40 is 80.

Then 2x - 5 = 2(15) - 5 = 25 and 2x + 10 = 2(15) + 10 = 40.
Thus, the numbers are 15, 25, and 40.

11.   Let W = width of the rectangle
2W + 1 = length of the rectangle

$$2W + 2(2W + 1) = 26$$
$$2W + 4W + 2 = 26$$
$$6W + 2 = 26$$
$$\underline{\qquad - 2 \qquad -2}$$
$$6W \qquad = 24$$
$$\frac{6W}{6} = \frac{24}{6}$$

$$W \qquad = 4$$

CHECK: 9 is one more than twice 4, and 2(4) + 2(9) = 8 + 18 = 26.

Then $2W + 1 = 2(4) + 1 = 9$.   Thus, the rectangle has a width of 4 cm. and a length of 9 cm.

13.   Let x = second side of the triangle
$x + 10$ = first side of the triangle
$3x$ = third side of the triangle

$$x + (x + 10) + 3x = 45$$
$$5x + 10 = 45$$
$$\underline{ - 10 \quad -10}$$
$$5x = 35$$
$$\frac{\cancel{5}x}{\cancel{5}} = \frac{35}{5}$$
$$x = 7$$

CHECK: 17 is 10 more than 7, 21 is three times 7, and $7 + 17 + 21 = 45$.

Then $x + 10 = 7 + 10 = 17$ and $3x = 3(7) = 21$.   Thus, the lengths of the three sides are 7 inches, 17 inches, and 21 inches.

15.   Let W = width of the rectangle
$3W - 2$ = length of the rectangle
New perimeter = original perimeter + 12

$$2(3W) + 2(3W - 2 - 2) = 2W + 2(3W - 2) + 12$$
$$2(3W) + 2(3W - 4) = 2W + 2(3W - 2) + 12$$
$$6W + 6W - 8 = 2W + 6W - 4 + 12$$
$$12W - 8 = 8W + 8$$
$$\underline{-8W \qquad\qquad -8W}$$
$$4W - 8 = 8$$
$$\underline{+ 8 \qquad\qquad + 8}$$
$$4W = 16$$
$$\frac{\cancel{4}W}{\cancel{4}} = \frac{16}{4}$$
$$W = 4$$

CHECK: 10 is 2 less than 3 times 4. Original perimeter is $2(4) + 2(1) = 28$. New perimeter is $2(12) + 2(8) = 40$, which is 12 more than 28.

Then $3W - 2 = 3(4) - 2 = 10$.   Thus, the original dimensions of the rectangle are 4 and 10.

17.   Let x = number of 12¢ stamps
        29 - x = number of 15¢ stamps

$$12x + 15(29 - x) = 399$$
$$12x + 435 - 15x = 399$$
$$-3x + 435 = 399$$
$$- 435 \quad -435$$
$$-3x = -36$$
$$\frac{-3x}{-3} = \frac{-36}{-3}$$

$$x = 12$$

CHECK: 12 + 17 = 29. 12 12¢ stamps cost $1.44 and 17 15¢ stamps cost $2.55. The total cost is $1.44 + $2.55 = $3.99.

Then 29 - x = 29 - 12 = 17. Thus, Jack bought 12 12¢ stamps and 17 15¢ stamps.

19.   Let x = number of nickels
            2x = number of dimes
        2x - 3 = number of quarters

$$5x + 10(2x) + 25(2x - 3) = 450$$
$$5x + 20x + 50x - 75 = 450$$
$$75x - 75 = 450$$
$$+ 75 \quad +75$$
$$75x = 525$$
$$\frac{75x}{75} = \frac{525}{75}$$

$$x = 7$$

CHECK: The value of 7 nickels is $.35. The value of 14 dimes is $1.40. The value of 11 quarters is $2.75. The total value of the coins is $.35 + $1.40 + $2.75 = $4.50.

Then 2x = 2(7) = 14 and 2x - 3 = 2(7) - 3 = 11. Thus, there are 7 nickels, 14 dimes and 11 quarters in the collection.

21.   Let x = number of books that Susan sold.
        80 - x = number of magazine subscriptions that Susan sold.

$$1.50x + 2.25(80 - x) = 157.50$$
$$1.50x + 180 - 2.25x = 157.50$$
$$-.75x + 180 = 157.50$$
$$- 180 \quad -180$$
$$-.75x = -22.50$$
$$\frac{-.75x}{-.75} = \frac{-22.50}{-.75}$$

$$x = 30$$

CHECK: Susan earned 30($1.50) = $45 from selling books and 50($2.25) = $112.50 from selling magazine subscriptions. Her total commission was $45 + $112.50 = $157.50

Thus, Susan sold 30 books.

23.   Let t = the time (in hours) that each train travels up to the
              point that they pass by each other.
      Using d = rt,
          20t = distance traveled by slower train and
          40t = distance traveled by faster train
      Then

      20t + 40t = 300   CHECK: In 5 hours, the slower
            60t = 300   train travels 20(5) = 100
            ~~60t~~ = ~~300~~   miles and the faster one
            ~~60~~   60   travels 40(5) = 200 miles.
                                       100 + 200 = 300 miles.
              t =   5

      Thus, the trains pass by each other five hours later than 10:00
      a.m., or at 3:00 p.m.

25.   Let t = the time (in hours) traveled by the person who left
              earlier
      t - 1 = the time (in hours) traveled by the person who left 1 hour
              later

      55t + 45(t - 1) = 355   CHECK: The person who left earlier
       55t + 45t - 45 = 355   travels 4(55) = 220 km.
          100t - 45 = 355   The person who left later
                + 45   +45   travels 3(45) = 135 km.
          _____   The distance between them
          100t   = 400   is 220 + 135 = 355 km.
          ~~100t~~   = 400
          ~~100~~   100

              t   =   4

      Thus, the people will be 355 kilometers apart four hours later
      than 2:00 p.m., or at 6:00 p.m.

27.   Let t = number of hours needed to complete the running section
      6 - t = number of hours needed to complete the bicycling
              section

      18t + 50(6 - t) = 172   CHECK: The first person runs a
       18t + 300 - 50t = 172   distance of 18(4) = 72 km.
          -32t + 300 = 172   The second person bicycles
               - 300   -300   a distance of 50(6 - 4) =
          _____   50(2) = 100 km. The total
              -32t   =-128   distance covered is 72 +
              ~~-32t~~   =-128   100 = 172 km.
              ~~-32~~   -32

              t   =   4

Thus, it takes 4 hours to complete the running section of the course. Since the running rate is 18 k.p.h., the running section of the course is 18(4) = 72 kilometers.

29. Let t = number of hours that the trainee works.
     t - 2 = number of hours that the secretary works.

$$7t + 15(t - 2) = 124$$
$$7t + 15t - 30 = 124$$
$$22t - 30 = 124$$
$$\underline{+ 30 \quad +30}$$
$$22t = 154$$
$$\frac{22t}{22} = \frac{154}{22}$$
$$t = 7$$

CHECK: The trainee processes 7(7) = 49 forms. The secretary processes 15(7 - 2) = 15(5) = 75 forms. The total number of forms is 49 + 75 = 124.

Thus, the pile of forms will be finished 7 hours after 9:00 a.m., or at 4:00 p.m.

Exercises 3.4

1. $x + 4 < 3$

     $-2 + 4 \overset{?}{<} 3$

     $2 \overset{\checkmark}{<} 3$ Therefore, -2 satisfies the inequality.

3. $a - 2 > -1$

     $-3 - 2 \overset{?}{>} -1$

     $-5 \overset{\checkmark}{>} -1$ Therefore, -3 does not satisfy the inequality.

5. $-y + 3 \leq 5$

     $-(-2) + 3 \overset{?}{\leq} 5$

     $2 + 3 \overset{?}{\leq} 5$

     $5 \overset{\checkmark}{\leq} 5$ Therefore, -2 satisfies the inequality.

7. $2 - x \geq -8$

     $2 - 6 \overset{?}{\geq} -8$

     $-4 \overset{\checkmark}{\geq} -8$ Therefore, 6 satisfies the inequality.

9. $2z - 5 < -3$

   $2(1) - 5 \overset{?}{<} -3$

   $2 - 5 \overset{?}{<} -3$

   $-3 \not< -3$ Therefore, 1 does not satisfy the inequality.

11. $5 + 2u > 12$

   $5 + 2(3) \overset{?}{>} 12$

   $5 + 6 \overset{?}{>} 12$

   $11 \not> 12$ Therefore, 3 does not satisfy the inequality.

13. $7 - 4x < 8$

   $7 - 4(-4) \overset{?}{<} 8$

   $7 + 16 \overset{?}{<} 8$

   $23 \not< 8$ Therefore, -4 does not satisfy the inequality.

15. $-2 < 8 - x < 3$

   $-2 \overset{?}{<} 8 - 6 \overset{?}{<} 3$

   $-2 \overset{\checkmark}{<} \quad 2 \quad \overset{\checkmark}{<} 3$ Therefore, 6 satisfies the inequality.

17. $6 + 2(a - 3) < 1$

   $6 + 2(-2 - 3) \overset{?}{<} 1$

   $6 + 2(-5) \overset{?}{<} 1$

   $6 - 10 \overset{?}{<} 1$

   $-4 \overset{\checkmark}{<} 1$ Therefore, -2 satisfies the inequality.

19. $-12 < 9 - 5(x + 1) < -5$

   $-12 \overset{?}{<} 9 - 5(3 + 1) \overset{?}{<} -5$

   $-12 \overset{?}{<} 9 - 5(4) \overset{?}{<} -5$

   $-12 \overset{?}{<} 9 - 20 \overset{?}{<} -5$

   $-12 \overset{\checkmark}{<} -11 \overset{\checkmark}{<} -5$

   Therefore, 3 satisfies the inequality.

21. $x - 3 < 2$
       $\underline{\ \ + 3\ \ \ +3}$
       $x\ \ \ \ \ \ < 5$

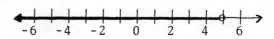

23. $a + 7 > 4$
       $\underline{\ \ - 7\ \ \ -7}$
       $a\ \ \ \ \ \ > -3$

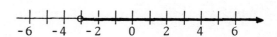

25. $w + 2 < -4$
       $\underline{\ \ - 2\ \ \ -2}$
       $w\ \ \ \ \ \ < -6$

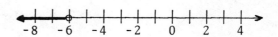

27. $x + 3 > 0$
       $\underline{\ \ - 3\ \ \ -3}$
       $x\ \ \ \ \ \ > -3$

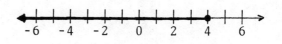

29. $3x \leq 12$

       $\dfrac{\cancel{3}x}{\cancel{3}} \leq \dfrac{12}{3}$

       $x \leq 4$

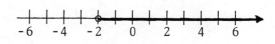

31. $4y > -8$

       $\dfrac{\cancel{4}y}{\cancel{4}} > \dfrac{-8}{4}$

       $y > -2$

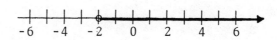

33. $-3x < 6$

       $\dfrac{-3x}{-3} > \dfrac{6}{-3}$

       $x > -2$

35. $-3x < -6$

$\dfrac{\cancel{-3}x}{\cancel{-3}} > \dfrac{-6}{-3}$

$x > -2$

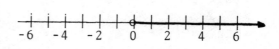

37. $7a > 0$

$\dfrac{\cancel{7}a}{\cancel{7}} > \dfrac{0}{7}$

$a > 0$

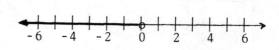

39. $-7a \geq 0$

$\dfrac{\cancel{-7}a}{\cancel{-7}} \leq \dfrac{0}{-7}$

$a \leq 0$

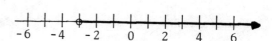

41. $-x < 3$
$(-1)(-x) > (-1)(3)$
$x > -3$

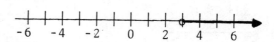

43. $-x < -3$
$(-1)(-x) > (-1)(-3)$
$x > 3$

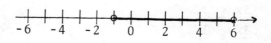

45.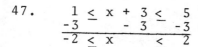

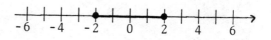

47.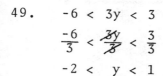

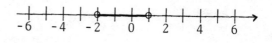

49. $-6 < 3y < 3$

$\dfrac{-6}{3} < \dfrac{\cancel{3}y}{\cancel{3}} < \dfrac{3}{3}$

$-2 < y < 1$

51. $0 \leq -2x < 2$

$\dfrac{0}{-2} \geq \dfrac{\cancel{-2}x}{\cancel{-2}} > \dfrac{2}{-2}$

$0 \geq x > -1$
or
$-1 < x \leq 0$

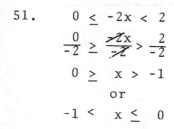

53. $-5 < -x < -1$
       $(-1)(-5) > (-1)(-x) > (-1)(-1)$
       $\qquad 5 > \qquad x > 1$

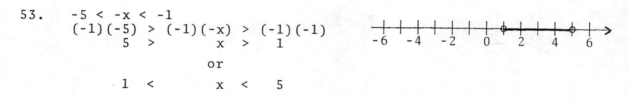

                              or

       $1 < \qquad x < 5$

55.   One number is less than a second number if the first number is
       located to the left of the second on the number line. (Equi-
       valently, we could say that the second number is located to the
       right of the first on the number line.)

56.   If we begin with an inequality, we may add the same quantity to
       both sides, subtract the same quantity from both sides or
       multiply or divide both sides by the same positive quantity and
       get another inequality with the same symbol. If we multiply or
       divide both sides by the same negative quantity, we get another
       inequality with the reversed symbol.

57.   When we multiply or divide both sides of an equality by the
       same quantity, it does not matter whether the quantity is
       positive or negative. This is not the case for inequalities
       (see (56)).

58. $2 < x \leq 5$ means that x is between 2 and 5 on the number line,
       possibly equal to 5, but not equal to 2.

Exercises 3.5

1. $x + 5 < 3$
      $\underline{\quad - 5 \qquad -5}$
      $x \qquad < -2$

3. $a - 2 > -3$
      $\underline{\quad + 2 \qquad +2}$
      $a \qquad > -1$

5. $2y < 8$

      $\dfrac{2y}{2} < \dfrac{8}{2}$

      $y < 4$

7. $2y > -8$

      $\dfrac{2y}{2} > \dfrac{-8}{2}$

      $y > -4$

9. $-2y < 8$

$\dfrac{-2y}{-2} > \dfrac{8}{-2}$

$y > -4$

11. $-2y > -8$

$\dfrac{-2y}{-2} < \dfrac{-8}{-2}$

$y < 4$

13. $-x < 4$

$\dfrac{-x}{-1} > \dfrac{4}{-1}$ or

$x > -4$

$-x < 4$

$(-1)(-x) > (-1)(4)$

$x > -4$

15. $-1 > -y$

$\dfrac{-1}{-1} < \dfrac{-y}{-1}$ or

$-1 < y$

$-1 > -y$

$(-1)(-1) < (-1)(-y)$

$1 < y$

17. $5x + 3 \le 8$

$ -3 \quad -3$

$\overline{5x \qquad \le \quad 5}$

$\dfrac{5x}{5} \qquad \le \dfrac{5}{5}$

$x \qquad \le 1$

19. $2x - 9 \ge 15$

$ + 9 \quad +9$

$\overline{2x \qquad \ge \ 24}$

$\dfrac{2x}{2} \qquad \ge \dfrac{24}{2}$

$x \qquad \ge 12$

21. $2(z - 3) + 4 > -6$

$2z - 6 + 4 > -6$

$2z - 2 > -6$

$ + 2 \qquad +2$

$\overline{2z \qquad > -4}$

$\dfrac{2z}{2} \qquad > \dfrac{-4}{2}$

$z \qquad > -2$

23. $3(x + 4) + 2(x - 1) < 20$

$$3x + 12 + 2x - 2 < 20$$

$$5x + 10 < 20$$

$$\underline{\quad - 10 \quad -10}$$

$$5x \qquad < 10$$

$$\frac{\cancel{5}x}{\cancel{5}} \quad < \frac{10}{5}$$

$$x \qquad < \quad 2$$

25. $5(w + 3) - 7w \leq 7$

$$15w + 15 - 7w \leq 7$$

$$-2w + 15 \leq 7$$

$$\underline{\quad - 15 \quad -15}$$

$$\frac{\cancel{-2}w}{\cancel{-2}} \qquad \geq \frac{-8}{-2}$$

$$w \qquad \geq \quad 4$$

27. $3(a + 4) - 4(a - 1) < 10$

$$3a + 12 - 4a + 4 < 10$$

$$-a + 16 < 10$$

$$\underline{\quad - 16 \quad -16}$$

$$-a \qquad < -6$$

$$\frac{-a}{-1} \qquad > \frac{-6}{-1}$$

$$a \qquad > \quad 6$$

29. $4(y - 3) - (3y - 12) \geq 2$

$$4y - 12 - 3y + 12 \geq 2$$

$$y \geq 2$$

31. $2(u + 2) - 2(u - 1) < 5$

$$2u + 4 - 2u + 2 < 5$$

$$6 < 5 \qquad \text{contradiction}$$

33. $4(x - 2) - (4x - 3) < 6$

$$4x - 8 - 4x + 3 < 6$$

$$-5 < 6 \qquad \text{identity}$$

35. $x + 3 < 2x + 7$

$$\underline{-x \qquad -x}$$

$$3 < x + 7$$

$$\underline{-7 \qquad - 7}$$

$$-4 < x$$

37.
$$
\begin{array}{rcr}
5t - 3 & \geq & 3t - 9 \\
-3t & & -3t \\
\hline
2t - 3 & \geq & 9 \\
+ 3 & & + 3 \\
\hline
2t & \geq & 12 \\
\dfrac{2t}{2} & \geq & \dfrac{12}{2} \\
t & \geq & 6
\end{array}
$$

39.
$$
\begin{array}{rcl}
2(a - 5) + 3a & > & 6a - 6 \\
2a - 10 + 3a & > & 6a - 6 \\
5a - 10 & > & 6a - 6 \\
-5a & & -5a \\
\hline
-10 & > & a - 6 \\
+ 6 & & + 6 \\
\hline
-4 & > & a
\end{array}
$$

41.
$$
\begin{array}{rcl}
4(w + 2) - 3(w - 1) & > & 5(w - 1) - 5w \\
4w + 8 - 3w + 3 & > & 5w - 5 - 5w \\
w + 11 & > & -5 \\
- 11 & & -11 \\
\hline
w & > & -16
\end{array}
$$

43.
$$
\begin{array}{rcl}
2y - 4(y + 1) & \leq & 8 - (y + 2) \\
2y - 4y - 4 & \leq & 8 - y - 2 \\
-2y - 4 & \leq & 6 - y \\
+2y & & +2y \\
\hline
-4 & \leq & 6 + y \\
-6 & & -6 \\
\hline
-10 & \leq & y
\end{array}
$$

45.
$$
\begin{array}{rcccc}
2 & < & x + 7 & < & 10 \\
-7 & & - 7 & & -7 \\
\hline
-5 & < & x & < & 3
\end{array}
$$

47.
$$
\begin{array}{rcccc}
3 & < & 2a + 5 & < & 7 \\
-5 & & - 5 & & -5 \\
\hline
-2 & < & 2a & < & 2 \\
\dfrac{-2}{2} & < & \dfrac{2a}{2} & < & \dfrac{2}{2} \\
-1 & < & a & < & 1
\end{array}
$$

49.
$$
\begin{array}{rcccc}
-5 & \leq & -4y + 3 & < & 7 \\
-3 & & - 3 & & -3 \\
\hline
-8 & \leq & -4y & < & 4 \\
\dfrac{-8}{-4} & \geq & \dfrac{-4y}{-4} & > & \dfrac{4}{-4} \\
2 & \geq & y & > & -1
\end{array}
$$

51.
$$\begin{array}{rcccc} 1 & \leq & 6 & - x < & 3 \\ -6 & & -6 & & -6 \\ \hline -5 & \leq & & -x < & -3 \end{array}$$

$$\frac{-5}{-1} \geq \quad \frac{-x}{-1} > \frac{-3}{-1}$$

$$5 \geq \quad x > 3$$

53.
$$\begin{array}{rccc} x & + 4 & < 2x & - 1 \\ -x & & -x & \\ \hline & 4 & < x & - 1 \\ & +1 & & + 1 \\ \hline & 5 & < x \end{array}$$

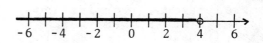

55.
$$\begin{array}{rcccc} 3(a & + 2) & - 5a & \geq 2 & - a \\ 3a & + 6 & - 5a & \geq 2 & - a \\ & -2a & + 6 & \geq 2 & - a \\ & +2a & & & +2a \\ \hline & & 6 & > 2 & + a \\ & & -2 & & -2 \\ \hline & & 4 & \geq & a \end{array}$$

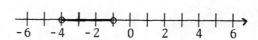

57.
$$\begin{array}{rcccc} -1 & < & x + 3 & < & 2 \\ -3 & & - 3 & & -3 \\ \hline -4 & < & x & < & -1 \end{array}$$

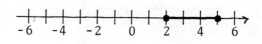

59.
$$\begin{array}{rcccc} -1 & \leq & y - 3 & \leq & 2 \\ +3 & & + 3 & & +3 \\ \hline 2 & \leq & y & \leq & 5 \end{array}$$

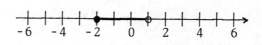

61.
$$\begin{array}{rcccc} -3 & \leq & 4t + 5 & < & 9 \\ -5 & & - 5 & & -5 \\ \hline -8 & \leq & 4t & < & 4 \end{array}$$

$$\frac{-8}{4} \leq \frac{4t}{4} \quad < \frac{4}{4}$$

$$-2 \leq t \quad < 1$$

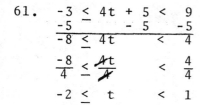

63.
$$\begin{array}{rcccc} -5 & < & 3 - 2x & \leq & 9 \\ -3 & & -3 & & -3 \\ \hline -8 & < & -2x & \leq & 6 \end{array}$$

$$\frac{-8}{2} > \frac{-2x}{-2} \geq \frac{6}{-2}$$

$$4 > \quad x \geq -3$$

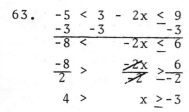

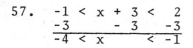
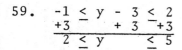
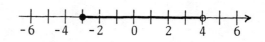

65. (a) Starting with $2 \leq -2x$, we must divide both sides of this
         inequality by -2, obtaining $\frac{2}{-2} \geq \frac{-2x}{-2}$ or $-1 \geq x$.

     (b) When we subtract 4 from both sides of the original inequality,
         the resulting inequality should read $2x < -2$, not $2x > -2$.
         (We only reverse the inequality sign when we multiply or
         divide by a negative quantity.)

     (c) We must divide both sides of the inequality $-9 > 3x$ by 3,
         giving $\frac{-9}{3} > \frac{\cancel{3}x}{\cancel{3}}$ or $-3 > x$.

66. Only part (a) makes sense, since it requires that x be a number
     between -3 and 2. Parts (b), (c), (e), and (f) all lead to
     contradictions. For instance, the inequality $-5 < x < -8$
     implies that $-5 < -8$, which is false. (The others are similar.)
     Part (d) makes no sense, since we cannot write double inequali-
     ties in which the inequality symbols point in opposite directions.

Chapter 3 Review Exercises

1. $5(x - 4) - 3(x - 3) = 3 - (14 - 2x)$
       $5x - 20 - 3x + 9 = 3 - 14 + 2x$
         $2x - 11 = 2x - 11$
    $\underline{\qquad -2x \qquad\qquad -2x \qquad}$
              $-11 = -11$ identity

3. $3a(a + 3) - a(2a + 4) = a^2 + 10$
      $3a^2 + 9a - 2a^2 - 4a = a^2 + 10$
              $a^2 + 5a = a^2 + 10$
    $\underline{\qquad -a^2 \qquad\qquad -a^2 \qquad}$
                   $5a = 10$
                   $\frac{\cancel{5}a}{\cancel{5}} = \frac{10}{5}$
                    $a = 2$ conditional equation

5. $2x - 5 = -7$
    Check $x = -6$: $2(-6) - 5 \overset{?}{\underset{?}{=}} -7$
                       $-12 - 5 \overset{?}{=} -7$
                       $-17 \neq -7$ So -6 does not satisfy the
                                            equation.
    Check $x = -1$: $2(-1) - 5 \overset{?}{=} -7$
                       $-2 - 5 \overset{?}{=} -7$
                       $-7 \overset{\checkmark}{=} -7$ So -1 satisfies the equation.

7. $4y + 3 \leq 10 - 3y$

Check $y = -1$: $4(-1) + 3 \overset{?}{\leq} 10 - 3(-1)$

$-4 + 3 \overset{?}{\leq} 10 + 3$

$-1 \overset{\checkmark}{\leq} 13$

So -1 satisfies the inequality.

Check $y = 1$: $4(1) + 3 \overset{?}{\leq} 10 - 3(1)$

$4 + 3 \overset{?}{\leq} 10 - 3$

$7 \overset{\checkmark}{\leq} 7$

So 1 satisfies the inequality.

9. $3t + 2(t - 5) = 3t - 14$

Check $t = -2$: $3(-2) + 2(-2 - 5) \overset{?}{=} 3(-2) - 14$

$3(-2) + 2(-7) \overset{?}{=} 3(-2) - 14$

$-6 - 14 \overset{?}{=} -6 - 14$

$-20 \overset{\checkmark}{=} -20$

So -2 satisfies the equation.

Check $t = 2$: $3(2) + 2(2 - 5) \overset{?}{=} 3(2) - 14$

$3(2) + 2(-3) \overset{?}{=} 3(2) - 14$

$6 - 6 \overset{?}{=} 6 - 14$

$0 \neq -8$

So 2 does not satisfy the equation.

11. $8 - 3(x - 2) > x - 4$

Check $x = -5$: $8 - 3(-5 - 2) \overset{?}{>} -5 - 4$

$8 - 3(-7) \overset{?}{>} -5 - 4$

$8 + 21 \overset{?}{>} -5 - 4$

$29 \overset{\checkmark}{>} -9$

So -5 satisfies the inequality.

Check $x = 5$: $8 - 3(5 - 2) \overset{?}{>} 5 - 4$

$8 - 3(3) \overset{?}{>} 5 - 4$

$8 - 9 \overset{?}{>} 5 - 4$

$-1 \not> 1$

So 5 does not satisfy the inequality.

13. $a^2 + (a - 2)^2 = 20$

Check a = -2: $(-2)^2 + (-2 - 2)^2 \stackrel{?}{=} 20$

$(-2)^2 + (-4)^2 \stackrel{?}{=} 20$

$4 + 16 \stackrel{?}{=} 20$

$20 \stackrel{\checkmark}{=} 20$

So -2 satisfies the equation.

Check a = 2: $(2)^2 + (2 - 2)^2 \stackrel{?}{=} 20$

$(2)^2 + (0)^2 \stackrel{?}{=} 20$

$4 + 0 \stackrel{?}{=} 20$

$4 \neq 20$

So 2 does not satisfy the equation.

15. $\begin{aligned} 5x + 8 &= 2x - 7 \\ -2x \quad\quad &\quad -2x \\ \hline 3x + 8 &= \quad -7 \\ -8 &\quad -8 \\ \hline 3x &= \quad -15 \\ \frac{3x}{3} &= \frac{-15}{3} \\ x &= \quad -5 \end{aligned}$

17. $2(y + 4) - 2y = 8$

$2y + 8 - 2y = 8$

$8 = 8$ identity

19. $2(3a + 4) + 4 = 3(a - 1)$

$6a + 8 + 4 = 3a - 3$

$\begin{aligned} 6a + 12 &= 3a - 3 \\ -3a \quad\quad &\quad -3a \\ \hline 3a + 12 &= \quad -3 \\ -12 &\quad -12 \\ \hline 3a &= \quad -15 \\ \frac{3a}{3} &= \frac{-15}{3} \\ a &= \quad -5 \end{aligned}$

21. $8x - 3(x - 4) = 4(x + 3) + 28$

$$8x - 3x + 12 = 4x + 12 + 28$$
$$5x + 12 = 4x + 40$$
$$\underline{-4x \qquad\qquad -4x}$$
$$\underline{x + 12 = \qquad 40}$$
$$\underline{\quad - 12 \qquad - 12}$$
$$x \qquad = \qquad 28$$

23. $a(a + 3) - 2(a - 1) = a(a - 1) + 6$

$$a^2 + 3a - 2a + 2 = a^2 - a + 6$$
$$a^2 + a + 2 = a^2 - a + 6$$
$$\underline{-a^2 \qquad\qquad -a^2}$$
$$\underline{a + 2 = \qquad -a + 6}$$
$$\underline{+a \qquad\qquad +a}$$
$$\underline{2a + 2 = \qquad 6}$$
$$\underline{\quad - 2 \qquad -2}$$
$$\underline{2a \quad = \qquad 4}$$
$$\frac{\cancel{2}a}{\cancel{2}} \quad = \quad \frac{4}{2}$$
$$a \quad = \quad 2$$

25. $8 - 3(x - 1) < 2$

$$8 - 3x + 3 < 2$$
$$-3x + 11 < 2$$
$$\underline{\quad - 11 \quad -11}$$
$$-3x \qquad < -9$$
$$\frac{\cancel{-3}x}{\cancel{-3}} \qquad > \frac{-9}{-3}$$
$$x \qquad > 3$$

27. $2(x - 3) - 4(x - 1) \geq 7 - x$

$$2x - 6 - 4x + 4 \geq 7 - x$$
$$-2x - 2 \geq 7 - x$$
$$\underline{+2x \qquad\qquad +2x}$$
$$\underline{-2 \geq 7 + x}$$
$$\underline{-7 \quad -7}$$
$$-9 \geq \qquad x$$

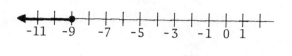

29. $2 \leq 3a + 8 < 20$

$$\underline{-8 \qquad\quad - 8 \qquad -8}$$
$$\underline{-6 \leq 3a \qquad < 12}$$
$$\frac{-6}{3} \leq \frac{\cancel{3}a}{\cancel{3}} \qquad < \frac{12}{3}$$
$$-2 \leq \quad a \qquad < 4$$

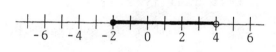

31. Let x = one of the numbers
     2x - 3 = the other number

     x + (2x - 3) = 18   CHECK: 11 is 3 less than twice 7.
          3x - 3 = 18   The sum of 7 and 11 is 18.
             + 3   +3
     ─────────────────────
            3x   = 21

            $\dfrac{3x}{3}$ = $\dfrac{21}{3}$

             x   = 7

     Then 2x - 3 = 2(7) - 3 = 11.   Thus, the numbers are 7 and 11.

33. Let W = width of the rectangle
     5W + 4 = length of the rectangle

     2W + 2(5W + 4) = 80   CHECK: 34 is 4 more than 5 times
      2W + 10W + 8 = 80   6. 2(6) + 2(34) = 80.
          12W + 8   = 80
              - 8   -8
     ──────────────────────
           12W   = 72

           $\dfrac{12W}{12}$ = $\dfrac{72}{12}$

            W   = 6

     Then 5W + 4 = 5(6) + 4 = 34.   Thus, the dimensions of the
     rectangle are 6 cm and 34 cm.

35. Let x = number of first quality skirts bought
     150-x = number of irregular skirts bought

     12x + 7(150 - x) = 1500   CHECK: 90 first quality skirts
      12x + 1050 - 7x = 1500   cost 12(90) = $1080. 60
          5x + 1050   = 1500   irregular skirts cost
               - 1050   -1050   7(60) = $420. The total
     ──────────────────────   cost of the skirts is
            5x   = 450 $1080 + $420 = $1500.

            $\dfrac{5x}{5}$ = $\dfrac{450}{5}$

             x   = 90

     Then 150 - x = 150 - 90 = 60.   Thus, the wholesaler bought 90
     first quality skirts and 60 irregular skirts.

37. Let x = number of overtime hours the laborer must work.

     6(40) + 9x > 348
       240 + 9x ≥ 348
       -240   -240
     ──────────────────
          9x > 108

          $\dfrac{9x}{9}$ ≥ $\dfrac{108}{9}$

           x > 12

Thus, the minimum number of overtime hours that laborer must work is 12.

Chapter 3 Practice Test

1. (a) $3x - 5(x - 2) = -2x + 8$
    $$3x - 5x + 10 = -2x + 8$$
    $$-2x + 10 = -2x + 8$$
    $$\underline{+2x \qquad\quad +2x}$$
    $$10 = 8 \quad \text{contradiction}$$

    (b) $3x - 5(x - 2) = -2x + 10$
    $$3x - 5x + 10 = -2x + 10$$
    $$-2x + 10 = -2x + 10 \quad \text{identity}$$

    (c) $3x - 5(x - 2) = 2x - 10$
    $$3x - 5x + 10 = 2x - 10$$
    $$-2x + 10 = 2x - 10$$
    $$\underline{+2x \qquad\quad +2x}$$
    $$10 = 4x - 10$$
    $$\underline{+10 \qquad\quad + 10}$$
    $$20 = 4x$$
    $$\frac{20}{4} = \frac{\cancel{4}x}{\cancel{4}}$$
    $$5 = x \qquad\qquad \text{conditional}$$

3. (a) $8 - 3x = 3x - 10$
    $$\underline{+ 3x \quad +3x}$$
    $$8 = 6x - 10$$
    $$\underline{+10 \qquad\quad + 10}$$
    $$18 = 6x$$
    $$\frac{18}{6} = \frac{\cancel{6}x}{\cancel{6}}$$
    $$3 = x$$

    (b) $2(3y - 5) - 4y = 2 - (y + 12)$
    $$6y - 10 - 4y = 2 - y - 12$$
    $$2y - 10 = -y - 10$$
    $$\underline{+ y \qquad\quad +y}$$
    $$3y - 10 = -10$$
    $$\underline{+ 10 \qquad\quad +10}$$
    $$3y = 0$$
    $$\frac{\cancel{3}y}{\cancel{3}} = \frac{0}{3}$$
    $$y = 0$$

(c) $2a^2 - 3(a - 4) = 2a(a - 6) + 3a$

$\quad\quad 2a^2 - 3a + 12 = 2a^2 - 12a + 3a$

$\quad\quad 2a^2 - 3a + 12 = 2a^2 - 9a$

$\quad\quad \underline{-2a^2 \quad\quad\quad\quad\quad -2a^2}$

$\quad\quad\quad\quad \underline{-3a + 12 = \quad\quad -9a}$

$\quad\quad\quad\quad \underline{+3a \quad\quad\quad\quad +3a}$

$\quad\quad\quad\quad\quad\quad 12 = \quad\quad -6a$

$\quad\quad\quad\quad\quad\quad \dfrac{12}{-6} = \dfrac{-6a}{-6}$

$\quad\quad\quad\quad\quad\quad -2 = \quad\quad a$

(d) $9 - 5(x - 2) \geq 4$

$\quad\quad 9 - 5x + 10 \geq 4$

$\quad\quad\quad -5x + 10 \geq 4$

$\quad\quad\quad\quad \underline{- 19 \quad -19}$

$\quad\quad\quad\quad -5x \quad\quad \geq -15$

$\quad\quad\quad\quad \dfrac{-5x}{-5} \quad\quad \leq \dfrac{-15}{-5}$

$\quad\quad\quad\quad x \quad\quad\quad \leq 3$

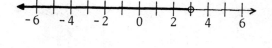

(e) $1 < 3 - x \leq 5$

$\quad\quad \underline{-3 \quad -3 \quad\quad -3}$

$\quad\quad -2 < \quad -x \leq 2$

$\quad\quad \dfrac{-2}{-1} > \quad \dfrac{-x}{-1} \geq \dfrac{2}{-1}$

$\quad\quad 2 > \quad\quad x \geq -2 \quad$ or $\quad -2 \leq x < 2$

5. Let x = number of \$1 cassettes

$20 - x$ = number of \$3 cassettes

$1x + 3(20 - x) = 46$

$\quad x + 60 - 3x = 46$

$\quad\quad -2x + 60 = 46$

$\quad\quad\quad \underline{- 60 \quad -60}$

$\quad\quad\quad -2x \quad\quad = -14$

$\quad\quad\quad \dfrac{-2x}{-2} \quad = \dfrac{-14}{-2}$

$\quad\quad\quad x \quad\quad = 7$

CHECK: $7 + 13 \overset{\checkmark}{=} 20$. 7 cassettes at \$1 each cost \$7. 13 cassettes at \$3 each cost $13(3) = \$39$. $\$7 + \$39 \overset{\checkmark}{=} \$46$.

Then $20 - x = 20 - 7 = 13$. Thus, the person bought 7 one-dollar cassettes and 13 three-dollar cassettes.

Cumulative Review: Chapters 1-3

1. $-8 - 5 - 7 = -13 - 7 = -20$

3. $12 - 4(3 - 5) = 12 - 4(-2) = 12 + 8 = 20$

5. $-5^2 = -(5 \cdot 5) = -25$

7. $xx^2x^3 = x^{1+2+3} = x^6$

9. $x^2y - 2xy^2 - xy^2 - 3x^2y = x^2y - 3x^2y - 2xy^2 - xy^2$
$$= (1 - 3)x^2y + (-2 - 1)xy^2$$
$$= -2x^2y - 3xy^2$$

11. $2x(3x^2 - 4y) = 2x(3x^2) - 2x(4y) = 6x^3 - 8xy$

13. $-3u^2(u^3)(-5v) = ((-3)(-5))(u^2u^3)v = 15u^5v$

15. $4(m - 3n) + 3(2m - n) = 4m - 12n + 6m - 3n$
$$= 4m + 6m - 12n - 3n$$
$$= 10m - 15n$$

17. $2ab(a^2 - ab) - 4a^2(ab - b^2) = 2a^3b - 2a^2b^2 - 4a^3b + 4a^2b^2$
$$= 2a^3b - 4a^3b - 2a^2b^2 + 4a^2b^2$$
$$= (2 - 4)a^3b + (-2 + 4)a^2b^2$$
$$= -2a^3b + 2a^2b^2$$

19. $x^2y - xy^2 - (xy^2 - x^2y) = x^2y - xy^2 - xy^2 + x^2y$
$$= x^2y + x^2y - xy^2 - xy^2$$
$$= (1 + 1)x^2y + (-1 - 1)xy^2$$
$$= 2x^2y - 2xy^2$$

21. $x - 3\{x - 4(x - 5)\} = x - 3\{x - 4x + 20\}$
$$= x - 3\{-3x + 20\}$$
$$= x + 9x - 60$$
$$= 10x - 60$$

23. $3xy(4x^3y - 2y) - 2x(3y^2)(2x^3) = 12x^4y^2 - 6xy^2 - 12x^4y^2$
$$= 12x^4y^2 - 12x^4y^2 - 6xy^2$$
$$= (12 - 12)x^4y^2 - 6xy^2$$
$$= -6xy^2$$

25. $x^2 = (-2)^2 = 4$

27. $xy^2 = (xy)^2 = (-2)(-3)^2 - ((-2)(-3))^2$
$$= -2(9) - (6)^2$$
$$= -18 - 36$$
$$= -54$$

29. $|x - y - z| = |(-2) - (-3) - (5)|$
$$= |-2 + 3 - 5|$$
$$= |-4|$$
$$= 4$$

31. $2x - 4y^2 = 2(-2) - 4(-3)^2$
$$= 2(-2) - 4(9)$$
$$= -4 - 36$$
$$= -40$$

33.
$$
\begin{array}{rcl}
2x - 11 &=& 5x + 10 \\
-2x & & -2x \\
\hline
-11 &=& 3x + 10 \\
-10 & & -10 \\
\hline
-21 &=& 3x \\
\dfrac{-21}{3} &=& \dfrac{3x}{3} \\
-7 &=& x
\end{array}
$$

35.
$$
\begin{array}{rcl}
9(a + 1) - 3(2a - 2) &=& 12 \\
9a + 9 - 6a + 6 &=& 12 \\
3a + 15 &=& 12 \\
- 15 & & -12 \\
\hline
3a & &= -3 \\
\dfrac{3a}{3} & &= \dfrac{-3}{3} \\
a & &= -1
\end{array}
$$

37.
$$
\begin{array}{rcl}
4(5 - x) - 2(6 - 2x) &=& 8 \\
20 - 4x - 12 - 4x &=& 8 \\
8 &=& 8 \qquad \text{identity}
\end{array}
$$

39. $2(s + 4) + 3(2s + 2) > 6s$
$$2s + 8 + 6s + 6 > 6s$$
$$8s + 14 > 6s$$
$$\underline{-8s \qquad\qquad -8s}$$
$$14 > -2s$$
$$\frac{14}{-2} < \frac{-2s}{-2}$$
$$-7 < s$$

41. $1 < 2y - 5 \le 3$
$$\underline{+5 \qquad + 5 \quad +5}$$
$$6 < 2y \qquad \le 8$$
$$\frac{6}{2} < \frac{2y}{2} \qquad \le \frac{8}{2}$$
$$3 < y \qquad \le 4$$

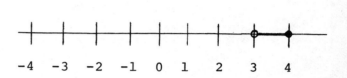

43. $4(3d - 2) + 6(8 - d) = 9d - 4(d - 10)$
$$12d - 8 + 48 - 6d = 9d - 4d + 40$$
$$6d + 40 = 5d + 40$$
$$\underline{-5d \qquad\qquad -5d}$$
$$d + 40 = \qquad 40$$
$$\underline{- 40 \qquad\qquad -40}$$
$$d = \qquad 0$$

45. Let x = one of the numbers.
$3x - 7$ = the other number.

$x + (3x - 7) = 41$ CHECK: 29 is 7 less than 3 times
$$4x - 7 = 41$$ 12. The sum of 12 and 29
$$\underline{+ 7 \quad +7}$$ is 41.
$$4x = 48$$
$$\frac{4x}{4} = \frac{48}{4}$$
$$x = 12$$

Then $3x - 7 = 3(12 - 7) = 29$. Thus, the numbers are 12 and 29.

47. Let x = number of danishes that Louise bought.
$18 - x$ = number of pastries that Louise bought.

$40x + 55(18 - x) = 825$ CHECK: 11 danishes cost 11($.40)
$$40x + 990 - 55x = 825$$ = $4.40.   7 pastries cost
$$-15x + 990 = 825$$ 7($.55) = $3.85. The total
$$\underline{- 990 \quad -990}$$ cost of the assortment is
$$-15x = -165$$ $4.40 + $3.85 = $8.25.
$$\frac{-15x}{-15} = \frac{-165}{-15}$$
$$x = 11$$

Then $18 - x = 18 - 11 = 7$.   Thus, Louise bought 11 danishes and 7 pastries.

Cumulative Practice Test: Chapters 1-3

1.   (a) $-3^4 + 3(-2)^3 = -(3 \cdot 3 \cdot 3 \cdot 3) + 3((-2)(-2)(-2))$
$$= -81 + 3(-8)$$
$$= -81 - 24$$
$$= -105$$

(b) $(3 - 7 - 2)^2 = (-4 - 2)^2 = (-6)^2 = (-6)(-6) = 36$

3.   (a) $5x^2 - 4x - 8 - 7x^2 - x + 11 = 5x^2 - 7x^2 - 4x - x - 8 + 11$
$$= -2x^2 - 5x + 3$$

(b) $2(x - 3y) + 5(y - x) = 2x - 6y + 5y - 5x$
$$= 2x - 5x - 6y + 5y$$
$$= -3x - y$$

(c) $3a(a^2 - 2b) - 5(a^3 - ab) = 3a^3 - 6ab - 5a^3 + 5ab$
$$= 3a^3 - 5a^3 - 6ab + 5ab$$
$$= -2a^3 - ab$$

(d) $2(u - 4v) - 3(v - 2u) - (8u - 11v)$
$$= 2u - 8v - 3v + 6u - 8u + 11v$$
$$= 2u + 6u - 8u - 8v - 3v + 11v$$
$$= 0u + 0v$$
$$= 0$$

(e) $4x^2y^3(x - 5y) - 2xy(5y^2)(-2xy)$
$$= 4x^3y^3 - 20x^2y^4 - 10xy^3(-2xy)$$
$$= 4x^3y^3 - 20x^2y^4 + 20x^2y^4$$
$$= 4x^3y^3$$

(f) $6 - a[6 - a(6 - a)] = 6 - a[6 - 6a + a^2]$
$$= 6 - 6a + 6a^2 - a^3$$

5. (a)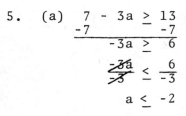

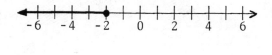

$$7 - 3a \geq 13$$
$$\underline{-7 \qquad\qquad -7}$$
$$-3a \geq 6$$
$$\frac{-3a}{-3} \leq \frac{6}{-3}$$
$$a \leq -2$$

(b)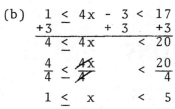

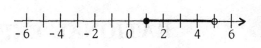

$$1 \leq 4x - 3 < 17$$
$$\underline{+3 \qquad\qquad + 3 \quad +3}$$
$$4 \leq 4x \qquad\quad < 20$$
$$\frac{4}{4} \leq \frac{4x}{4} \qquad\quad < \frac{20}{4}$$
$$1 \leq x \qquad\quad < 5$$

Chapter 4

RATIONAL EXPRESSIONS

1. $\dfrac{18}{30} = \dfrac{3 \cdot \cancel{6}}{5 \cdot \cancel{6}} = \dfrac{3}{5}$

3. $\dfrac{-9}{21} = \dfrac{-3 \cdot \cancel{3}}{7 \cdot \cancel{3}} = \dfrac{-3}{7} = -\dfrac{3}{7}$

5. $\dfrac{-15}{-6} = \dfrac{5\cancel{(-3)}}{2\cancel{(-3)}} = \dfrac{5}{2}$

7. $\dfrac{-5 + 8}{10 - 4} = \dfrac{3}{6} = \dfrac{1 \cdot \cancel{3}}{2 \cdot \cancel{3}} = \dfrac{1}{2}$

9. $\dfrac{8 - 5(2)}{6 - 4(3)} = \dfrac{8 - 10}{6 - 12} = \dfrac{-2}{-6} = \dfrac{1\cancel{(-2)}}{3\cancel{(-2)}} = \dfrac{1}{3}$

11. $\dfrac{x^3}{x} = \dfrac{x^2 \cdot \cancel{x}}{1 \cdot \cancel{x}} = \dfrac{x^2}{1} = x^2$

13. $\dfrac{x}{x^3} = \dfrac{1 \cdot \cancel{x}}{x^2 \cdot \cancel{x}} = \dfrac{1}{x^2}$

15. $\dfrac{10x}{4x^2} = \dfrac{5 \cdot \cancel{2x}}{2x \cdot \cancel{2x}} = \dfrac{5}{2x}$

17. $\dfrac{-3z^6}{5z^2} = \dfrac{-3z^4 \cdot \cancel{z^2}}{5\cancel{z^2}} = \dfrac{-3z^4}{5} = -\dfrac{3z^4}{5}$

19. $\dfrac{12t^5}{30t^{10}} = \dfrac{2 \cdot \cancel{6t^5}}{5t^5 \cdot \cancel{6t^5}} = \dfrac{2}{5t^5}$

21. $\dfrac{6ab^5}{-2a^3b^2} = \dfrac{3b^3 \cdot 2ab^2}{-a^2 \cdot 2ab^2} = \dfrac{3b^3}{-a^2} = -\dfrac{3b^3}{a^2}$

23. $\dfrac{(2x^3)(6x^2)}{(4x)(3x^4)} = \dfrac{1 \cdot 12x^5}{1 \cdot 12x^5} = \dfrac{1}{1} = 1$

25. $\dfrac{(r^3t^2)(-rt^3)}{2r^2t^7} = \dfrac{-r^4t^5}{2r^2t^7} = \dfrac{-r^2 \cdot r^2t^5}{2t^2 \cdot r^2t^5} = \dfrac{-r^2}{2t^2} = \dfrac{r^2}{2t^2}$

27. $\dfrac{3a(5b)(-4ab^3)}{6ab(2a^2b^2)} = \dfrac{-60a^2b^4}{12a^3b^3} = \dfrac{-5b \cdot 12a^2b^3}{a \cdot 12a^2b^3} = \dfrac{-5b}{a} = -\dfrac{5b}{a}$

29. $\dfrac{(2x)^5}{(4x)^3} = \dfrac{32x^5}{64x^3} = \dfrac{x^2 \cdot 32x^3}{2 \cdot 32x^3} = \dfrac{x^2}{2}$

31. $\dfrac{(-4x^3)^2}{(-2x^4)^3} = \dfrac{16x^6}{-8x^{12}} = \dfrac{2 \cdot 8x^6}{-x^6 \cdot 8x^6} = \dfrac{2}{-x^6} = -\dfrac{2}{x^6}$

33. $\dfrac{(2xy^2)^3}{(4x^2y^3)^3} = \dfrac{8x^3y^6}{64x^6y^9} = \dfrac{1 \cdot 8x^3y^6}{8x^3y^3 \cdot 8x^3y^6} = \dfrac{1}{8x^3y^3}$

35. $\dfrac{5x - 2x}{10x - 4x} = \dfrac{3x}{6x} = \dfrac{1 \cdot 3x}{2 \cdot 3x} = \dfrac{1}{2}$

37. $\dfrac{5a(2x)}{15a(8x)} = \dfrac{10ax}{120ax} = \dfrac{1 \cdot 10ax}{12 \cdot 10ax} = \dfrac{1}{12}$

39. $\dfrac{4s - 3t}{8s - 9t}$ cannot be reduced.

41. $\dfrac{7a^2 - 5a^2 - 6a^2}{4a - 8a} = \dfrac{-4a^2}{-4a} = \dfrac{a(-4a)}{1(-4a)} = \dfrac{a}{1} = a$

43. $\dfrac{5x^2 - 3x - x^2 + 2x}{6x^2 - 5x - 2x^2 + 4x} = \dfrac{4x^2 - x}{4x^2 - x} = \dfrac{1}{1} = 1$

45. The value of a fraction is unchanged when its numerator and denominator are both either multiplied or divided by the same nonzero amount.

46. We would conclude that 2 = 4. It was incorrect to write $\dfrac{4 + 2}{1 + 2} = \dfrac{4}{1}$. The 2's cannot be crossed out, since 2 is a common term, not a common factor.

47. (a) The factor of x in the reduced fraction should be in its numerator.

(b)   When both factors in the numerator are crossed out, a factor of 1 remains.

(c)   As in part (b), a factor of 1 remains in the numerator, so that the reduced fraction is $\dfrac{1}{3x^2y}$.

(d)   Crossing out x's amounts to crossing out terms rather than factors.

48.   The fractions in (a), (c), (d), and (e) are equivalent. So are the fractions in (b), (f), and (g).

Exercises 4.2

1. $\dfrac{-4}{9} \cdot \dfrac{-2}{3} = \dfrac{(-4)(-2)}{9 \cdot 3} = \dfrac{8}{27}$

3. $\dfrac{\cancel{-6}^{\,2}{}^1}{\cancel{10}_{2}{}_1} \cdot \dfrac{\cancel{15}^{\,3}{}^1}{\cancel{9}_{3}{}_1} = \dfrac{-1}{1} = -1$

5. $\dfrac{2}{3y} \cdot \dfrac{x}{5} = \dfrac{2x}{3y \cdot 5} = \dfrac{2x}{15y}$

7. $\dfrac{x^2}{4y} \cdot \dfrac{5x}{3y} = \dfrac{x^2 \cdot 5x}{4y \cdot 3y} = \dfrac{5x^3}{12y^2}$

9. $\dfrac{4}{5} \div \dfrac{5}{4} = \dfrac{4}{5} \cdot \dfrac{4}{5} = \dfrac{4 \cdot 4}{5 \cdot 5} = \dfrac{16}{25}$

11. $\dfrac{6x}{y} \div \dfrac{y^2}{2x^2} = \dfrac{6x}{y} \cdot \dfrac{2x^2}{y^2} = \dfrac{6x \cdot 2x^2}{y \cdot y^2} = \dfrac{12x^3}{y^3}$

13. $\dfrac{\cancel{3}^{\,1}}{2\cancel{t}} \cdot \dfrac{\cancel{t}w}{\cancel{6}_{2}} = \dfrac{1 \cdot w}{2 \cdot 2} = \dfrac{w}{4}$

15. $4 \cdot \dfrac{x}{12} = \dfrac{\cancel{4}^{\,1}}{1} \cdot \dfrac{x}{\cancel{12}_{3}} = \dfrac{1 \cdot x}{1 \cdot 3} = \dfrac{x}{3}$

17. $4 \div \dfrac{x}{12} = \dfrac{4}{1} \div \dfrac{x}{12} = \dfrac{4}{1} \cdot \dfrac{12}{x} = \dfrac{4 \cdot 12}{1 \cdot x} = \dfrac{48}{x}$

19. $\dfrac{x}{12} \div 4 = \dfrac{x}{12} \div \dfrac{4}{1} = \dfrac{x}{12} \cdot \dfrac{1}{4} = \dfrac{x \cdot 1}{12 \cdot 4} = \dfrac{x}{48}$

21. $\dfrac{-2\cancel{x}^{\,1}}{\cancel{3y^2}_{y}} \cdot \dfrac{-\cancel{9y}^{\,3}}{\cancel{4x}_{2}} = \dfrac{(-1)(-3)}{2y} = \dfrac{3}{2y}$

23. $\dfrac{m^2 n^2}{2m} \cdot \dfrac{6}{n^3} = \dfrac{m^2 \cdot 3}{1 \cdot n} = \dfrac{3m^2}{n}$

25. $\dfrac{3uv^2}{5w} \div \dfrac{6u^2v}{15w} = \dfrac{3uv^2}{5w} \cdot \dfrac{15w}{6u^2v} = \dfrac{v \cdot 3}{2 \cdot u} = \dfrac{3v}{2u}$

27. $6xy \cdot \dfrac{2x}{3y} = \dfrac{6xy}{1} \cdot \dfrac{2x}{3y} = \dfrac{2x \cdot 2x}{1 \cdot 1} = \dfrac{4x^2}{1} = 4x^2$

29. $6xy \div \dfrac{2x}{3y} = \dfrac{6xy}{1} \cdot \dfrac{3y}{2x} = \dfrac{3y \cdot 3y}{1 \cdot 1} = \dfrac{9y^2}{1} = 9y^2$

31. $\dfrac{2x}{3y} \div (6xy) = \dfrac{2x}{3y} \div \dfrac{6xy}{1} = \dfrac{2x}{3y} \cdot \dfrac{1}{6xy} = \dfrac{1 \cdot 1}{3y \cdot 3y} = \dfrac{1}{9y^2}$

33. $\dfrac{-4x}{9y} \cdot \dfrac{x^2}{y^2} \cdot \dfrac{3y}{2x} = \dfrac{-2 \cdot x^2}{3 \cdot y^2} = -\dfrac{2x^2}{3y^2}$

35. $\dfrac{9}{a^2} \cdot \left(\dfrac{a}{3} \div \dfrac{3}{a}\right) = \dfrac{9}{a^2} \cdot \left(\dfrac{a}{3} \cdot \dfrac{a}{3}\right) = \dfrac{9}{a^2} \cdot \dfrac{a^2}{9} = \dfrac{1 \cdot 1}{1 \cdot 1} = \dfrac{1}{1} = 1$

37. $\dfrac{9}{a^2} \div \left(\dfrac{a}{3} \cdot \dfrac{3}{a}\right) = \dfrac{9}{a^2} \div \dfrac{1}{1} = \dfrac{9}{a^2} \cdot \dfrac{1}{1} = \dfrac{9 \cdot 1}{a^2 \cdot 1} = \dfrac{9}{a^2}$

39. $\dfrac{9}{a^2} \div \left(\dfrac{a}{3} \div \dfrac{3}{a}\right) = \dfrac{9}{a^2} \div \left(\dfrac{a}{3} \cdot \dfrac{a}{3}\right) = \dfrac{9}{a^2} \div \dfrac{a^2}{9} = \dfrac{9}{a^2} \cdot \dfrac{9}{a^2}$

$= \dfrac{9 \cdot 9}{a^2 \cdot a^2} = \dfrac{81}{a^4}$

41. $\left(\dfrac{9}{a^2} \div \dfrac{a}{3}\right) \div \dfrac{a}{3} = \left(\dfrac{9}{a^2} \cdot \dfrac{3}{a}\right) \div \dfrac{a}{3} = \dfrac{27}{a^3} \div \dfrac{a}{3} = \dfrac{27}{a^3} \cdot \dfrac{3}{a}$

$= \dfrac{27 \cdot 3}{a^3 \cdot a} = \dfrac{81}{a^4}$

43. $\dfrac{\frac{2x}{3}}{\frac{10x}{9}} = \dfrac{2x}{3} \div \dfrac{10x}{9} = \dfrac{2x}{3} \cdot \dfrac{9}{10x} = \dfrac{1 \cdot 3}{1 \cdot 5} = \dfrac{3}{5}$

45. $\dfrac{\frac{x^2}{3}}{\frac{x}{6}} = \dfrac{x^2}{3} \div \dfrac{x}{6} = \dfrac{x^2}{3} \cdot \dfrac{6}{x} = \dfrac{x \cdot 2}{1 \cdot 1} = \dfrac{2x}{1} = 2x$

47. $\dfrac{\dfrac{x}{y^2}}{\dfrac{y}{x^2}} = \dfrac{x}{y^2} \div \dfrac{y}{x^2} = \dfrac{x}{y^2} \cdot \dfrac{x^2}{y} = \dfrac{x \cdot x^2}{y^2 \cdot y} = \dfrac{x^3}{y^3}$

49. $\dfrac{\dfrac{2u}{z^2}}{\dfrac{4z}{u}} = \dfrac{2u}{z^2} \div \dfrac{4z}{u} = \dfrac{\overset{1}{\cancel{2u}}}{z^2} \cdot \dfrac{u}{\underset{2}{\cancel{4z}}} = \dfrac{u \cdot u}{z^2 \cdot 2z} = \dfrac{u^2}{2z^3}$

51. $\dfrac{3x^2 - x^2}{4y^2 - y^2} \cdot \dfrac{2y + y}{x^2 + x^2} = \dfrac{\overset{1}{\cancel{2x^2}}}{\underset{y}{\cancel{3y^2}}} \cdot \dfrac{\overset{1}{\cancel{3y}}}{\underset{1}{\cancel{2x^2}}} = \dfrac{1 \cdot 1}{y \cdot 1} = \dfrac{1}{y}$

53. $\dfrac{4x^2 - x^2}{2y + y} \div \dfrac{4x - x}{2y^2 + y^2} = \dfrac{3x^2}{3y} \div \dfrac{3x}{3y^2} = \dfrac{\overset{x}{\cancel{3x^2}}}{\underset{1}{\cancel{3y}}} \cdot \dfrac{\overset{y}{\cancel{3y^2}}}{\underset{1}{\cancel{3x}}} = \dfrac{x \cdot y}{1 \cdot 1} = \dfrac{xy}{1} = xy$

55. To divide by a fraction, multiply by its reciprocal. This rule works because division is defined to be the inverse of multiplication.

56. (a) The fraction $\dfrac{2y}{3x}$ must be inverted, leading to $\dfrac{3x}{2y} \cdot \dfrac{3x}{2y}$

    $= \dfrac{9x^2}{4y^2}.$

    (b) The factor of 5 is $\dfrac{5}{1}$, not $\dfrac{5}{5}$. Thus, $5 \cdot \dfrac{3x}{2} = \dfrac{5}{1} \cdot \dfrac{3x}{2}$

    $= \dfrac{5 \cdot 3x}{1 \cdot 2} = \dfrac{15x}{2}.$

Exercises 4.3

1. $\dfrac{5}{3} + \dfrac{4}{3} = \dfrac{5 + 4}{3} = \dfrac{\overset{3}{\cancel{9}}}{\underset{1}{\cancel{3}}} = \dfrac{3}{1} = 3$

3. $\dfrac{3}{5} - \dfrac{7}{5} = \dfrac{3 - 7}{5} = \dfrac{-4}{5} = -\dfrac{4}{5}$

5. $\dfrac{7}{9} - \dfrac{5}{9} - \dfrac{8}{9} = \dfrac{7 - 5 - 8}{9} = \dfrac{\overset{2}{\cancel{-6}}}{\underset{3}{\cancel{9}}} = -\dfrac{2}{3}$

7. $\dfrac{2}{3} + \dfrac{4}{5} = \dfrac{2(5)}{3(5)} + \dfrac{4(3)}{5(3)} = \dfrac{10}{15} + \dfrac{12}{15} = \dfrac{10 + 12}{15} = \dfrac{22}{15}$

9. $\dfrac{2}{3} \cdot \dfrac{4}{5} = \dfrac{2 \cdot 4}{3 \cdot 5} = \dfrac{8}{15}$

11. $\dfrac{2}{3} - \dfrac{5}{6} = \dfrac{2(2)}{3(2)} - \dfrac{5}{6} = \dfrac{4}{6} - \dfrac{5}{6} = \dfrac{4 - 5}{6} = \dfrac{-1}{6} = -\dfrac{1}{6}$

13. $3 + \dfrac{3}{4} - \dfrac{3}{8} = \dfrac{3}{1} + \dfrac{3}{4} - \dfrac{3}{8} = \dfrac{3(8)}{1(8)} + \dfrac{3(2)}{4(2)} - \dfrac{3}{8} = \dfrac{24}{8} + \dfrac{6}{8} - \dfrac{3}{8}$

$= \dfrac{24 + 6 - 3}{8} = \dfrac{27}{8}$

15. $\dfrac{3}{2} - \dfrac{4}{5} + \dfrac{7}{10} = \dfrac{3(5)}{2(5)} - \dfrac{4(2)}{5(2)} + \dfrac{7}{10} = \dfrac{15}{10} - \dfrac{8}{10} + \dfrac{7}{10}$

$= \dfrac{15 - 8 + 7}{10} = \dfrac{\overset{7}{\cancel{14}}}{\underset{5}{\cancel{10}}} = \dfrac{7}{5}$

17. $\dfrac{5}{6} - \dfrac{3}{8} + \dfrac{1}{4} = \dfrac{5(4)}{6(4)} - \dfrac{3(3)}{8(3)} + \dfrac{1(6)}{4(6)} = \dfrac{20}{24} - \dfrac{9}{24} + \dfrac{6}{24}$

$= \dfrac{20 - 9 + 6}{24} = \dfrac{17}{24}$

19. $2 + \dfrac{1}{3} - \dfrac{1}{2} = \dfrac{2}{1} + \dfrac{1}{3} - \dfrac{1}{2} = \dfrac{2(6)}{1(6)} + \dfrac{1(2)}{3(2)} - \dfrac{1(3)}{2(3)} = \dfrac{12}{6} + \dfrac{2}{6} - \dfrac{3}{6}$

$= \dfrac{12 + 2 - 3}{6} = \dfrac{11}{6}$

21. $\dfrac{8}{3x} + \dfrac{4}{3x} = \dfrac{8 + 4}{3x} = \dfrac{\overset{4}{\cancel{12}}}{\underset{1}{\cancel{3x}}} = \dfrac{4}{x}$

23. $\dfrac{8}{3x} \cdot \dfrac{4}{3x} = \dfrac{8 \cdot 4}{3x \cdot 3x} = \dfrac{32}{9x^2}$

25. $\dfrac{7}{6x} + \dfrac{13}{6x} - \dfrac{11}{6x} = \dfrac{7 + 13 - 11}{6x} = \dfrac{\overset{3}{\cancel{9}}}{\underset{2}{\cancel{6x}}} = \dfrac{3}{2x}$

27. $\dfrac{3y}{7x} - \dfrac{5y}{7x} + \dfrac{4y}{7x} = \dfrac{3y - 5y + 4y}{7x} = \dfrac{2y}{7x}$

29. $\dfrac{w}{9z} - \dfrac{5w}{9z} + \dfrac{4w}{9z} = \dfrac{w - 5w + 4w}{9z} = \dfrac{0}{9z} = 0$

31. $\dfrac{-5a}{7b} + \dfrac{3a}{7b} - \dfrac{12a}{7b} = \dfrac{-5a + 3a - 12a}{7b} = \dfrac{\overset{2}{\cancel{-14}}a}{\underset{1}{\cancel{7}}b} = \dfrac{-2a}{b} = -\dfrac{2a}{b}$

33. $\dfrac{x + 3}{3x} + \dfrac{x - 6}{3x} = \dfrac{x + 3 + x - 6}{3x} = \dfrac{2x - 3}{3x}$

35. $\dfrac{3y^2 - 5}{4y} + \dfrac{5 - 4y^2}{4y} = \dfrac{3y^2 - 5 + 5 - 4y^2}{4y} = \dfrac{\overset{y}{\cancel{-y^2}}}{\cancel{4y}} = \dfrac{-y}{4} = -\dfrac{y}{4}$

37. $\dfrac{5x + 2}{10x} - \dfrac{x + 2}{10x} = \dfrac{5x + 2 - (x + 2)}{10x} = \dfrac{5x + 2 - x - 2}{10x} = \dfrac{\overset{2}{\cancel{4x}}}{\underset{5}{\cancel{10x}}} = \dfrac{2}{5}$

39. $\dfrac{2a - 1}{3a} - \dfrac{5a - 1}{3a} = \dfrac{2a - 1 - (5a - 1)}{3a} = \dfrac{2a - 1 - 5a + 1}{3a}$

$= \dfrac{-3a}{\underset{1}{\cancel{3a}}} = \dfrac{-1}{1} = -1$

41. $\dfrac{w - 4}{6w} - \dfrac{w - 3}{6w} + \dfrac{5}{6w} = \dfrac{w - 4 - (w - 3) + 5}{6w} = \dfrac{w - 4 - w + 3 + 5}{6w}$

$= \dfrac{\overset{2}{\cancel{4}}}{\underset{3}{\cancel{6}}w} = \dfrac{2}{3w}$

43. $\dfrac{t^2 - 3t + 2}{5t^2} - \dfrac{7t + t^2}{5t^2} = \dfrac{t^2 - 3t + 2 - (7t + t^2)}{5t^2}$

$= \dfrac{t^2 - 3t + 2 - 7t - t^2}{5t^2} = \dfrac{-10t + 2}{5t^2}$

45. $\dfrac{3}{x} + \dfrac{2}{y} = \dfrac{3(y)}{x(y)} + \dfrac{2(x)}{y(x)} = \dfrac{3y}{xy} + \dfrac{2x}{xy} = \dfrac{3y + 2x}{xy}$

47. $\dfrac{3}{x} \cdot \dfrac{2}{y} = \dfrac{3 \cdot 2}{x \cdot y} = \dfrac{6}{xy}$

49. $\dfrac{5}{3x} - \dfrac{7}{2} = \dfrac{5(2)}{3x(2)} - \dfrac{7(3x)}{2(3x)} = \dfrac{10}{6x} - \dfrac{21x}{6x} = \dfrac{10 - 21x}{6x}$

51. $\dfrac{5}{4x} + \dfrac{3}{2y} = \dfrac{5(y)}{4x(y)} + \dfrac{3(2x)}{2y(2x)} = \dfrac{5y}{4xy} + \dfrac{6x}{4xy} = \dfrac{5y + 6x}{4xy}$

53. $\dfrac{4}{x^2} - \dfrac{3}{2x} = \dfrac{4(2)}{x^2(2)} - \dfrac{3(x)}{2x(x)} = \dfrac{8}{2x^2} - \dfrac{3x}{2x^2} = \dfrac{8 - 3x}{2x^2}$

55. $\dfrac{\overset{2}{4}}{x^2} \cdot \dfrac{3}{2x} = \dfrac{2 \cdot 3}{x^2 \cdot x} = \dfrac{6}{x^3}$

57. $\dfrac{2}{3x^2} + \dfrac{3}{2x^2} = \dfrac{2(2)}{3x^2(2)} + \dfrac{3(3)}{2x^2(3)} = \dfrac{4}{6x^2} + \dfrac{9}{6x^2} = \dfrac{4 + 9}{6x^2} = \dfrac{13}{6x^2}$

59. $\dfrac{7}{4a^2} - \dfrac{9}{20a} = \dfrac{7(5)}{4a^2(5)} - \dfrac{9(a)}{20a(a)} = \dfrac{35}{20a^2} - \dfrac{9a}{20a^2} = \dfrac{35 - 9a}{20a^2}$

61. $\dfrac{1}{x} + 2 = \dfrac{1}{x} + \dfrac{2}{1} = \dfrac{1}{x} + \dfrac{2(x)}{1(x)} = \dfrac{1}{x} + \dfrac{2x}{x} = \dfrac{1 + 2x}{x}$

63. $\dfrac{5}{3xy} + \dfrac{1}{6y^2} = \dfrac{5(2y)}{3xy(2y)} + \dfrac{1(x)}{6y^2(x)} = \dfrac{10y}{6xy^2} + \dfrac{x}{6xy^2} = \dfrac{10y + x}{6xy^2}$

65. $\dfrac{7}{6a^2b} + \dfrac{3}{4ab^3} = \dfrac{7(2b^2)}{6a^2b(2b^2)} + \dfrac{3(3a)}{4ab^3(3a)} = \dfrac{14b^2}{12a^2b^3} + \dfrac{9a}{12a^2b^3}$

$= \dfrac{14b^2 + 9a}{12a^2b^3}$

67. $\dfrac{7}{\overset{1}{\underset{2}{\cancel{6}}}a^2b} \cdot \dfrac{\overset{1}{\cancel{3}}}{4ab^3} = \dfrac{7 \cdot 1}{2a^2b \cdot 4ab^3} = \dfrac{7}{8a^3b^4}$

69. $\dfrac{4y}{3x^2} - \dfrac{3}{2x} + \dfrac{y}{x^2} = \dfrac{4y(2)}{3x^2(2)} - \dfrac{3(3x)}{2x(3x)} + \dfrac{y(6)}{x^2(6)} = \dfrac{8y}{6x^2} - \dfrac{9x}{6x^2} + \dfrac{6y}{6x^2}$

$= \dfrac{8y - 9x + 6y}{6x^2} = \dfrac{14y - 9x}{6x^2}$

71. $\dfrac{3}{4m^2n} - \dfrac{5}{6mn^3} + \dfrac{1}{8n^2} = \dfrac{3(6n^2)}{4m^2n(6n^2)} - \dfrac{5(4m)}{6mn^3(4m)} + \dfrac{1(3m^2n)}{8n^2(3m^2n)}$

$= \dfrac{18n^2}{24m^2n^3} - \dfrac{20m}{24m^2n^3} + \dfrac{3m^2n}{24m^2n^3}$

$= \dfrac{18n^2 - 20m + 3m^2n}{24m^2n^3}$

73. $\dfrac{x}{y} + \dfrac{y}{x} + \dfrac{3x}{2y} = \dfrac{x(2x)}{y(2x)} + \dfrac{y(2y)}{x(2y)} + \dfrac{3x(x)}{2y(x)} = \dfrac{2x^2}{2xy} + \dfrac{2y^2}{2xy} + \dfrac{3x^2}{2xy}$

$= \dfrac{2x^2 + 2y^2 + 3x^2}{2xy} = \dfrac{5x^2 + 2y^2}{2xy}$

75. $t - \dfrac{3}{t} = \dfrac{t}{1} - \dfrac{3}{t} = \dfrac{t(t)}{1(t)} - \dfrac{3}{t} = \dfrac{t^2}{t} - \dfrac{3}{t} = \dfrac{t^2 - 3}{t}$

77. $3x^2 + \dfrac{1}{x} - \dfrac{2}{x^2} = \dfrac{3x^2}{1} + \dfrac{1}{x} - \dfrac{2}{x^2} = \dfrac{3x^2(x^2)}{1(x^2)} + \dfrac{1(x)}{x(x)} - \dfrac{2}{x^2}$

$= \dfrac{3x^4}{x^2} + \dfrac{x}{x^2} - \dfrac{2}{x^2} = \dfrac{3x^4 + x - 2}{x^2}$

79. $\dfrac{2x + 3}{x} + \dfrac{x}{2} = \dfrac{(2x + 3)(2)}{x(2)} + \dfrac{x(x)}{2(x)} = \dfrac{4x + 6}{2x} + \dfrac{x^2}{2x} = \dfrac{4x + 6 + x^2}{2x}$

81. $\dfrac{a - 5}{2} + \dfrac{3}{a} = \dfrac{(a - 5)(a)}{2(a)} + \dfrac{3(2)}{a(2)} = \dfrac{a^2 - 5a}{2a} + \dfrac{6}{2a} = \dfrac{a^2 - 5a + 6}{2a}$

83. The least common denominator (LCD) is the "smallest" expression that is exactly divisible by each of the denominators in a problem. We need the LCD in order to add or subtract two or more fractions. (Actually, a common denominator is really

all that is needed, but the LCD is the most efficient one to use.)

84. Each of the original denominators is a factor of the LCD, so this is a common denominator. Since each factor of the LCD was chosen the maximum number of times that it appears as a factor in any one of the denominators, there are no extra factors. Thus, this must be the smallest common denominator possible.

85. The LCD for $\frac{3}{10}$ and $\frac{7}{9}$ is 90. The LCD for $\frac{5}{6}$ and $\frac{3}{4}$ is 12. The LCD of two fractions will simply be the product of the two denominators when these denominators have no prime factor in common.

86. (a) We must subtract the entire expression $(5 - x)$ from $x + 3$ in the numerator. This gives $\frac{x + 3 - (5 - x)}{x} =$
$\frac{x + 3 - 5 + x}{x} = \frac{2x - 2}{x}$.

(b) We cannot cancel when performing addition.

(c) When building fractions, we must multiply both numerator and denominator by the same quantity. So $\frac{5x}{2y} = \frac{5x(3x)}{2y(3x)} = \frac{15x^2}{6xy}$ and $\frac{7y}{6x} = \frac{7y(y)}{6x(y)} = \frac{7y^2}{6xy}$. Then $\frac{5x}{2y} + \frac{7y}{6x} = \frac{15x^2}{6xy} + \frac{7y^2}{6xy} = \frac{15x^2 + 7y^2}{6xy}$.

(d) The cancellation step undoes the building step and brings the problem back to its original form. The final step is incorrect, since we cannot add two fractions with unlike denominators.

(e) The cancellation is not allowed, since there are no common factors to be crossed out.

87. Reducing these fractions would reverse the building process and bring us back to the original problem.

Exercises 4.4

1. $\frac{x}{3} - 2 = \frac{2}{3}$ LCD = 3

$3(\frac{x}{3} - 2) = 3 \cdot \frac{2}{3}$

$\frac{\cancel{3}}{1} \cdot \frac{x}{\cancel{3}} - 3 \cdot 2 = \frac{\cancel{3}}{1} \cdot \frac{2}{\cancel{3}}$

$x - 6 = 2$

$x = 8$

3. $\frac{3a}{4} + 2 = \frac{5}{4}$ LCD = 4

$4(\frac{3a}{4} + 2) = 4 \cdot \frac{5}{4}$

$\frac{\cancel{4}}{1} \cdot \frac{3a}{\cancel{4}} + 4 \cdot 2 = \frac{\cancel{4}}{1} \cdot \frac{5}{\cancel{4}}$

$3a + 8 = 5$

$3a = -3$

$a = -1$

5. $\frac{u}{2} - \frac{u}{4} = 2$ LCD = 4

$4(\frac{u}{2} - \frac{u}{4}) = 4 \cdot 2$

$\frac{\cancel{4}^2}{1} \cdot \frac{u}{\cancel{2}_1} - \frac{\cancel{4}^1}{1} \cdot \frac{u}{\cancel{4}_1} = 4 \cdot 2$

$2u - u = 8$

$u = 8$

7. $\frac{y}{3} + \frac{y}{5} < \frac{8}{5}$ LCD = 15

$15(\frac{y}{3} + \frac{y}{5}) < 15 \cdot \frac{8}{5}$

$\frac{\cancel{15}^5}{1} \cdot \frac{y}{\cancel{3}_1} + \frac{\cancel{15}^3}{1} \cdot \frac{y}{\cancel{5}_1} < \frac{\cancel{15}^3}{1} \cdot \frac{8}{\cancel{5}_1}$

$5y + 3y < 24$

$8y < 24$

$y < 3$

9. $x - \frac{2}{3}x = \frac{4}{3}$ LCD = 3

$3(x - \frac{2}{3}x) = 3 \cdot \frac{4}{3}$

$3 \cdot x - \frac{\cancel{3}^1}{1} \cdot \frac{2x}{\cancel{3}_1} = \frac{\cancel{3}^1}{1} \cdot \frac{4}{\cancel{3}_1}$

$3x - 2x = 4$

$x = 4$

11. $\frac{a}{4} - \frac{a}{3} \geq \frac{5}{2}$ LCD = 12

$12(\frac{a}{4} - \frac{a}{3}) \geq 12 \cdot \frac{5}{2}$

$\frac{\cancel{12}^3}{1} \cdot \frac{a}{\cancel{4}_1} - \frac{\cancel{12}^4}{1} \cdot \frac{a}{\cancel{3}_1} \geq \frac{\cancel{12}^6}{1} \cdot \frac{5}{\cancel{2}_1}$

$3a - 4a \geq 30$

$-a \geq 30$

$a \leq -30$

(Remember to reverse the inequality symbol when multiplying or dividing by a negative quantity.)

13. $.7x + .4x = 5.5$ LCD = 10

$10(.7x + .4x) = 10(5.5)$

$10(.7x) + 10(.4x) = 10(5.5)$

$7x + 4x = 55$

$11x = 55$

$x = 5$

15. $.3x - .25x = 2$ LCD = 100

$100(.3x - .25x) = 100(2)$

$100(.3x) - 100(.25x) = 100(2)$

$30x - 25x = 200$

$5x = 200$

$x = 40$

17. $.8m + .05m = .34$ LCD $= 100$

$100(.8m + .05m) = 100(.34)$

$100(.8m) + 100(.05m) = 100(.34)$

$80m + 5m = 34$

$85m = 34$

$m = \dfrac{34}{85} = \dfrac{2 \cdot \cancel{17}}{5 \cdot \cancel{17}} = \dfrac{2}{5}$

19. $\dfrac{w + 3}{4} = \dfrac{w + 4}{3}$ LCD $= 12$

$\dfrac{\cancel{12}^3}{1} \cdot \dfrac{w + 3}{\cancel{4}_1} = \dfrac{\cancel{12}^4}{1} \cdot \dfrac{w + 4}{\cancel{3}_1}$

$3(w + 3) = 4(w + 4)$

$3w + 9 = 4(w + 4)$

$9 = w + 16$

$-7 = w$

21. $\dfrac{w + 3}{4} + 1 = \dfrac{w + 4}{3}$ LCD $= 12$

$12(\dfrac{w + 3}{4} + 1) = 12 \cdot \dfrac{w + 4}{3}$

$\dfrac{\cancel{12}^3}{1} \cdot \dfrac{w + 3}{\cancel{4}_1} + 12 \cdot 1 = \dfrac{\cancel{12}^4}{1} \cdot \dfrac{w + 4}{\cancel{3}_1}$

$3(w + 3) + 12 = 4(w + 4)$

$3w + 9 + 12 = 4w + 16$

$3w + 21 = 4w + 16$

$21 = w + 16$

$5 = w$

23. $\dfrac{x + 1}{2} + x = 11$ LCD $= 2$

$2(\dfrac{x + 1}{2} + x) = 2 \cdot 11$

$\dfrac{\cancel{2}^1}{1} \cdot \dfrac{x + 1}{\cancel{2}_1} + 2 \cdot x = 2 \cdot 11$

$x + 1 + 2x = 22$

$3x + 1 = 22$

$3x = 21$

$x = 7$

25. $\dfrac{y}{6} - \dfrac{y - 2}{4} > 1$ LCD = 12

$12(\dfrac{y}{6} - \dfrac{y - 2}{4}) > 12 \cdot 1$

$\dfrac{\cancel{12}^2}{1} \cdot \dfrac{y}{\cancel{6}_1} - \dfrac{\cancel{12}^3}{1} \cdot \dfrac{y - 2}{\cancel{4}_1} > 12 \cdot 1$

$2y - 3(y - 2) > 12$

$2y - 3y + 6 > 12$

$-y + 6 > 12$

$-y > 6$

$y < -6$

27. $3 - \dfrac{a + 1}{4} = \dfrac{a + 4}{2}$ LCD = 4

$4(3 - \dfrac{a + 1}{4}) = 4 \cdot \dfrac{a + 4}{2}$

$4 \cdot 3 - \dfrac{\cancel{4}^1}{1} \cdot \dfrac{a + 1}{\cancel{4}_1} = \dfrac{\cancel{4}^2}{1} \cdot \dfrac{a + 4}{\cancel{2}_1}$

$12 - (a + 1) = 2(a + 4)$

$12 - a - 1 = 2a + 8$

$11 - a = 2a + 8$

$11 = 3a + 8$

$3 = 3a$

$1 = a$

29. $\dfrac{2y - 3}{2} - \dfrac{y - 5}{3} = \dfrac{1}{6}$ LCD = 6

$6(\dfrac{2y - 3}{2} - \dfrac{y - 5}{3}) = 6 \cdot \dfrac{1}{6}$

$\dfrac{\cancel{6}^3}{1} \cdot \dfrac{2y - 3}{\cancel{2}_1} - \dfrac{\cancel{6}^2}{1} \cdot \dfrac{y - 5}{\cancel{3}_1} = \dfrac{\cancel{6}^1}{1} \cdot \dfrac{1}{\cancel{6}_1}$

$3(2y - 3) - 2(y - 5) = 1$

$6y - 9 - 2y + 10 = 1$

$4y + 1 = 1$

$4y = 0$

$y = 0$

31. $\dfrac{x + 2}{3} - \dfrac{2x + 3}{4} = \dfrac{x + 4}{8}$ LCD = 24

$24\left(\dfrac{x + 2}{3} - \dfrac{2x + 3}{4}\right) = 24 \cdot \dfrac{x + 4}{8}$

$\dfrac{\overset{8}{\cancel{24}}}{1} \cdot \dfrac{x + 2}{\underset{1}{\cancel{3}}} - \dfrac{\overset{6}{\cancel{24}}}{1} \cdot \dfrac{2x + 3}{\underset{1}{\cancel{4}}} = \dfrac{\overset{3}{\cancel{24}}}{1} \cdot \dfrac{x + 4}{\underset{1}{\cancel{8}}}$

$8(x + 2) - 6(2x + 3) = 3(x + 4)$

$8x + 16 - 12x - 18 = 3x + 12$

$-4x - 2 = 3x + 12$

$-2 = 7x + 12$

$-14 = 7x$

$-2 = x$

33. $\dfrac{t}{2} + \dfrac{t - 1}{3} + \dfrac{t - 6}{4} = t - 2$ LCD = 12

$12\left(\dfrac{t}{2} + \dfrac{t - 1}{3} + \dfrac{t - 6}{4}\right) = 12(t - 2)$

$\dfrac{\overset{6}{\cancel{12}}}{1} \cdot \dfrac{t}{\underset{1}{\cancel{2}}} + \dfrac{\overset{4}{\cancel{12}}}{1} \cdot \dfrac{t - 1}{\underset{1}{\cancel{3}}} + \dfrac{\overset{3}{\cancel{12}}}{1} \cdot \dfrac{t - 6}{\underset{1}{\cancel{4}}} = 12(t - 2)$

$6t + 4(t - 1) + 3(t - 6) = 12(t - 2)$

$6t + 4t - 4 + 3t - 18 = 12t - 24$

$13t - 22 = 12t - 24$

$t - 22 = -24$

$t = -2$

35. $.5(x + 2) - .3(x - 4) = 3$ LCD = 10

$10(.5(x + 2) - .3(x - 4)) = 10 \cdot 3$

$10(.5(x + 2)) - 10(.3(x - 4)) = 10 \cdot 3$

$5(x + 2) - 3(x - 4) = 30$

$5x + 10 - 3x + 12 = 30$

$2x + 22 = 30$

$2x = 8$

$x = 4$

37. $3(y + 2) + \dfrac{y + 3}{5} = \dfrac{9y + 8}{2}$ LCD = 10

$10(3(y + 2) + \dfrac{y + 3}{5}) = 10 \cdot \dfrac{9y + 8}{2}$

$10(3(y + 2)) + \dfrac{\cancel{10}^2}{1} \cdot \dfrac{y + 3}{\cancel{5}_1} = \dfrac{\cancel{10}^5}{1} \cdot \dfrac{9y + 8}{\cancel{2}_1}$

$30(y + 2) + 2(y + 3) = 5(9y + 8)$

$30y + 60 + 2y + 6 = 45y + 40$

$32y + 66 = 45y + 40$

$66 = 13y + 40$

$26 = 13y$

$2 = y$

39. $z + \dfrac{z + 5}{3} - \dfrac{z - 2}{6} = \dfrac{z + 4}{4} + 1$ LCD = 12

$12(z + \dfrac{z + 5}{3} - \dfrac{z - 2}{6}) = 12(\dfrac{z + 4}{4} + 1)$

$12 \cdot z + \dfrac{\cancel{12}^4}{1} \cdot \dfrac{z + 5}{\cancel{3}_1} - \dfrac{\cancel{12}^2}{1} \cdot \dfrac{z - 2}{\cancel{6}_1} = \dfrac{\cancel{12}^3}{1} \cdot \dfrac{z + 4}{\cancel{4}_1} + 12 \cdot 1$

$12z + 4(z + 5) - 2(z - 2) = 3(z + 4) + 12$

$12z + 4z + 20 - 2z + 4 = 3z + 12 + 12$

$14z + 24 = 3z + 24$

$11z + 24 = 24$

$11z = 0$

$z = 0$

41. $3 \leq \dfrac{x}{3} - \dfrac{x + 1}{2} \leq 6$ LCD = 6

$6 \cdot 3 \leq 6(\dfrac{x}{3} - \dfrac{x + 1}{2}) \leq 6 \cdot 6$

$18 \leq \dfrac{\cancel{6}^2}{1} \cdot \dfrac{x}{\cancel{3}_1} - \dfrac{\cancel{6}^3}{1} \cdot \dfrac{x + 1}{\cancel{2}_1} \leq 36$

$18 \leq 2x - 3(x + 1) \leq 36$

$18 \leq 2x - 3x - 3 \leq 36$

$18 \leq -x - 3 \leq 36$

$21 \leq -x \leq 39$

$-21 \geq x \geq -39$

43. LCD of 3, 2, and 5 is 30. So

$$\frac{x}{3} + \frac{x}{2} + \frac{x}{5} = \frac{x(10)}{3(10)} + \frac{x(15)}{2(15)} + \frac{x(6)}{5(6)}$$

$$= \frac{10x}{30} + \frac{15x}{30} + \frac{6x}{30}$$

$$= \frac{10x + 15x + 6x}{30}$$

$$= \frac{31x}{30}$$

45. $\frac{x}{3} + \frac{x}{2} + \frac{x}{5} = 62$ LCD = 30

$$30\left(\frac{x}{3} + \frac{x}{2} + \frac{x}{5}\right) = 30 \cdot 62$$

$$\frac{\overset{10}{\cancel{30}}}{1} \cdot \frac{x}{\cancel{3}_1} + \frac{\overset{15}{\cancel{30}}}{1} \cdot \frac{x}{\cancel{2}_1} + \frac{\overset{6}{\cancel{30}}}{1} \cdot \frac{x}{\cancel{5}_1} = 1860$$

$$10x + 15x + 6x = 1860$$
$$31x = 1860$$
$$x = 60$$

47. $\frac{x + 5}{2} - \frac{x - 1}{4} = 2$ LCD = 4

$$4\left(\frac{x + 5}{2} - \frac{x - 1}{4}\right) = 4 \cdot 2$$

$$\frac{\overset{2}{\cancel{4}}}{1} \cdot \frac{x + 5}{\cancel{2}_1} - \frac{\overset{1}{\cancel{4}}}{1} \cdot \frac{x - 1}{\cancel{4}_1} = 4 \cdot 2$$

$$2(x + 5) - (x - 1) = 8$$
$$2x + 10 - x + 1 = 8$$
$$x + 11 = 8$$
$$x = -3$$

49. LCD of 2 and 4 is 4. So

$$\frac{x + 5}{2} - \frac{x - 1}{4} = \frac{(x + 5)(2)}{2(2)} - \frac{x - 1}{4}$$

$$= \frac{2(x + 5)}{4} - \frac{x - 1}{4}$$

$$= \frac{2(x + 5) - (x - 1)}{4} = \frac{2x + 10 - x + 1}{4}$$

$$= \frac{x + 11}{4}$$

Exercises 4.5

1. $\dfrac{\text{\# red}}{\text{\# black}} = \dfrac{7}{5}$

3. $\dfrac{\text{\# black}}{\text{\# red}} = \dfrac{5}{7}$

5. $\dfrac{\text{\# with}}{\text{\# without}} = \dfrac{11}{5}$

7. $\dfrac{\overset{1}{x}}{3\underset{1}{x}} = \dfrac{1}{3}$

9. $\dfrac{a}{b + c}$

11. $\dfrac{x}{5} = \dfrac{12}{3}$

$15 \cdot \dfrac{x}{5} = 15 \cdot \dfrac{12}{3}$

$\dfrac{\overset{3}{\cancel{15}}}{1} \cdot \dfrac{x}{\underset{1}{\cancel{5}}} = \dfrac{\overset{5}{\cancel{15}}}{1} \cdot \dfrac{12}{\underset{1}{\cancel{3}}}$

$3x = 60$

$x = 20$

13. $\dfrac{a}{6} = \dfrac{5}{3}$

$6 \cdot \dfrac{a}{6} = 6 \cdot \dfrac{5}{3}$

$\dfrac{\overset{1}{\cancel{6}}}{1} \cdot \dfrac{a}{\cancel{6}} = \dfrac{\overset{2}{\cancel{6}}}{1} \cdot \dfrac{5}{\underset{1}{\cancel{3}}}$

$a = 10$

15. $\dfrac{y}{15} = \dfrac{20}{6}$

$\dfrac{\overset{2}{\cancel{30}}}{} \cdot \dfrac{y}{\underset{1}{\cancel{15}}} = \dfrac{\overset{5}{\cancel{30}}}{} \cdot \dfrac{20}{\underset{1}{\cancel{6}}}$

$2y = 100$

$y = 50$

17. $\dfrac{y}{9} = \dfrac{4}{3}$

$9 \cdot \dfrac{y}{9} = 9 \cdot \dfrac{4}{3}$

$\dfrac{\overset{1}{\cancel{9}}}{1} \cdot \dfrac{y}{\underset{1}{\cancel{9}}} = \dfrac{\overset{3}{\cancel{9}}}{1} \cdot \dfrac{4}{\underset{1}{\cancel{3}}}$

$y = 12$

19. Let x = number of red marbles in the jar.

$\dfrac{x}{210} = \dfrac{7}{5}$

$210 \cdot \dfrac{x}{210} = 210 \cdot \dfrac{7}{5}$

$\dfrac{\overset{1}{\cancel{210}}}{1} \cdot \dfrac{x}{\underset{1}{\cancel{210}}} = \dfrac{\overset{42}{\cancel{210}}}{1} \cdot \dfrac{7}{\underset{1}{\cancel{5}}}$

$x = 294$

There are 294 red marbles in the jar.

21. Let x = number of students who got 90 or above.

$$\frac{x}{24} = \frac{3}{8}$$

$$24 \cdot \frac{x}{24} = 24 \cdot \frac{3}{8}$$

$$\frac{\cancel{24}^{1}}{1} \cdot \frac{x}{\cancel{24}_{1}} = \frac{\cancel{24}^{3}}{1} \cdot \frac{3}{\cancel{8}_{1}}$$

$$x = 9$$

There were 9 students who got 90 or above.

23. Let W = width of the rectangle.

$$\frac{18}{W} = \frac{9}{4}$$

$$4W \cdot \frac{18}{W} = 4W \cdot \frac{9}{4}$$

$$\frac{\cancel{4W}}{1} \cdot \frac{18}{\cancel{W}_{1}} = \frac{\cancel{4W}}{1} \cdot \frac{9}{\cancel{4}_{1}}$$

$$72 = 9W$$

$$8 = W$$

The width of the rectangle is 8 cm.

25. $$\frac{\text{shorter side}}{\text{longer side}} = \frac{\overset{2}{\cancel{6x}}}{\underset{5}{\cancel{15x}}} = \frac{2}{5}$$

27. Let x = length of scale drawing of the 20 meter wall (in cm).

$$\frac{x}{20} = \frac{5}{12}$$

$$60 \cdot \frac{x}{20} = 60 \cdot \frac{5}{12}$$

$$\frac{\cancel{60}^{3}}{1} \cdot \frac{x}{\cancel{20}_{1}} = \frac{\cancel{60}^{5}}{1} \cdot \frac{5}{\cancel{12}_{1}}$$

$$3x = 25$$

$$x = \frac{25}{3} = 8.33 \text{ (to the nearest hundredth)}$$

The scale drawing of the 20 meter wall is 8.33 cm.

29. Let x = number of kilograms in 10 lbs.

$$\frac{10}{x} = \frac{2.2}{1}$$

$$x \cdot \frac{10}{x} = x \cdot \frac{2.2}{1}$$

$$\frac{\cancel{x}}{1} \cdot \frac{10}{\cancel{x}} = 2.2x$$

$$10 = 2.2x$$

$$\frac{10}{2.2} = x$$

   4.55 = x (to the nearest hundredth)

There are 4.55 kilograms in 10 lbs.

31. Let x = number of yards in 100 meters.

$$\frac{100}{x} = \frac{.92}{1}$$

$$x \cdot \frac{100}{x} = x \cdot \frac{.92}{1}$$

$$\frac{\cancel{x}}{1} \cdot \frac{100}{\cancel{x}} = .92x$$

$$100 = .92x$$

$$\frac{100}{.92} = x$$

  108.70 = x (to the nearest hundredth)

There are 108.70 yards in 100 meters.

33. Let x = number of untagged deer in the entire area.

$$\frac{48}{x} = \frac{18}{42} \quad \text{(42 = 60 - 18 untagged deer in the second group.)}$$

$$42x \cdot \frac{48}{x} = 42x \cdot \frac{18}{42}$$

$$\frac{42\cancel{x}}{1} \cdot \frac{48}{\cancel{x}_1} = \frac{\cancel{42}x}{1} \cdot \frac{18}{\cancel{42}_1}$$

$$2016 = 18x$$

$$112 = x$$

Then the total number of deer estimated in the entire area is 48 + 112 = 160.

Exercises 4.6

1. Let x = the number

$$\frac{2}{3}x + 5 = 9$$

$$3\left(\frac{2}{3}x + 5\right) = 3 \cdot 9$$

$$\frac{\cancel{3}}{1} \cdot \frac{2}{\cancel{3}}x + 3 \cdot 5 = 3 \cdot 9 \qquad \text{CHECK: } \frac{2}{3} \text{ of 6 is 4, and}$$

$$2x + 15 = 27 \qquad\qquad\qquad 5 \text{ more than 4 is 9.}$$

$$2x = 12$$

$$x = 6$$

Thus, the number is 6.

3. Let x = the number

$$\frac{3}{4}x - 2 = \frac{1}{8}x - 7$$

$$8\left(\frac{3}{4}x - 2\right) = 8\left(\frac{1}{8}x - 7\right)$$

$$\frac{\cancel{8}^2}{1} \cdot \frac{3}{\cancel{4}_1}x - 8 \cdot 2 = \frac{\cancel{8}^1}{1} \cdot \frac{1}{\cancel{8}_1}x - 8 \cdot 7$$

$$6x - 16 = x - 56 \qquad \text{CHECK: } 2 \text{ less than } \frac{3}{4} \text{ of -8 is}$$

$$5x - 16 = -56 \qquad\qquad 2 \text{ less than -6 or -8.}$$

$$5x = -40 \qquad\qquad \frac{1}{8} \text{ of -8 is -1, and -8 is}$$

$$x = -8$$

Thus, the number is -8.   7 less than -1.

5. Let L = length of the rectangle (in meters)

$$\frac{1}{2}L = \text{width of the rectangle (in meters)}$$

$$2(L) + 2\left(\frac{1}{2}L\right) = 36 \qquad \text{CHECK: } 6 \text{ is } \frac{1}{2} \text{ of 12, and}$$

$$2L + \frac{\cancel{2}^1}{1} \cdot \frac{1}{\cancel{2}_1}L = 36 \qquad\qquad 2(6) + 2(12) = 12 + 24$$

$$2L + L = 36 \qquad\qquad\qquad\qquad = 36.$$

$$3L = 36$$

$$L = 12$$

Then $\frac{1}{2}L = \frac{1}{2}(12) = 6$. Thus, the dimensions of the rectangle are 12 meters and 6 meters.

7. Let x = length of the longest side of the triangle (in inches)

$\frac{3}{4}x$ = length of the medium side of the triangle (in inches)

$\frac{1}{2}(\frac{3}{4}x)$ = length of the shortest side of the triangle (in inches)

$x + \frac{3}{4}x + \frac{1}{2}(\frac{3}{4}x) = 17$ CHECK: 6 is $\frac{3}{4}$ of 8, and 3

$\quad x + \frac{3}{4}x + \frac{3}{8}x = 17$ is $\frac{1}{2}$ of 6. The sum

$8(x + \frac{3}{4}x + \frac{3}{8}x) = 8 \cdot 17$ of 8, 6, and 3 is 17.

$8 \cdot x + \frac{\overset{2}{\cancel{8}}}{1} \cdot \frac{3}{\underset{1}{\cancel{4}}}x + \frac{\overset{1}{\cancel{8}}}{1} \cdot \frac{3}{\underset{1}{\cancel{8}}}x = 8 \cdot 17$

$$8x + 6x + 3x = 136$$
$$17x = 136$$
$$x = 8$$

Then $\frac{3}{4}x = \frac{3}{4}(8) = 6$ and $\frac{1}{2}(\frac{3}{4}x) = \frac{1}{2}(\frac{3}{4}(8)) = 3$. Thus, the sides of the triangle are 8 inches, 6 inches, and 3 inches.

9. Let x = number of regular tickets sold

$350-x$ = number of combination tickets sold

$3x + 7(350 - x) = 1990$ CHECK: 115 regular tickets at \$3

$\quad 3x + 2450 - 7x = 1990$ each gives \$345.   235

$\qquad -4x + 2450 = 1990$ combination tickets at \$7

$\qquad\qquad -4x = -460$ each gives \$1645. The

$\qquad\qquad\quad x = 115$ total amount collected is

$345 + \$1645 = \$1990$.

Then $350 - x = 350 - 115 = 235$. Thus, there were 115 regular tickets and 235 combination tickets sold.

11. Let x = number of quarters in the collection

$2x + 3$ = number of dimes in the collection

$25x + 10(2x + 3) = 255$ CHECK: 13 is 3 more than twice

$\quad 25x + 20x + 30 = 255$ 5. 5 quarters are worth

$\qquad 45x + 30 = 255$ $5(\$.25) = \$1.25$, while 13

$\qquad\qquad 45x = 225$ dimes are worth $13(\$.10)$

$\qquad\qquad\quad x = 5$ $= \$1.30$. Total value $=$

$1.25 + \$1.30 = \$2.55$.

Then $2x + 3 = 2(5) + 3 = 13$. Thus, there are 5 quarters and 13 dimes in the collection.

13. Let t = number of minutes that the older machine works
     t - 15 = number of minutes that the newer machine works

$$175t + 250(t - 15) = 13675$$

CHECK: The older machine sorts
175(41) = 7175 screws,
while the newer one sorts
250(41 - 15) = 250(26) =
6500 screws. In all,
7175 + 6500 = 13,675
screws are sorted.

$$175t + 250t - 3750 = 13675$$
$$425t - 3750 = 13675$$
$$425t = 17425$$
$$t = 41$$

Since the older machine began the sorting process at 10:00
a.m. and worked for 41 minutes, the sorting is completed at
10:41 a.m.

15.   Let x = amount of money invested at 8%

x+4000 = amount of money invested at 11%

$$.08x + .11(x + 4000) = 1390$$
$$100(.08x + .11(x + 4000)) = 100(1390)$$
$$100(.08x) + 100(.11(x + 4000)) = 100(1390)$$
$$8x + 11(x + 4000) = 139000$$

CHECK: $5000 at 8% yields $400
interest. $9000 at 11%
yields $990 interest.
The total interest earned
is $400 + $990 = $1390.

$$8x + 11x + 44000 = 139000$$
$$19x + 44000 = 139000$$
$$19x = 95000$$
$$x = 5000$$

Then x + 4000 = 5000 + 4000 = 9000. Thus, $9000 was invested
at 11%.

17.   Let x = amount of money invested at 9%
      800-x = amount of money invested at 6%

$$.09x + .06(800 - x) = 67.50$$
$$100(.09x + .06(800 - x)) = 100(67.50)$$
$$100(.09x) + 100(.06(800 - x)) = 100(67.50)$$
$$9x + 6(800 - x) = 6750$$

CHECK: The interest on the
9% investment is
.09($650) = $58.50. The
interest on the 6%
investment is .06($150)
= $9.00. Total interest
= $58.50 + $9.00 = $67.50.

$$9x + 4800 - 6x = 6750$$
$$3x + 4800 = 6750$$
$$3x = 1950$$
$$x = 650$$

Then 800 - x = 800 - 650 = 150. Thus, $650 was invested at
9% and $150 was invested at 6%.

19. Let x = amount of money invested at 8%
     6000-x = amount of money invested at 12%

     .08x + .12(6000 - x) = .09(6000)

     100(.08x + .12(6000 - x)) = 100(.09(6000))

     100(.08x) + 100(.12(6000 - x)) = 100(.09(6000))

     8x + 12(6000 - x) = 9(6000)   CHECK: The interest on the 8%
       8x + 72000 - 12x = 54000   investment is .08($4500)
                                                = $360. The interest on
           -4x + 72000 = 54000   the 12% investment is
                                                .12($1500) = $180. The
                  -4x = -18000   total interest $360 +
                                                $180 = $540 is 9% of
                    x = 4500 $6000.

     Then 6000 - x = 6000 - 4500 = 1500. Thus, $4500 should be
     invested at 8% and $1500 should be invested at 12%.

21. Let x = number of ml of 30% hydrochloric acid solution

     .30x + .50(30) = .45(x + 30)

     100(.30x + .50(30)) = 100(.45(x + 30))

     100(.30x) + 100(.50(30)) = 100(.45(x + 30))

     30x + 50(30) = 45(x + 30)   CHECK: In 10 ml of a 30%
        30x + 1500 = 45x + 1350   solution, there are 3
                                                ml of acid. In 30 ml
              1500 = 15x + 1350   of a 50% solution, there
                                                are 15 ml of acid. So
               150 = 15x   there are 3 + 15 = 18 ml
                                                of acid in the mixture,
                10 = x   which is 45% of 40 ml.

     Thus, 10 ml of 30% hydrochloric acid solution should be used
     in the mixture.

23. Let x = number of liters of 25% salt solution
     90 - x = number of liters of 55% salt solution

     .25x + .55(90 - x) = .50(90)

     100(.25x + .55(90 - x)) = 100(.50(90))

     100(.25x) + 100(.55(90 - x)) = 100(.50(90))

     25x + 55(90 - x) = 50(90)   CHECK: In 15 l of a 25% salt
     25x + 4950 - 55x = 4500   solution, there are
                                                .25(15) = 3.75 l of
         -30x + 4950 = 4500   salt. In 75 l of a 55%
                                                salt solution, there are
               -30x = -450   .55(75) = 41.25 l of
                                                salt. In the mixture,
                  x = 15   there are 3.75 + 41.25
                                                = 45 l of salt, which is
                                                50% of 90 l.

Then $90 - x = 90 - 15 = 75$. Thus, 15 liters of the 25% solution should be mixed with 75 liters of the 55% solution.

25. Let x = number of gallons of pure anti-freeze to be used

$1.00x + .30(10) = .50(x + 10)$

$100(1.00x + .30(10)) = 100(.50(x + 10))$

$100(1.00x) + 100(.30(10)) = 100(.50(x + 10))$

$100x + 30(10) = 50(x + 10)$ CHECK: 10 gallons of a 30% anti-freeze solution

$100x + 300 = 50x + 500$ contains 3 gallons of anti-freeze. If we add

$50x + 300 = 500$ 4 gallons of anti-freeze we get 14 gallons in the

$50x = 200$ solution, 7 of which are anti-freeze. This is

$x = 4$ 50%.

Thus, 4 gallons of pure anti-freeze should be added to the radiator.

27. Let x = number of pounds of candy that sells for \$3.75/lb.

$3.75x + 5.00(35) = 4.25(x + 35)$

$100(3.75x + 5.00(35)) = 100(4.25(x + 35))$

$100(3.75x) + 100(5.00(35)) = 100(4.25(x + 35))$

$375x + 500(35) = 425(x + 35)$ CHECK: 52.5 lbs at \$3.75/lb =

$375x + 17500 = 425x + 14875$ \$196.87½.   35 lbs at

$17500 = 50x + 14875$ \$5/lb = \$175.   Total =

$2625 = 50x$ \$371.87½.   87.5 lbs

$52.5 = x$ at \$4.25/lb = \$371.87½.

Thus, 52.5 pounds of candy that sells for \$3.75/lb. should be added to the mixture.

29. Let t = number of hours that John and Susan must travel before they meet

$4t + 8t = 9$ CHECK: John walks $4\left(\frac{3}{4}\right) = 3$

$12t = 9$ miles and Susan jogs

$t = \dfrac{9}{12} = \dfrac{3}{4}$ $8\left(\frac{3}{4}\right) = 6$ miles.

$3 + 6 = 9$.

Since each must travel for $\frac{3}{4}$ of an hour or for 45 minutes, they will meet at 8:45 a.m.

31. Let t = number of hours that John must travel before they meet

$t - \dfrac{1}{4}$ = number of hours that Susan must travel before they meet

$4t + 8(t - \dfrac{1}{4}) = 9$ 　　　　CHECK: John walks $4(\dfrac{11}{12}) = \dfrac{11}{3} = 3\dfrac{2}{3}$

$4t + 8t - 8 \cdot \dfrac{1}{\underset{1}{4}} = 9$ 　　　　miles and Susan jogs

$12t - 2 = 9$ 　　　　$8(\dfrac{11}{12} - \dfrac{1}{4}) = 8(\dfrac{8}{12}) = \dfrac{16}{3} =$

$12t = 11$ 　　　　$5\dfrac{1}{3}$ miles. $\quad 3\dfrac{2}{3} + 5\dfrac{1}{3} = 9.$

$t = \dfrac{11}{12}$

Since John must travel $\dfrac{11}{12}$ hours or 55 minutes before he meets Susan, they will meet at 8:40 a.m.

33. Let t = number of hours that David spends jogging
$2 - t$ = number of hours that David spends walking

$5(2 - t) + 9t = 16$ 　　　　CHECK: David jogs $9(\dfrac{3}{2}) = \dfrac{27}{2}$

$10 - 5t + 9t = 16$ 　　　　$= 13\dfrac{1}{2}$ miles and walks

$10 + 4t = 16$ 　　　　$5(\dfrac{1}{2}) = \dfrac{5}{2} = 2\dfrac{1}{2}$ miles.

$4t = 6$ 　　　　$13\dfrac{1}{2} + 2\dfrac{1}{2} = 16$.

$t = \dfrac{6}{4} = \dfrac{3}{2}$

Thus, David jogs for $1\dfrac{1}{2}$ hours.

35. Recall that $C = \dfrac{5}{9}(F - 32)$, where C is the temperature in degrees Celsius and F is the temperature in degrees Fahrenheit.

$25 < C < 40$

$25 < \dfrac{5}{9}(F - 32) < 40$

$9(25) < 9(\dfrac{5}{9}(F - 32)) < 9(40)$

$225 < 5(F - 32) < 360$

$45 < F - 32 < 72$

$77 < F < 104$

Thus, the corresponding temperature range in degrees Fahrenheit is between 77°F and 104°F.

37. Let x = original price of a skirt
     .80x = sale price of the skirt

$$12.60 < .80x < 20.76$$

$$100(12.60) < 100(.80x) < 100(20.76)$$

$$1260 < 80x < 2076$$

$$15.75 < x < 25.95$$

Thus, the original range of prices on the skirts was between $15.75 and $25.95.

Chapter 4 - Review Exercises

1. $\dfrac{-18}{42} = \dfrac{-3 \cdot \cancel{6}}{7 \cdot \cancel{6}} = \dfrac{-3}{7} = -\dfrac{3}{7}$

3. $\dfrac{15x^6}{6x^2} = \dfrac{5x^4 \cdot \cancel{3x^2}}{2 \cdot \cancel{3x^2}} = \dfrac{5x^4}{2}$

5. $\dfrac{-10x^3y^5}{4xy^{10}} = \dfrac{-5x^2 \cdot \cancel{2xy^5}}{2y^5 \cdot \cancel{2xy^5}} = \dfrac{-5x^2}{2y^5} = -\dfrac{5x^2}{2y^5}$

7. $\dfrac{3t - 7t - t}{-2t^2 - 3t^2} = \dfrac{-5t}{-5t^2} = \dfrac{1\cancel{(-5t)}}{t\cancel{(-5t)}} = \dfrac{1}{t}$

9. $\dfrac{a}{4} \cdot \dfrac{a}{4} = \dfrac{a^2}{16}$

11. $\dfrac{7a}{6} - \dfrac{5a}{6} = \dfrac{7a - 5a}{6} = \dfrac{\overset{1}{\cancel{2}}a}{\underset{3}{\cancel{6}}} = \dfrac{a}{3}$

13. $\dfrac{4x - 3}{6x} - \dfrac{x - 1}{6x} = \dfrac{4x - 3 - (x - 1)}{6x} = \dfrac{4x - 3 - x + 1}{6x} = \dfrac{3x - 2}{6x}$

15. $\dfrac{2y^2 - 3y}{4} - \dfrac{y^2 - 3y}{4} + \dfrac{y^2}{4} = \dfrac{2y^2 - 3y - (y^2 - 3y) + y^2}{4}$

$$= \dfrac{2y^2 - 3y - y^2 + 3y + y^2}{4}$$

$$= \dfrac{\overset{1}{\cancel{2}}y^2}{\underset{2}{\cancel{4}}} = \dfrac{y^2}{2}$$

17. $\left(\dfrac{\cancel{x}}{\underset{2}{\cancel{4}}} \cdot \dfrac{\cancel{6}^3}{\cancel{xy}^2}\right) \div (2xy) = \dfrac{3x}{2y^2} \div \dfrac{2xy}{1} = \dfrac{3\cancel{x}}{2y^2} \cdot \dfrac{1}{2\cancel{x}y} = \dfrac{3}{4y^3}$

19. $\dfrac{a}{2} \cdot \dfrac{a}{4} = \dfrac{a^2}{8}$

21. $\dfrac{x^2}{2} - \dfrac{x^2}{6} + \dfrac{x^2}{3} = \dfrac{x^2(3)}{2(3)} - \dfrac{x^2}{6} + \dfrac{x^2(2)}{3(2)} = \dfrac{3x^2}{6} - \dfrac{x^2}{6} + \dfrac{2x^2}{6}$

$\qquad\qquad = \dfrac{3x^2 - x^2 + 2x^2}{6} = \dfrac{\overset{2}{4x^2}}{\underset{3}{6}} = \dfrac{2x^2}{3}$

23. $\dfrac{4}{x^2} + \dfrac{3}{2x} = \dfrac{4(2)}{x^2(2)} + \dfrac{3(x)}{2x(x)} = \dfrac{8}{2x^2} + \dfrac{3x}{2x^2} = \dfrac{8 + 3x}{2x^2}$

25. $\dfrac{3}{4a^2b} - \dfrac{5}{6ab} + \dfrac{7}{8b^3} = \dfrac{3(6b^2)}{4a^2b(6b^2)} - \dfrac{5(4ab^2)}{6ab(4ab^2)} + \dfrac{7(3a^2)}{8b^3(3a^2)}$

$\qquad\qquad = \dfrac{18b^2}{24a^2b^3} - \dfrac{20ab^2}{24a^2b^3} + \dfrac{21a^2}{24a^2b^3}$

$\qquad\qquad = \dfrac{18b^2 - 20ab^2 + 21a^2}{24a^2b^3}$

27. $\dfrac{x}{6} - \dfrac{1}{4} = \dfrac{7}{12}$

$12(\dfrac{x}{6} - \dfrac{1}{4}) = 12(\dfrac{7}{12})$

$\dfrac{\overset{2}{\cancel{12}}}{1} \cdot \dfrac{x}{\underset{1}{\cancel{6}}} - \dfrac{\overset{3}{\cancel{12}}}{1} \cdot \dfrac{1}{\underset{1}{\cancel{4}}} = \dfrac{\overset{1}{\cancel{12}}}{1} \cdot \dfrac{7}{\underset{1}{\cancel{12}}}$

$2x - 3 = 7$

$\qquad 2x = 10$

$\qquad\ x = 5$

29. $\dfrac{t + 1}{2} + \dfrac{t + 2}{3} < \dfrac{t + 7}{6}$

$6(\dfrac{t + 1}{2} + \dfrac{t + 2}{3}) < 6(\dfrac{t + 7}{6})$

$\dfrac{\overset{3}{\cancel{6}}}{1} \cdot \dfrac{t + 1}{\underset{1}{\cancel{2}}} + \dfrac{\overset{2}{\cancel{6}}}{1} \cdot \dfrac{t + 2}{\underset{1}{\cancel{3}}} < \dfrac{\overset{1}{\cancel{6}}}{1} \cdot \dfrac{t + 7}{\underset{1}{\cancel{6}}}$

$3(t + 1) + 2(t + 2) < t + 7$

$\qquad 3t + 3 + 2t + 4 < t + 7$

$\qquad\qquad\quad 5t + 7 < t + 7$

$\qquad\qquad\quad 4t + 7 < 7$

$\qquad\qquad\qquad\quad 4t < 0$

$\qquad\qquad\qquad\ \ t < 0$

31. $\dfrac{y + 3}{5} - \dfrac{y - 2}{3} = 1$

$15\left(\dfrac{y + 3}{5} - \dfrac{y - 2}{3}\right) = 15(1)$

$\dfrac{\cancel{15}^3}{1} \cdot \dfrac{y + 3}{\cancel{5}_1} - \dfrac{\cancel{15}^5}{1} \cdot \dfrac{y - 2}{\cancel{3}_1} = 15$

$3(y + 3) - 5(y - 2) = 15$

$3y + 9 - 5y + 10 = 15$

$-2y + 19 = 15$

$-2y = -4$

$y = 2$

33. $\dfrac{x}{3} = \dfrac{x + 1}{6}$

$6 \cdot \dfrac{x}{3} = 6 \cdot \dfrac{x + 1}{6}$

$\dfrac{\cancel{6}^2}{1} \cdot \dfrac{x}{\cancel{3}_1} = \dfrac{\cancel{6}^1}{1} \cdot \dfrac{x + 1}{\cancel{6}_1}$

$2x = x + 1$

$x = 1$

35. $2x + .2(x + 6) = 10$

$10(2x + .2(x + 6)) = 10 \cdot 10$

$10(2x) + 10(.2(x + 6)) = 100$

$20x + 2(x + 6) = 100$

$20x + 2x + 12 = 100$

$22x + 12 = 100$

$22x = 88$

$x = 4$

37. Let x = number of ounces in 1 kilogram (1000 grams)

$\dfrac{1000}{x} = \dfrac{28.4}{1}$

$\dfrac{\cancel{x}^1}{1} \cdot \dfrac{1000}{\cancel{x}_1} = x \cdot \dfrac{28.4}{1}$

$1000 = 28.4x$

$\dfrac{1000}{28.4} = x$

$35.21 = x$ (to the nearest hundredth)

Thus, there are 35.21 ounces in 1 kilogram.

39. Let x   = amount invested at 6%
        2x   = amount invested at 7%
     7000-3x = amount invested at 8%

.06x + .07(2x) + .08(7000 - 3x) $\geq$ 500

100(.06x + .07(2x) + .08(7000 - 3x)) $\geq$ 100(500)

100(.06x) + 100(.07(2x)) + 100(.08(7000 - 3x)) $\geq$ 50000

6x + 7(2x) + 8(7000 - 3x) $\geq$ 50000

6x + 14x + 56000 - 24x $\geq$ 50000

-4x + 56000 $\geq$ 50000

-4x $\geq$ -6000

x $\leq$ 1500

Thus, the most that can be invested at 6% is $1500.

41. Let x = Bill's present speed

5x = 3(x + 20)   CHECK: After 5 hours, Bill
                                covered (30)(5) = 150
5x = 3x + 60   miles. In 3 hours, he
                                would cover (50)(3) =
2x = 60   150 miles at the faster
                                rate as well.
 x = 30

Thus, Bill's present speed is 30 mph.

Chapter 4 Practice Test

1. (a) $\dfrac{-10}{24} = \dfrac{\cancel{2}(-5)}{\cancel{2}(12)} = \dfrac{-5}{12} = -\dfrac{5}{12}$

(b) $\dfrac{\overset{8}{\cancel{x^{10}}}}{\underset{1}{\cancel{x^{2}}}} = \dfrac{x^8}{1} = x^8$

(c) $\dfrac{\overset{2a^3}{\cancel{-6a^6}}}{\underset{1}{\cancel{-3a^3}}} = \dfrac{2a^3}{1} = 2a^3$

(d) $\dfrac{\overset{5\quad t^2}{\cancel{25r^2t^3}}}{\underset{3r^2}{\cancel{-15r^4t}}} = \dfrac{5t^2}{-3r^2} = -\dfrac{5t^2}{3r^2}$

3.   (a) $\frac{x}{3} + \frac{x}{5} = 8$

$$15\left(\frac{x}{3} + \frac{x}{5}\right) = 15 \cdot 8$$

$$\frac{\cancel{15}^5}{1} \cdot \frac{x}{\cancel{3}_1} + \frac{\cancel{15}^3}{1} \cdot \frac{x}{\cancel{5}_1} = 120$$

$$5x + 3x = 120$$

$$8x = 120$$

$$x = 15$$

(b) $\frac{x - 5}{2} + \frac{x}{5} \geq 8$

$$10\left(\frac{x - 5}{2} + \frac{x}{5}\right) \geq 10 \cdot 8$$

$$\frac{\cancel{10}^5}{1} \cdot \frac{x - 5}{\cancel{2}_1} + \frac{\cancel{10}^2}{1} \cdot \frac{x}{\cancel{5}_1} \geq 80$$

$$5(x - 5) + 2x \geq 80$$

$$5x - 25 + 2x \geq 80$$

$$7x - 25 \geq 80$$

$$\underline{+ 25 \quad + 25}$$

$$7x \quad\quad \geq 105$$

$$\frac{\cancel{7}x}{\cancel{7}} \quad\quad \geq \frac{105}{7}$$

$$x \quad\quad \geq 15$$

(c) $\frac{a + 3}{5} - \frac{a - 2}{4} = 1$

$$20\left(\frac{a + 3}{5} - \frac{a - 2}{4}\right) = 20 \cdot 1$$

$$\frac{\cancel{20}^4}{1} \cdot \frac{a + 3}{\cancel{5}_1} - \frac{\cancel{20}^5}{1} \cdot \frac{a - 2}{\cancel{4}_1} = 20$$

$$4(a + 3) - 5(a - 2) = 20$$

$$4a + 12 - 5a + 10 = 20$$

$$-a + 22 = 20$$

$$\underline{- 22 \quad - 22}$$

$$-a \quad\quad = -2$$

$$\frac{-a}{-1} \quad\quad = \frac{-2}{-1}$$

$$a \quad\quad = 2$$

(d) $.03t + .5t = 10.6$

$\quad 100(.03t + .5t) = 100(10.6)$

$\quad 100(.03t) + 100(.5t) = 100(10.6)$

$\quad 3t + 50t = 1060$

$\qquad 53t = 1060$

$$\frac{\cancel{53}t}{\cancel{53}} = \frac{1060}{53}$$

$\qquad\quad t = 20$

5. Let x = the number

$x + \frac{2}{3}x = 2x - 5$

$3(x + \frac{2}{3}x) = 3(2x - 5)$

$3x + \frac{\cancel{3}}{1} \cdot \frac{2}{\cancel{3}_1}x = 3(2x - 5)$

$3x + 2x = 6x - 15$ CHECK: $\frac{2}{3}$ of $15 = \frac{2}{\cancel{3}_1} \cdot \frac{\cancel{15}^5}{1} = \frac{10}{1}$

$\quad 5x = 6x - 15$ $= 10$. Then $15 + 10 =$

$\quad\underline{-6x \quad -6x}$ 25, which is 5 less

$\quad\overline{-x =} \qquad -15$ than twice 15.

$\quad \dfrac{-x}{-1} = \dfrac{-15}{-1}$

$\qquad x = \qquad 15$

7. Let x = amount invested at 8%
$7000-x$ = amount invested at 13%

$.08x + .13(7000 - x) = 750$

$100(.08x + .13(7000 - x)) = 100(750)$

$100(.08x) + 100(.13(7000 - x)) = 100(750)$

$8x + 13(7000 - x) = 75000$ CHECK: $3200 + 3800 = 7000$.
The interest on \$3200 at

$\quad 8x + 91000 - 13x = 75000$ 8% is \$256 (= .08(3200)).
The interest on \$3800 at

$\qquad -5x + 91000 = 75000$ 13% is \$494 (= .13(3800)).

$\qquad\qquad \underline{-91000 \quad -91000}$ Then \$256 + \$494 = \$750,

$\qquad\overline{-5x} \qquad\qquad =-16000$ as required.

$\qquad \dfrac{\cancel{-5}x}{\cancel{-5}} \qquad = \dfrac{-16000}{-5}$

$\qquad\quad x \qquad = 3200$

Then $7000 - x = 7000 - 3200 = 3800$. Thus, \$3200 is invested
at 8% and \$3800 is invested at 13%.

9. Let x = # of hours that the first person drives
   x - 4 = # of hours that the second person drives

   $48x + 55(x - 4) = 604$

   $48x + 55x - 220 = 604$

   $103x - 220 = 604$
   $ + 220 \quad +220$
   $103x = 824$

   $\dfrac{103x}{103} = \dfrac{824}{103}$

   $x = 8$

   CHECK: In 8 hours, the first person covers 48(8) = 384 km. In 8 - 4 = 4 hours, the second person covers 55(4) = 220 km. 384 + 220 = 604.

Thus, they will be 604 kilometers apart after the first person drives for 8 hours, or at 7:00 p.m.

Chapter 5

EXPONENTS AND POLYNOMIALS

1. $x^3 x^2 = x^{3+2} = x^5$

3. $(x^3)^2 = x^{3 \cdot 2} = x^6$

5. $x^3 x x^5 = x^{3+1+5} = x^9$

7. $10^4 10^5 = 10^{4+5} = 10^9$

9. $2^3 3^4$ cannot be simplified

11. $\dfrac{y^3 y^5}{y^2 y^4} = \dfrac{y^{3+5}}{y^{2+4}} = \dfrac{y^8}{y^6} = y^{8-6} = y^2$

13. $\dfrac{9u^9 v^8}{3u^3 v^4} = \dfrac{9}{3} u^{9-3} v^{8-4} = 3u^6 v^4$

15. $\dfrac{(a^3)^5}{(a^4)^2} = \dfrac{a^{3 \cdot 5}}{a^{4 \cdot 2}} = \dfrac{a^{15}}{a^8} = a^{15-8} = a^7$

17. $(-x^2)^4 = (-1)^4 (x^2)^4 = 1 \cdot x^{2 \cdot 4} = x^8$

19. $(x^2 y)^2 = (x^2)^2 y^2 = x^{2 \cdot 2} y^2 = x^4 y^2$

21. $(x^2 y^3)^5 = (x^2)^5 (y^3)^5 = x^{2 \cdot 5} y^{3 \cdot 5} = x^{10} y^{15}$

23. $(2r^3 s^5)^4 = 2^4 (r^3)^4 (s^5)^4 = 16r^{3 \cdot 4} s^{5 \cdot 4} = 16r^{12} s^{20}$

25. $(-x^3 y)^3 = (-1)^3 (x^3)^3 y^3 = -1 x^{3 \cdot 3} y^3 = -x^9 y^3$

27. $(\dfrac{x^3}{y^2})^4 = \dfrac{(x^3)^4}{(y^2)^4} = \dfrac{x^{3\cdot4}}{y^{2\cdot4}} = \dfrac{x^{12}}{y^8}$

29. $(2x^3)^4(3x^2)^2 = 2^4(x^3)^4 \cdot 3^2(x^2)^2 = 16x^{3\cdot4} \cdot 9x^{2\cdot2}$

$\qquad = (16 \cdot 9)x^{12}x^4 = 144x^{12+4} = 144x^{16}$

31. $\dfrac{(x^4y^2)^3}{x^5(y^3)^2} = \dfrac{(x^4)^3(y^2)^3}{x^5(y^3)^2} = \dfrac{x^{4\cdot3}y^{2\cdot3}}{x^5y^{3\cdot2}} = \dfrac{x^{12}\cancel{y^6}}{x^5\cancel{y^6}} = \dfrac{x^{12}}{x^5} = x^{12-5} = x^7$

33. $\dfrac{(3x^5y^4)^2}{9(x^3y)^3} = \dfrac{3^2(x^5)^2(y^4)^2}{9(x^3)^3y^3} = \dfrac{9x^{5\cdot2}y^{4\cdot2}}{9x^{3\cdot3}y^3} = \dfrac{\cancel{9}x^{10}y^8}{\cancel{9}x^9y^3} = \dfrac{x^{10}}{x^9} \cdot \dfrac{y^8}{y^3}$

$\qquad = x^{10-9}y^{8-3} = xy^5$

35. $(\dfrac{x^2y}{4u})^4 = \dfrac{(x^2y)^4}{(4u)^4} = \dfrac{(x^2)^4y^4}{4^4u^4} = \dfrac{x^{2\cdot4}y^4}{256u^4} = \dfrac{x^8y^4}{256u^4}$

37. $(\dfrac{2x^3y^4}{xy^6})^5 = (2 \cdot \dfrac{x^3}{x} \cdot \dfrac{y^4}{y^6})^5 = (2x^{3-1} \cdot \dfrac{1}{y^2})^5 = (\dfrac{2x^2}{y^2})^5$

$\qquad = \dfrac{(2x^2)^5}{(y^2)^5} = \dfrac{2^5(x^2)^5}{(y^2)^5} = \dfrac{32x^{2\cdot5}}{y^{2\cdot5}} = \dfrac{32x^{10}}{y^{10}}$

39. $(\dfrac{-3a^2b^3}{2c})^3 = \dfrac{(-3a^2b^3)^3}{(2c)^3} = \dfrac{(-3)^3(a^2)^3(b^3)^3}{2^3c^3} = \dfrac{-27a^{2\cdot3}b^{3\cdot3}}{8c^3}$

$\qquad = \dfrac{-27a^6b^9}{8c^3}$

41. $\dfrac{-3^2}{(-3)^2} = \dfrac{-\cancel{9}^1}{\cancel{9}_1} = \dfrac{-1}{1} = -1$

43. $\dfrac{-x^2}{(-x)^2} = \dfrac{-\cancel{x}^{\,1}}{(-1)^2\cancel{x}^2_1} = \dfrac{-1}{1} = -1$

45. $\dfrac{-u^3}{(-u)^3} = \dfrac{-u^3}{(-1)^3u^3} = \dfrac{-\cancel{u}^{\,1}}{-\cancel{u}^3_1} = \dfrac{-1}{-1} = 1$

47. $\dfrac{(-x^2)^4}{-(x^3)^2} = \dfrac{(-1)^4(x^2)^4}{-(x^3)^2} = \dfrac{1 \cdot x^{2\cdot4}}{-x^{3\cdot2}} = \dfrac{x^8}{-x^6} = -x^{8-6} = -x^2$

49. $\dfrac{-2^4 + 3^2}{(-4+3)^2} = \dfrac{-16 + 9}{(-1)^2} = \dfrac{-7}{1} = -7$

51. When we multiply two powers of the same base, we keep the base and add the exponents. When we raise a power to a power, we keep the base and multiply the exponents.

52. (a) $\dfrac{x^8}{x^8} = x^{8-8} = x^0$

    (b) $\dfrac{x^4}{x^7} = x^{4-7} = x^{-3}$

53. (a) According to Exponent Rule 2, we must multiply the exponents, not add them.

    (b) According to Exponent Rule 1, we must add the exponents, not multiply them.

    (c) According to Exponent Rule 3, we must subtract the exponents, not divide them.

    (d) Since x^2 and x^3 are unlike terms, we cannot combine them when they are added.

Exercises 5.2

1. (a) $-3(2) = -6$

    (b) $x^2 x^{-3} = x^{2+(-3)} = x^{-1} = \dfrac{1}{x}$

    (c) $(x^2)^{-3} = x^{2(-3)} = x^{-6} = \dfrac{1}{x^6}$

    (d) $2^{-3} = \dfrac{1}{2^3} = \dfrac{1}{8}$

3. (a) $-4(3) = -12$

    (b) $x^3 x^{-4} = x^{3+(-4)} = x^{-1} = \dfrac{1}{x}$

    (c) $(x^3)^{-4} = x^{3(-4)} = x^{-12} = \dfrac{1}{x^{12}}$

    (d) $3^{-4} = \dfrac{1}{3^4} = \dfrac{1}{81}$

5. $8^0 = 1$

7. $5 \cdot 4^0 = 5 \cdot 1 = 5$

9. $xy^0 = x \cdot 1 = x$

11. $5^{-2} = \dfrac{1}{5^2} = \dfrac{1}{25}$

13. $\dfrac{1}{5^{-2}} = \dfrac{1}{\frac{1}{5^2}} = \dfrac{1}{\frac{1}{25}} = 1 \cdot \dfrac{25}{1} = 25$

15. $x^{-4}x^4 = x^{-4+4} = x^0 = 1$

17. $x^{-4}x^{-6} = x^{-4+(-6)} = x^{-10} = \dfrac{1}{x^{10}}$

19. $a^2a^{-4}aa^{-7} = a^{2+(-4)+1+(-7)} = a^{-8} = \dfrac{1}{a^8}$

21. $10^{-3}10^8 = 10^{-3+8} = 10^5 = 100{,}000$

23. $10^6 10^{-5} 10^{-4} = 10^{6+(-5)+(-4)} = 10^{-3} = \dfrac{1}{10^3} = \dfrac{1}{1000}$

25. $10^7 10^{-7} = 10^{7+(-7)} = 10^0 = 1$

27. $(xy)^4 = x^4 y^4$

29. $2a^{-3} = \dfrac{2}{1} \cdot \dfrac{1}{a^3} = \dfrac{2}{a^3}$

31. $-3y^{-2} = \dfrac{-3}{1} \cdot \dfrac{1}{y^2} = -\dfrac{3}{y^2}$

33. $-(3y^{-2}) = -\left(\dfrac{3}{1} \cdot \dfrac{1}{y^2}\right) = -\left(\dfrac{3}{y^2}\right) = -\dfrac{3}{y^2}$

35. $xy^{-1} = \dfrac{x}{1} \cdot \dfrac{1}{y} = \dfrac{x}{y}$

37. $(a^4b^3)^{-2} = (a^4)^{-2}(b^3)^{-2} = a^{4(-2)}b^{3(-2)} = a^{-8}b^{-6}$

$\quad\quad = \dfrac{1}{a^8} \cdot \dfrac{1}{b^6} = \dfrac{1}{a^8 b^6}$

39. $(a^{-4}b^3)^{-2} = (a^{-4})^{-2}(b^3)^{-2} = a^{-4(-2)}b^{3(-2)} = a^8 b^{-6}$

$\quad\quad = \dfrac{a^8}{1} \cdot \dfrac{1}{b^6} = \dfrac{a^8}{b^6}$

41. $(3x^{-2}y^3z^{-4})^2 = 3^2(x^{-2})^2(y^3)^2(z^{-4})^2 = 9x^{-2(2)}y^{3(2)}z^{-4(2)}$

$\quad\quad = 9x^{-4}y^6z^{-8} = \dfrac{9}{1} \cdot \dfrac{1}{x^4} \cdot \dfrac{y^6}{1} \cdot \dfrac{1}{z^8} = \dfrac{9y^6}{x^4 z^8}$

43. $4(x^{-1}y)^{-3} = 4(x^{-1})^{-3}y^{-3} = 4x^{-1(-3)}y^{-3} = 4x^3y^{-3}$

$$= \frac{4}{1} \cdot \frac{x^3}{1} \cdot \frac{1}{y^3} = \frac{4x^3}{y^3}$$

45. $\dfrac{x^5}{x^2} = x^{5-2} = x^3$

47. $\dfrac{-3a^{-3}}{9a^9} = \dfrac{-\cancel{3}^1}{\cancel{9}_3} \cdot \dfrac{a^{-3}}{a^9} = -\dfrac{1}{3}a^{-3-9} = -\dfrac{1}{3}a^{-12} = -\dfrac{1}{3} \cdot \dfrac{1}{a^{12}} = -\dfrac{1}{3a^{12}}$

49. $x^{-2} + y^{-1} = \dfrac{1}{x^2} + \dfrac{1}{y} = \dfrac{y}{x^2y} + \dfrac{x^2}{x^2y} = \dfrac{y + x^2}{x^2y}$

51. $\dfrac{x^4x^{-10}}{x^{-2}x^{-5}} = \dfrac{x^{4+(-10)}}{x^{-2+(-5)}} = \dfrac{x^{-6}}{x^{-7}} = x^{-6-(-7)} = x^1 = x$

53. $\dfrac{x^4y^{-10}}{x^{-2}y^{-5}} = \dfrac{x^4}{x^{-2}} \cdot \dfrac{y^{-10}}{y^{-5}} = x^{4-(-2)}y^{-10-(-5)} = x^6y^{-5} = \dfrac{x^6}{1} \cdot \dfrac{1}{y^5} = \dfrac{x^6}{y^5}$

55. $\dfrac{10^{-3}10^5}{10^6 10^{-10}} = \dfrac{10^{-3+5}}{10^{6+(-10)}} = \dfrac{10^2}{10^{-4}} = 10^{2-(-4)} = 10^6 = 1{,}000{,}000$

57. $\dfrac{12(10^{-3})}{4(10^{-7})} = \dfrac{\cancel{12}^3}{\cancel{4}_1} \cdot \dfrac{10^{-3}}{10^{-7}} = 3 \cdot 10^{-3-(-7)} = 3 \cdot 10^4$

$$= 3 \cdot 10000 = 30000$$

59. $\left(\dfrac{a^{-2}}{a^3}\right)^{-3} = (a^{-2-3})^{-3} = (a^{-5})^{-3} = a^{-5(-3)} = a^{15}$

61. $\dfrac{(x^2y^{-1})^{-1}}{(x^3y^{-2})^2} = \dfrac{(x^2)^{-1}(y^{-1})^{-1}}{(x^3)^2(y^{-2})^2} = \dfrac{x^{2(-1)}y^{-1(-1)}}{x^{3(2)}y^{-2(2)}} = \dfrac{x^{-2}y^1}{x^6y^{-4}}$

$$= \dfrac{x^{-2}}{x^6} \cdot \dfrac{y^1}{y^{-4}} = x^{-2-6}y^{1-(-4)} = x^{-8}y^5 = \dfrac{1}{x^8} \cdot \dfrac{y^5}{1} = \dfrac{y^5}{x^8}$$

63. $\left(\dfrac{2m^{-2}n^{-3}}{m^{-6}n^{-1}}\right)^{-2} = \left(\dfrac{2}{1} \cdot \dfrac{m^{-2}}{m^{-6}} \cdot \dfrac{n^{-3}}{n^{-1}}\right)^{-2} = (2m^{-2-(-6)}n^{-3-(-1)})^{-2}$

$$= (2m^4n^{-2})^{-2} = 2^{-2}(m^4)^{-2}(n^{-2})^{-2}$$

$$= \dfrac{1}{2^2} \cdot m^{4(-2)}n^{-2(-2)} = \dfrac{1}{4}m^{-8}n^4 = \dfrac{1}{4} \cdot \dfrac{1}{m^8} \cdot \dfrac{n^4}{1}$$

$$= \dfrac{n^4}{4m^8}$$

65. $(\dfrac{x^{-1}y^{-2}}{3x^{-2}y^{-3}})^{-1} = (\dfrac{1}{3} \cdot \dfrac{x^{-1}}{x^{-2}} \cdot \dfrac{y^{-2}}{y^{-3}})^{-1} = (\dfrac{1}{3}x^{-1-(-2)}y^{-2-(-3)})^{-1}$

$= (\dfrac{1}{3}xy)^{-1} = (\dfrac{1}{3})^{-1}x^{-1}y^{-1} = \dfrac{1}{\frac{1}{3}}x^{-1}y^{-1}$

$= \dfrac{3}{1} \cdot \dfrac{1}{x} \cdot \dfrac{1}{y} = \dfrac{3}{xy}$

67. $\dfrac{(2m^{-2}n^{-3})^{-4}}{(m^{-6}n^{-1})^{-2}} = \dfrac{2^{-4}(m^{-2})^{-4}(n^{-3})^{-4}}{(m^{-6})^{-2}(n^{-1})^{-2}} = \dfrac{2^{-4}m^{-2(-4)}n^{-3(-4)}}{m^{-6(-2)}n^{-1(-2)}}$

$= \dfrac{2^{-4}m^{8}n^{12}}{m^{12}n^{2}} = \dfrac{1}{2^{4}} \cdot \dfrac{m^{8}}{m^{12}} \cdot \dfrac{n^{12}}{n^{2}} = \dfrac{1}{16}m^{8-12}n^{12-2}$

$= \dfrac{1}{16}m^{-4}n^{10} = \dfrac{1}{16} \cdot \dfrac{1}{m^{4}} \cdot \dfrac{n^{10}}{1} = \dfrac{n^{10}}{16m^{4}}$

69. $\dfrac{(x^{5}y)^{-2}(x^{-2}y^{3})^{2}}{(x^{-3}y^{-4})^{-2}} = \dfrac{(x^{5})^{-2}y^{-2} \cdot (x^{-2})^{2}(y^{3})^{2}}{(x^{-3})^{-2}(y^{-4})^{-2}}$

$= \dfrac{x^{5(-2)}y^{-2}x^{-2(2)}y^{3(2)}}{x^{-3(-2)}y^{-4(-2)}} = \dfrac{x^{-10}y^{-2}x^{-4}y^{6}}{x^{6}y^{8}}$

$= \dfrac{x^{-10+(-4)}y^{-2+6}}{x^{6}y^{8}} = \dfrac{x^{-14}y^{4}}{x^{6}y^{8}} = \dfrac{x^{-14}}{x^{6}} \cdot \dfrac{y^{4}}{y^{8}}$

$= x^{-14-6}y^{4-8} = x^{-20}y^{-4} = \dfrac{1}{x^{20}} \cdot \dfrac{1}{y^{4}}$

$= \dfrac{1}{x^{20}y^{4}}$

71. $\dfrac{x^{6}}{x^{4}}$ requires us to divide x^{6} by x^{4}, whereas $\dfrac{x^{6}}{x^{-4}} = \dfrac{x^{6}}{\frac{1}{x^{4}}}$

$= x^{6} \cdot \dfrac{x^{4}}{1}$ asks us to multiply x^{6} by x^{4}.

72. When -1 appears in the exponent, it tells us to take the reciprocal of the base. Thus, $3^{-1} = \dfrac{1}{3}$. When the minus sign appears in front of the 3, it tells us to take the opposite of 3. Put another way, 3^{-1} is the multiplicative inverse of 3, while -3 is the additive inverse of 3.

Exercises 5.3

1. $4530 = 4.53 \times 10^{3}$ 3. $.0453 = 4.53 \times 10^{-2}$

5. $.00007 = 7 \times 10^{-5}$ 7. $7,000,000 = 7 \times 10^6$

9. $85,370 = 8.537 \times 10^4$ 11. $.0085370 = 8.537 \times 10^{-3}$

13. $90 = 9 \times 10^1$ 15. $9 = 9 \times 10^0 = 9 \times 1 = 9$

17. $.9 = 9 \times 10^{-1}$ 19. $.09 = 9 \times 10^{-2}$

21. $.00000003 = 3 \times 10^{-8}$ 23. $28 = 2.8 \times 10^1$

25. $47.5 = 4.75 \times 10^1$ 27. $9727.3 = 9.7273 \times 10^3$

29. $2.8 \times 10^4 = 28,000$ 31. $2.8 \times 10^{-4} = .00028$

33. $4.29 \times 10^7 = 42,900,000$ 35. $4.29 \times 10^{-7} = .000000429$

37. $3.52 \times 10^{-3} = .00352$ 39. $3.5286 \times 10^5 = 352,860$

41. $.026 \times 10^{-3} = .000026$

43. $\begin{aligned}
(.004)(250) &= (4 \times 10^{-3})(2.5 \times 10^2) \\
&= (4)(2.5) \times 10^{-3}10^2 = 10 \times 10^{-3+2} \\
&= 10 \times 10^{-1} = 1.0 \times 10^0 = 1 \times 1 = 1
\end{aligned}$

45. $\dfrac{.003}{6000} = \dfrac{3 \times 10^{-3}}{6 \times 10^3} = \dfrac{3}{6} \times \dfrac{10^{-3}}{10^3} = .5 \times 10^{-3-3} = .5 \times 10^{-6} = 5 \times 10^{-7}$

47. $\begin{aligned}
\dfrac{(480)(.008)}{(.24)(4000)} &= \dfrac{(4.8 \times 10^2)(8 \times 10^{-3})}{(2.4 \times 10^{-1})(4 \times 10^3)} = \dfrac{\overset{2}{\cancel{(4.8)}}\overset{2}{\cancel{(8)}}}{\underset{1}{\cancel{(2.4)}}\underset{1}{\cancel{(4)}}} \times \dfrac{10^210^{-3}}{10^{-1}10^3} \\
&= 4 \times \dfrac{10^{2+(-3)}}{10^{-1+3}} = 4 \times \dfrac{10^{-1}}{10^2} = 4 \times 10^{-1-2} \\
&= 4 \times 10^{-3}
\end{aligned}$

49. $\begin{aligned}
\dfrac{(.0036)(.005)}{(.01)(.06)} &= \dfrac{(3.6 \times 10^{-3})(5 \times 10^{-3})}{(1 \times 10^{-2})(6 \times 10^{-2})} = \dfrac{\overset{.6}{\cancel{(3.6)}}(5)}{(1)\underset{1}{\cancel{(6)}}} \times \dfrac{10^{-3}10^{-3}}{10^{-2}10^{-2}} \\
&= 3 \times \dfrac{10^{-3+(-3)}}{10^{-2+(-2)}} = 3 \times \dfrac{10^{-6}}{10^{-4}} = 3 \times 10^{-6-(-4)} \\
&= 3 \times 10^{-2}
\end{aligned}$

51. 5.98×10^{27} kg

53. $\begin{aligned}
(80,000)(9.3 \times 10^{-23}) &= (8 \times 10^4)(9.3 \times 10^{-23}) \\
&= (8)(9.3) \times 10^410^{-23} = 74.4 \times 10^{4+(-23)} \\
&= 74.4 \times 10^{-19} = 7.44 \times 10^{-18} \text{ grams}
\end{aligned}$

55. $.00000001 = 1 \times 10^{-8}$ cm

57. $(153)(1 \times 10^{-8}) = 153 \times 10^{-8} = 1.53 \times 10^{-6}$ cm

59. 4250 million $= (4250)(1,000,000) = (4.25 \times 10^3)(1 \times 10^6)$

$$= (4.25)(1) \times 10^3 10^6 = 4.25 \times 10^{3+6}$$

$$= 4.25 \times 10^9 \text{ miles}$$

61. Let w = weight of the Earth in tons.

$$\frac{5.98 \times 10^{27}}{w} = \frac{888.9}{1}$$

$$5.98 \times 10^{27} = (8.889 \times 10^2)w$$

$$\frac{5.98 \times 10^{27}}{8.889 \times 10^2} = w$$

$$(\frac{5.98}{8.889}) \times \frac{10^{27}}{10^2} = w$$

$$.6727 \times 10^{27-2} = w$$

$$.6727 \times 10^{25} = 6.727 \times 10^{24} = w$$

Thus, the weight of the Earth is 6.727×10^{24} tons.

63. There are $(365)(24)(60)(60) = 31,536,000$ seconds in one year.
Then one light year equals $(186,000)(31,536,000)$ miles.
$$(186,000)(31,536,000) = (1.86 \times 10^5)(3.1536 \times 10^7)$$

$$= (1.86)(3.1536) \times 10^5 10^7$$

$$= 5.865696 \times 10^{5+7}$$

$$= 5.865696 \times 10^{12} \text{ miles}$$

65. $(5 \times 10^9)(5.865696 \times 10^{12})(1.6) = (5)(5.865696)(1.6) \times 10^9 10^{12}$

$$= 46.925568 \times 10^{9+12}$$

$$= 46.925568 \times 10^{21}$$

$$= 4.6925568 \times 10^{22} \text{ kilometers}$$

67. First multiply 3.74 by 6.38; then multiply 10^{-5} by 10^4. Take
the product of these two results and express this product in
scientific notation.

$$(3.74)(6.38) = 23.8612$$

$$10^{-5}10^4 = 10^{-5+4} = 10^{-1}$$
$$23.8612 \times 10^{-1} = 2.38612 \times 10^0 = 2.38612$$

68. If the number is bigger than 1, the exponent cannot be
     negative; if the number is smaller than 1, the exponent
     must be negative.

Exercises 5.4

1. (a) one term: $3x^5$

    (b) degree of $3x^5$: 5

    (c) degree of polynomial: 5

3. (a) two terms: 3x, 4

    (b) degree of 3x: 1
        degree of 4:   0

    (c) degree of polynomial: 1

5. (a) two terms: x^2, y^3

    (b) degree of x^2: 2
        degree of y^3: 3

    (c) degree of polynomial: 3

7. (a) one term: x^2y^3

    (b) degree of x^2y^3: 5 (= 2 + 3)

    (c) degree of polynomial: 5

9. (a) one term: 8

    (b) degree of 8: 0

    (c) degree of polynomial: 0

11. (a) three terms: $2x^3$, $-5x^2$, x

    (b) degree of $2x^3$: 3
        degree of $-5x^2$: 2
        degree of x: 1

    (c) degree of polynomial: 3

13.   (a) two terms: $2x^3$, y^5

(b) degree of $2x^3$:   3
degree of y^5:   5

(c) degree of polynomial: 5

15.   (a) one term: $2x^3y^5$

(b) degree of $2x^3y^5$:   8 (= 3 + 5)

(c) degree of polynomial: 8

17.   (a) four terms: x^5, $-x^3y^4$, $-2x^2y^3$, y^6

(b) degree of x^5:   5
degree of $-x^3y^4$:   7 (= 3 + 4)
degree of $-2x^2y^3$:   5 (= 2 + 3)
degree of y^6:   6

(c) degree of polynomial: 7

19.   (a) degree of x^2:   2
degree of $-5x$:   1
degree of 6:   0

(b) degree of polynomial: 2

(c) The coefficient of x^2 is 1.   The coefficient of $-5x$ is
-5.   6 is both a term and a coefficient.

21.   (a) degree of x^2:   2
degree of 4:   0

(b) degree of polynomial: 2

(c) Write the polynomial as x^2 + 0x + 4.   Then the coefficient
of x^2 is 1 and the coefficient of 0x is 0.   4 is both a
term and a coefficient.

23.   (a) degree of x^3:   3
degree of -1:   0

(b) degree of polynomial: 3

(c) Write the polynomial as x^3 + $0x^2$ + 0x - 1.   Then the
coefficient of x^3 is 1, and the coefficients of $0x^2$ and 0x
are 0.   -1 is both a term and a coefficient.

25. (a) degree of 1:   0

  degree of $-x^5$:   5

  (b) degree of polynomial: 5

  (c) Write the polynomial as $-x^5 + 0x^4 + 0x^3 + 0x^2 + 0x + 1$. Then the coefficient of $-x^5$ is -1, and the coefficients of $0x^4$, $0x^3$, $0x^2$ and $0x$ are all 0.   1 is both a term and a coefficient.

27. $(2x^2 - 5) + (3x^2 - 5) = 2x^2 + 3x^2 - 5 - 5 = 5x^2 - 10$

29. $(3u^3 - 2u + 7) + (u^3 - u^2 + 7u) = 3u^3 + u^3 - u^2 - 2u + 7u + 7$

$$= 4u^3 - u^2 + 5u + 7$$

31. $(3u^2 - 2u + 7) - (u^3 - u^2 + 7u) = 3u^2 - 2u + 7 - u^3 + u^2 - 7u$

$$= -u^3 + 3u^2 + u^2 - 2u - 7u + 7$$

$$= -u^3 + 4u^2 - 9u + 7$$

33. $(4t^3 - t) + (t^2 + t) - (t^3 - t^2) = 4t^3 - t + t^2 + t - t^3 + t^2$

$$= 4t^3 - t^3 + t^2 + t^2 - t + t$$

$$= 3t^3 + 2t^2$$

35. $(x^2y + 3xy - x^2y^2) + (x^2y - 5x^2y^2 - xy^2)$

$$= x^2y + x^2y + 3xy - x^2y^2 - 5x^2y^2 - xy^2$$

$$= 2x^2y + 3xy - 6x^2y^2 - xy^2$$

37. $(x^2y + 3xy - x^2y^2) - (x^2y - 5x^2y^2 - xy^2)$

$$= x^2y + 3xy - x^2y^2 - x^2y + 5x^2y^2 + xy^2$$

$$= x^2y - x^2y + 3xy - x^2y^2 + 5x^2y^2 + xy^2$$

$$= 3xy + 4x^2y^2 + xy^2$$

39. $2(y^2 - 4y + 1) + 3(2y^2 - y - 1) = 2y^2 - 8y + 2 + 6y^2 - 3y - 3$

$$= 2y^2 + 6y^2 - 8y - 3y + 2 - 3$$

$$= 8y^2 - 11y - 1$$

41. $5(x^2 - 3x + 2) - 3(2x^2 - 5x - 2) = 5x^2 - 15x + 10 - 6x^2 + 15x + 6$

$$= 5x^2 - 6x^2 - 15x + 15x + 10 + 6$$

$$= -x^2 + 16$$

43. $(x^2 + 3x - 7) + (5x - x^2) + (3x^2 - x - 2)$

$$= x^2 - x^2 + 3x^2 + 3x + 5x - x - 7 - 2$$

$$= 3x^2 + 7x - 9$$

45. $(2x^2 - 3x + 5) - (x^2 - 7x + 3) = 2x^2 - 3x + 5 - x^2 + 7x - 3$

$$= 2x^2 - x^2 - 3x + 7x + 5 - 3$$

$$= x^2 + 4x + 2$$

47. $(a^3 - b^2) + (a^2b + 2b^2) - (a^3 - a^2 - b + b^2)$

$$= a^3 - b^2 + a^2b + 2b^2 - a^3 + a^2 + b - b^2$$

$$= a^3 - a^3 - b^2 + 2b^2 - b^2 + a^2b + a^2 + b$$

$$= a^2b + a^2 + b$$

49. $2x - 1 - ((3x + 6) + (5x - 8)) = 2x - 1 - (8x - 2)$

$$= 2x - 1 - 8x + 2$$

$$= 2x - 8x - 1 + 2$$

$$= -6x + 1$$

51. $x^2 - x + 3 = (-5)^2 - (-5) + 3 = 25 + 5 + 3 = 33$

53. $y^4 + y^3 + y^2 + y + 1 = (-3)^4 + (-3)^3 + (-3)^2 + (-3) + 1$

$$= 81 - 27 + 9 - 3 + 1 = 61$$

55. $-3x^2y + 5xy^2 = -3(2)^2(-1) + 5(2)(-1)^2$

$$= -3(4)(-1) + 5(2)(1) = 12 + 10 = 22$$

57. In a sum, the expressions to be added are called terms;
in a product, the expressions to be multiplied are called
factors.

58. 3 is not a factor of the expression 6x + 8 because 3 does
not exactly divide 8.

59. 2 is a factor of the expression 6x + 8 because 2 does
exactly divide both 6x and 8. Here, we can write 6x + 8
= 2(3x + 4).

Exercises 5.5

1. $3x(5x^3)(4x^2) = (3)(5)(4)(x \cdot x^3 \cdot x^2) = 60x^6$

3. $3x(5x^3 + 4x^2) = 3x \cdot 5x^3 + 3x \cdot 4x^2 = 15x^4 + 12x^3$

5. $4xy(3yz)(-5xz) = (4)(3)(-5)(xx)(yy)(zz) = -60x^2y^2z^2$

7. $4xy(3yz - 5xz) = 4xy \cdot 3yz - 4xy \cdot 5xz = 12xy^2z - 20x^2yz$

9. $3x^2(x + 3y) + 4xy(x - 3y) = 3x^2 \cdot x + 3x^2 \cdot 3y + 4xy \cdot x - 4xy \cdot 3y$
$$= 3x^3 + 9x^2y + 4x^2y - 12xy^2$$
$$= 3x^3 + 13x^2y - 12xy^2$$

11. $5xy^2(xy - y) - 2y(x^2y^2 - xy^2)$
$$= 5xy^2 \cdot xy - 5xy^2 \cdot y - 2y \cdot x^2y^2 + 2y \cdot xy^2$$
$$= 5x^2y^3 - 5xy^3 - 2x^2y^3 + 2xy^3$$
$$= 3x^2y^3 - 3xy^3$$

13. $(x + 2)(x^2 - x + 3) = x(x^2 - x + 3) + 2(x^2 - x + 3)$
$$= x^3 - x^2 + 3x + 2x^2 - 2x + 6$$
$$= x^3 + x^2 + x + 6$$

15. $(y - 5)(y^2 + 2y - 6) = y(y^2 + 2y - 6) - 5(y^2 + 2y - 6)$
$$= y^3 + 2y^2 - 6y - 5y^2 - 10y + 30$$
$$= y^3 - 3y^2 - 16y + 30$$

17. $(3x - 2)(x^2 + 3x - 5) = 3x(x^2 + 3x - 5) - 2(x^2 + 3x - 5)$
$$= 3x^3 + 9x^2 - 15x - 2x^2 - 6x + 10$$
$$= 3x^3 + 7x^2 - 21x + 10$$

19. $(5z + 2)(3z^2 + 2z + 8) = 5z(3z^2 + 2z + 8) + 2(3z^2 + 2z + 8)$
$$= 15z^3 + 10z^2 + 40z + 6z^2 + 4z + 16$$
$$= 15z^3 + 16z^2 + 44z + 16$$

21. $(x + y)(x^2 - xy + y^2) = x(x^2 - xy + y^2) + y(x^2 - xy + y^2)$
$$= x^3 - x^2y + xy^2 + x^2y - xy^2 + y^3$$
$$= x^3 + y^3$$

23. $(x^2 + x + 1)(x^2 + x - 1) = x^2(x^2 + x - 1) + x(x^2 + x - 1) + 1(x^2 + x - 1)$

$$= x^4 + x^3 - x^2 + x^3 + x^2 - x + x^2 + x - 1$$

$$= x^4 + 2x^3 + x^2 - 1$$

25. $(x^3 + xy - y^2)(x^3 - 3xy + y^2) = x^3(x^3 - 3xy + y^2) + xy(x^3 - 3xy + y^2)$

$$- y^2(x^3 - 3xy + y^2)$$

$$= x^6 - 3x^4y + x^3y^2 + x^4y - 3x^2y^2 + xy^3$$

$$- x^3y^2 + 3xy^3 - y^4$$

$$= x^6 - 2x^4y - 3x^2y^2 + 4xy^3 - y^4$$

27. $(x + 5)(x + 3) = x^2 + 3x + 5x + 15 = x^2 + 8x + 15$

29. $(x - 5)(x - 3) = x^2 - 3x - 5x + 15 = x^2 - 8x + 15$

31. $(x - 5)(x + 3) = x^2 + 3x - 5x - 15 = x^2 - 2x - 15$

33. $(x + 5)(x - 3) = x^2 - 3x + 5x - 15 = x^2 + 2x - 15$

35. $(x + 2y)(x + 3y) = x^2 + 3xy + 2xy + 6y^2 = x^2 + 5xy + 6y^2$

37. $(a + 8b)(a - 5b) = a^2 - 5ab + 8ab - 40b^2 = a^2 + 3ab - 40b^2$

39. $(3x - 4)(4x - 1) = 12x^2 - 3x - 16x + 4 = 12x^2 - 19x + 4$

41. $(2r - s)(r + 3s) = 2r^2 + 6rs - rs - 3s^2 = 2r^2 + 5rs - 3s^2$

43. $(x^2 + 3)(x^2 + 2) = x^4 + 2x^2 + 3x^2 + 6 = x^4 + 5x^2 + 6$

45. $(x + 7)(x + 7) = x^2 + 7x + 7x + 49 = x^2 + 14x + 49$

47. $(x + 7)(x - 7) = x^2 - 7x + 7x - 49 = x^2 - 49$

49. $(x - 4)^2 = (x - 4)(x - 4) = x^2 - 4x - 4x + 16 = x^2 - 8x + 16$

51. $(x + 2)^3 = (x + 2)(x + 2)(x + 2) = (x + 2)(x^2 + 2x + 2x + 4)$

$$= (x + 2)(x^2 + 4x + 4)$$

$$= x(x^2 + 4x + 4) + 2(x^2 + 4x + 4)$$

$$= x^3 + 4x^2 + 4x + 2x^2 + 8x + 8$$

$$= x^3 + 6x^2 + 12x + 8$$

53. $(3x - 5)^2 = (3x - 5)(3x - 5) = 9x^2 - 15x - 15x + 25$

$$= 9x^2 - 30x + 25$$

55. $(2a - 9b)^2 = (2a - 9b)(2a - 9b) = 4a^2 - 18ab - 18ab + 81b^2$

$\qquad = 4a^2 - 36ab + 81b^2$

57. $2x^2(x + 4)(x - 8) = 2x^2(x^2 - 8x + 4x - 32)$

$\qquad = 2x^2(x^2 - 4x - 32) = 2x^4 - 8x^3 - 74x^2$

59. $3x(5x - 6)(3x - 2) = 3x(15x^2 - 10x - 18x + 12)$

$\qquad = 3x(15x^2 - 28x + 12) = 45x^3 - 84x^2 + 36x$

61. $(x + 4)(x - 3) + (x - 6)(x - 2) = x^2 - 3x + 4x - 12 + x^2 - 2x - 6x + 12$

$\qquad = 2x^2 - 7x$

63. $(a - 5)(a - 4) - (a - 3)(a - 2)$

$\qquad = a^2 - 4a - 5a + 20 - (a^2 - 2a - 3a + 6)$

$\qquad = a^2 - 9a + 20 - (a^2 - 5a + 6)$

$\qquad = a^2 - 9a + 20 - a^2 + 5a - 6 = -4a + 14$

65. $(x - 6)^2 - (x + 6)^2 = (x - 6)(x - 6) - (x + 6)(x + 6)$

$\qquad = x^2 - 6x - 6x + 36 - (x^2 + 6x + 6x + 36)$

$\qquad = x^2 - 12x + 36 - (x^2 + 12x + 36)$

$\qquad = x^2 - 12x + 36 - x^2 - 12x - 36 = -24x$

67. $(x + 2)^3 - (x + 2)^2 - (x + 2) + 2$

$\qquad = (x + 2)(x + 2)(x + 2) - (x + 2)(x + 2) - (x + 2) + 2$

$\qquad = x^3 + 6x^2 + 12x + 8 - (x^2 + 4x + 4) - (x + 2) + 2$

$\qquad$ (see Exercise (51) for details)

$\qquad = x^3 + 6x^2 + 12x + 8 - x^2 - 4x - 4 - x - 2 + 2$

$\qquad = x^3 + 5x^2 + 7x + 4$

69. (a) Both examples require us to find the square of an expression involving x and y.

(b) The first example asks us to square a product; the second asks us to square a sum.

(c) $(xy)^2 = x^2y^2$, by Exponent Rule 4.
$(x + y)^2 = x^2 + 2xy + y^2$ by the FOIL method.

70. $(x + y)^n = x^n + y^n$ only when $n = 1$.

71.   (a) $-4x^2(2x - 7) = -8x^3 + 28x^2$

$-4x^2(2x - 7)(3x + 1) = (-8x^3 + 28x^2)(3x + 1)$

$= -24x^4 - 8x^3 + 84x^3 + 28x^2$

$= -24x^4 + 76x^3 + 28x^2$

(b) $-4x^2(3x + 1) = -12x^3 - 4x^2$

$-4x^2(2x - 7)(3x + 1) = -4x^2(3x + 1)(2x - 7)$

$= (-12x^3 - 4x^2)(2x - 7)$

$= -24x^4 + 84x^3 - 8x^3 + 28x^2$

$= -24x^4 + 76x^3 + 28x^2$

(c) $(2x - 7)(3x + 1) = 6x^2 + 2x - 21x - 7 = 6x^2 - 19x - 7$

$-4x^2(2x - 7)(3x + 1) = -4x^2(6x^2 - 19x - 7)$

$= -24x^4 + 76x^3 + 28x^2$

The three answers are the same, and should be because of the
commutative and associative laws of multiplication.

Chapter 5 - Review Exercises

1. $3^{-4} = \dfrac{1}{3^4} = \dfrac{1}{81}$

3. $(3^{-1} + 2^{-2})^2 = (\dfrac{1}{3^1} + \dfrac{1}{2^2})^2 = (\dfrac{1}{3} + \dfrac{1}{4})^2 = (\dfrac{7}{12})^2 = \dfrac{7^2}{12^2} = \dfrac{49}{144}$

5. $\dfrac{(xy^2)^3}{(x^2y)^4} = \dfrac{x^3(y^2)^3}{(x^2)^4 y^4} = \dfrac{x^3 y^6}{x^8 y^4} = \dfrac{x^3}{x^8} \cdot \dfrac{y^6}{y^4} = x^{-5}y^2 = \dfrac{1}{x^5} \cdot \dfrac{y^2}{1} = \dfrac{y^2}{x^5}$

7. $\dfrac{(3x^3y^2)^4}{9(x^2y^4)^3} = \dfrac{3^4(x^3)^4(y^2)^4}{9(x^2)^3(y^4)^3} = \dfrac{81x^{12}y^8}{9x^6y^{12}} = \dfrac{81}{9} \cdot \dfrac{x^{12}}{x^6} \cdot \dfrac{y^8}{y^{12}}$

$= 9 \cdot x^6 \cdot y^{-4} = \dfrac{9}{1} \cdot \dfrac{x^6}{1} \cdot \dfrac{1}{y^4} = \dfrac{9x^6}{y^4}$

9. $(x^{-2})^{-3} = x^6$

11. $(\dfrac{2x^{-2}x^3}{x^{-3}})^{-2} = (\dfrac{2x}{x^{-3}})^{-2} = (2x^4)^{-2} = 2^{-2}(x^4)^{-2} = \dfrac{1}{2^2}x^{-8}$

$= \dfrac{1}{4} \cdot \dfrac{1}{x^8} = \dfrac{1}{4x^8}$

13. $58,700,000 = 5.87 \times 10^7$ 15. $.000002 = 2 \times 10^{-6}$

17. $2.56 \times 10^{-3} = .00256$ 19. $5.773 \times 10^8 = 577,300,000$

21. $(.008)(250000) = (8 \times 10^{-3})(2.5 \times 10^5)$
$$= (8)(2.5) \times 10^{-3}10^5 = 20 \times 10^2 = 2 \times 10^3 = 2000$$

23. $\dfrac{.001}{.000025} = \dfrac{1 \times 10^{-3}}{2.5 \times 10^{-5}} = \dfrac{1}{2.5} \times \dfrac{10^{-3}}{10^{-5}} = .4 \times 10^2 = 4 \times 10^1 = 40$

25. (a) three terms: x^2, $3x$, -7

     (b) degree of x^2: 2
         degree of $3x$: 1
         degree of -7: 0

     (c) degree of polynomial: 2

27. (a) three terms: $3x^3y$, $-5y^2$, $6xy$

     (b) degree of $3x^3y$: 4 (= 3 + 1)
         degree of $-5y^2$: 2
         degree of $6xy$: 2 (= 1 + 1)

     (c) degree of polynomial: 4

29. (a) two terms: $8x$, -5

     (b) degree of $8x$: 1
         degree of -5: 0

     (c) degree of polynomial: 1

31. (a) one term

     (b) degree of 9: 0

     (c) degree of polynomial: 0

33. (a) one term

     (b) degree of $(3x^5)(2x^3) = 6x^8$: 8

     (c) degree of polynomial: 8

35. $2x^3 - 7x^2 + 0x + 4$

37. $y^5 + 0y^4 + 0y^3 + y^2 - 2y - 1$

39. $(3x^2 - 5x + 7) + (5x - x^2 - 5) = 3x^2 - 5x + 7 + 5x - x^2 - 5$

$$= 2x^2 + 2$$

41. $(3x^2 - 5x + 7) - (5x - x^2 - 5) = 3x^2 - 5x + 7 - 5x + x^2 + 5$

$$= 4x^2 - 10x + 12$$

43. $2(x^2y - xy^2 - 5x^2y^2) + 3(xy^2 - x^2y + x^2y^2)$

$$= 2x^2y - 2xy^2 - 10x^2y^2 + 3xy^2 - 3x^2y + 3x^2y^2$$

$$= -x^2y + xy^2 - 7x^2y^2$$

45. $2(x^2y - xy^2) - 5x^2y^2 - 3(xy^2 - x^2y + x^2y^2)$

$$= 2x^2y - 2xy^2 - 5x^2y^2 - 3xy^2 + 3x^2y - 3x^2y^2$$

$$= 5x^2y - 5xy^2 - 8x^2y^2$$

47. $2a^2(a - 3b) + 4a(a^2 + ab) - 2(a^3 - a^2b)$

$$= 2a^3 - 6a^2b + 4a^3 + 4a^2b - 2a^3 + 2a^2b = 4a^3$$

49. $x^2 + 4x - (x^2 - 4x) = x^2 + 4x - x^2 + 4x = 8x$

51. $(x^2 + 4x - 3) + (2x^2 - x - 2) - (3x - 5)$

$$= x^2 + 4x - 3 + 2x^2 - x - 2 - 3x + 5 = 3x^3$$

53. $(x + 4)(x - 7) = x^2 - 7x + 4x - 28 = x^2 - 3x - 28$

55. $(2x - 3)(4x - 5) = 8x^2 - 10x - 12x + 15 = 8x^2 - 22x + 15$

57. $(3a - 4b)(2a + 5b) = 6a^2 + 15ab - 8ab - 20b^2$

$$= 6a^2 + 7ab - 20b^2$$

59. $(x + 2)(x - 3)(x + 1) = (x + 2)(x^2 + x - 3x - 3)$

$$= (x + 2)(x^2 - 2x - 3)$$

$$= x(x^2 - 2x - 3) + 2(x^2 - 2x - 3)$$

$$= x^3 - 2x^2 - 3x + 2x^2 - 4x - 6$$

$$= x^3 - 7x - 6$$

61. $(x + 6)^2 = (x + 6)(x + 6) = x^2 + 6x + 6x + 36$

$$= x^2 + 12x + 36$$

63. $(x - 5)^3 = (x - 5)(x - 5)(x - 5) = (x - 5)(x^2 - 5x - 5x + 25)$

$\qquad = (x - 5)(x^2 - 10x + 25)$

$\qquad = x(x^2 - 10x + 25) - 5(x^2 - 10x + 25)$

$\qquad = x^3 - 10x^2 + 25x - 5x^2 + 50x - 125$

$\qquad = x^3 - 15x^2 + 75x - 125$

65. $3x^2(x - 4)(x + 2) = 3x^2(x^2 + 2x - 4x - 8)$

$\qquad = 3x^2(x^2 - 2x - 8) = 3x^4 - 6x^3 - 24x^2$

67. $(x - 5)(x + 5) = x^2 + 5x - 5x - 25 = x^2 - 25$

69. $(x + 2)(x^2 - 3x + 4) = x(x^2 - 3x + 4) + 2(x^2 - 3x + 4)$

$\qquad = x^3 - 3x^2 + 4x + 2x^2 - 6x + 8$

$\qquad = x^3 - x^2 - 2x + 8$

71. $(x^2 + 2x - 1)(x^2 + 2x + 1) = x^2(x^2 + 2x + 1) + 2x(x^2 + 2x + 1)$

$\qquad - 1(x^2 + 2x + 1)$

$\qquad = x^4 + 2x^3 + x^2 + 2x^3 + 4x^2 + 2x$

$\qquad - x^2 - 2x - 1$

$\qquad = x^4 + 4x^3 + 4x^2 - 1$

73. $(2x - 3)(x + 4) - (x - 2)(x - 1)$

$\qquad = 2x^2 + 8x - 3x - 12 - (x^2 - x - 2x + 2)$

$\qquad = 2x^2 + 5x - 12 - (x^2 - 3x + 2)$

$\qquad = 2x^2 + 5x - 12 - x^2 + 3x - 2$

$\qquad = x^2 + 8x - 14$

Chapter 5 Practice Test

1. $5^0 + 2^{-2} + 4^{-1} = 1 + \dfrac{1}{2^2} + \dfrac{1}{4^1} = 1 + \dfrac{1}{4} + \dfrac{1}{4}$

$\qquad = \dfrac{4}{4} + \dfrac{1}{4} + \dfrac{1}{4} = \dfrac{6}{4} = \dfrac{3}{2}$

3. $x^{-4}x^{-5} = x^{-4+(-5)} = x^{-9} = \dfrac{1}{x^9}$

5. $\dfrac{(2x^{-3}y^4)^4}{4(x^{-2}y^{-1})^3} = \dfrac{2^4(x^{-3})^4(y^4)^4}{4(x^{-2})^3(y^{-1})^3} = \dfrac{16x^{-3(4)}y^{4(4)}}{4x^{-2(3)}y^{-1(3)}} = \dfrac{16x^{-12}y^{16}}{4x^{-6}y^{-3}}$

$\qquad = (\dfrac{16}{4})(\dfrac{x^{-12}}{x^{-6}})(\dfrac{y^{16}}{y^{-3}}) = 4x^{-12-(-6)}y^{16-(-3)}$

$\qquad = 4x^{-6}y^{19} = \dfrac{4}{1} \cdot \dfrac{1}{x^6} \cdot \dfrac{y^{19}}{1} = \dfrac{4y^{19}}{x^6}$

7. $-3x^2y(4x^2y)(-2x^3) = -3(4)(-2)x^2x^2x^3yy = 24x^{2+2+3}y^{1+1}$

$\qquad = 24x^7y^2$

9. $2x(x^2 - y) - 3(x - xy) - (2x^3 - 3x)$

$\qquad = 2x^3 - 2xy - 3x + 3xy - 2x^3 + 3x$

$\qquad = 2x^3 - 2x^3 - 2xy + 3xy - 3x + 3x = xy$

11. $3x^2(2x - y) - xy(x + y) = 6x^3 - 3x^2y - x^2y - xy^2$

$\qquad = 6x^3 - 4x^2y - xy^2$

13. $(a - 1)^2 - (a + 1)^2 = (a - 1)(a - 1) - (a + 1)(a + 1)$

$\qquad = a^2 - 2a + 1 - (a^2 + 2a + 1)$

$\qquad = a^2 - 2a + 1 - a^2 - 2a - 1$

$\qquad = a^2 - a^2 - 2a - 2a + 1 - 1 = -4a$

15. $\dfrac{(.24)(5000)}{.006} = \dfrac{(2.4 \times 10^{-1})(5 \times 10^3)}{6 \times 10^{-3}}$

$\qquad = \dfrac{(2.4)(5)}{6} \times \dfrac{10^{-1}10^3}{10^{-3}} = \dfrac{12}{6} \times \dfrac{10^2}{10^{-3}}$

$\qquad = 2 \times 10^{2-(-3)} = 2 \times 10^5 = 200,000$

Chapter 6

FACTORING

1. $(x + 4)(x + 3) = x^2 + 3x + 4x + 12 = x^2 + 7x + 12$

3. $(x - 4)(x - 3) = x^2 - 3x - 4x + 12 = x^2 - 7x + 12$

5. $(x + 4)(x - 3) = x^2 - 3x + 4x - 12 = x^2 + x - 12$

7. $(x - 4)(x + 3) = x^2 + 3x - 4x - 12 = x^2 - x - 12$

9. $(x + 6)(x + 2) = x^2 + 2x + 6x + 12 = x^2 + 8x + 12$

11. $(x - 6)(x - 2) = x^2 - 2x - 6x + 12 = x^2 - 8x + 12$

13. $(x + 6)(x - 2) = x^2 - 2x + 6x - 12 = x^2 + 4x - 12$

15. $(x - 6)(x + 2) = x^2 + 2x - 6x - 12 = x^2 - 4x - 12$

17. $(x + 12)(x + 1) = x^2 + x + 12x + 12 = x^2 + 13x + 12$

19. $(x - 12)(x - 1) = x^2 - x - 12x + 12 = x^2 - 13x + 12$

21. $(x + 12)(x - 1) = x^2 - x + 12x - 12 = x^2 + 11x - 12$

23. $(x - 12)(x + 1) = x^2 + x - 12x - 12 = x^2 - 11x - 12$

25. $(a + 8)(a + 8) = a^2 + 8a + 8a + 64 = a^2 + 16a + 64$
(perfect square)

27. $(a - 8)(a - 8) = a^2 - 8a - 8a + 64 = a^2 - 16a + 64$
(perfect square)

29. $(a + 8)(a - 8) = a^2 - 8a + 8a - 64 = a^2 - 64$
     (difference of two squares)

31. $(c - 4)^2 = (c - 4)(c - 4) = c^2 - 4c - 4c + 16 = c^2 - 8c + 16$
     (perfect square)

33. $(c + 4)^2 = (c + 4)(c + 4) = c^2 + 4c + 4c + 16 = c^2 + 8c + 16$
     (perfect square)

35. $(c + 4)(c - 4) = c^2 - 4c + 4c - 16 = c^2 - 16$
     (difference of two squares)

37. $(3x + 4)(x + 7) = 3x^2 + 21x + 4x + 28 = 3x^2 + 25x + 28$

39. $(3x + 7)(x + 4) = 3x^2 + 12x + 7x + 28 = 3x^2 + 19x + 28$

41. $(3x + 4)(x - 7) = 3x^2 - 21x + 4x - 28 = 3x^2 - 17x - 28$

43. $(3x - 4)(x + 7) = 3x^2 + 21x - 4x - 28 = 3x^2 + 17x - 28$

45. $(3x + 4)(5x + 7) = 15x^2 + 21x + 20x + 28 = 15x^2 + 41x + 28$

47. $(3x + 7)(5x + 4) = 15x^2 + 12x + 35x + 28 = 15x^2 + 47x + 28$

49. $(3x + 4)(5x - 7) = 15x^2 - 21x + 20x - 28 = 15x^2 - x - 28$

51. $(3x - 4)(5x + 7) = 15x^2 + 21x - 20x - 28 = 15x^2 + x - 28$

53. $(2a + 5)^2 = (2a + 5)(2a + 5) = 4a^2 + 10a + 10a + 25$
     $= 4a^2 + 20a + 25$ (perfect square)

55. $(2a + 5)(2a - 5) = 4a^2 - 10a + 10a - 25 = 4a^2 - 25$
     (difference of two squares)

57. $(3xy)^2 = 3^2 x^2 y^2 = 9x^2 y^2$

59. $(x^3 + y^2)^2 = (x^3 + y^2)(x^3 + y^2) = x^6 + x^3 y^2 + x^3 y^2 + y^4$
     $= x^6 + 2x^3 y^2 + y^4$ (perfect square)

61. $(2a + 5y)^2 = (2a + 5y)(2a + 5y) = 4a^2 + 10ay + 10ay + 25y^2$
     $= 4a^2 + 20ay + 25y^2$ (perfect square)

63. $(2a + 5y)(2a - 5y) = 4a^2 - 10ay + 10ay - 25y^2 = 4a^2 - 25y^2$
     (difference of two squares)

65. $(x + 6)(x + 4) = x^2 + 4x + 6x + 24 = x^2 + 10x + 24$

     $(x - 6)(x - 4) = x^2 - 4x - 6x + 24 = x^2 - 10x + 24$

     The effect of switching both + signs to - signs is to change
     the sign of the cross term from + to -.

66. $(x + 6)(x - 4) = x^2 - 4x + 6x - 24 = x^2 + 2x - 24$

    $(x - 6)(x + 4) = x^2 + 4x - 6x - 24 = x^2 - 2x - 24$

    The middle terms of the resulting trinomials have opposite signs.

67. (5) and (7)   (6) and (8)
     (13) and (15)   (14) and (16)
     (21) and (23)   (22) and (24)
     (41) and (43)   (42) and (44)
     (49) and (51)   (50) and (52)

    The middle terms will always have opposite signs, since

    $(x + a)(x - b) = x^2 + (a - b)x - ab$

    $(a - a)(x + b) = x^2 + (-a + b)x - ab$

    and $(a - b)$ and $(-a + b)$ are always opposites of one another.

Exercises 6.2

1. $5x + 20 = 5 \cdot x + 5 \cdot 4 = 5(x + 4)$

3. $8a - 12 = 4 \cdot 2a - 4 \cdot 3 = 4(2a - 3)$

5. $3a + 6b - 8c$ is not factorable.

7. $x^2 + 3x = x \cdot x + x \cdot 3 = x(x + 3)$

9. $a^2 + a = a \cdot a + a \cdot 1 = a(a + 1)$

11. $x^2 - 5x + xy = x \cdot x - x \cdot 5 + x \cdot y = x(x - 5 + y)$

13. $3c^6 - 6c^3 = 3c^3 \cdot c^3 - 3c^3 \cdot 2 = 3c^3(c^3 - 2)$

15. $x^2y - xy^2 = xy \cdot x - xy \cdot y = xy(x - y)$

17. $6x^2 + 3x = 3x \cdot 2x + 3x \cdot 1 = 3x(2x + 1)$

19. $8x^3y^2 - 25z^4$ is not factorable.

21. $12c^3d^5 + 4c^2d^3 = 4c^2d^3 \cdot 3cd^2 + 4c^2d^3 \cdot 1 = 4c^2d^3(3cd^2 + 1)$

23. $x^2y^3 - y^2z^4 + x^3z^2$ is not factorable.

25. $2x^2yz^3 + 8xyz^2 - 10x^2y^2z^2 = 2xyz^2 \cdot xz + 2xyz^2 \cdot 4 - 2xyz^2 \cdot 5xy$

    $= 2xyz^2(xz + 4 - 5xy)$

27. $6u^3v^2 + 18u^3v^3 - 12u^3v^5 = 6u^3v^2 \cdot 1 + 6u^3v^2 \cdot 3v - 6u^3v^2 \cdot 2v^3$

    $= 6u^3v^2(1 + 3v - 2v^3)$

29. $x(x - 5) + 4(x - 5) = (x - 5)(x + 4)$

31. $y(y + 6) - 3(y + 6) = (y + 6)(y - 3)$

33. $x^2 + 8x + xy + 8y = (x^2 + 8x) + (xy + 8y) = x(x + 8) + y(x + 8)$
$$= (x + 8)(x + y)$$

35. $m^2 + mn + 9m + 9n = (m^2 + mn) + (9m + 9n) = m(m + n) + 9(m + n)$
$$= (m + n)(m + 9)$$

37. $x^2 - xy - 4x + 4y = (x^2 - xy) + (-4x + 4y)$
$$= x(x - y) - 4(x - y) = (x - y)(x - 4)$$

39. $3x^2y + 6xy - 5x - 10 = (3x^2y + 6xy) + (-5x - 10)$
$$= 3xy(x + 2) - 5(x + 2) = (x + 2)(3xy - 5)$$

41. (a) $(x + 2)(x + 3)$

(b) $x^2y^2(x + y)$

42. Step 1: -x is replaced by -5x + 4x.
Step 2: The first two terms are grouped and the last two terms are grouped. The common factor is then removed from each group.
Step 3: The common factor of (x - 5) is removed from the sum.

43. There are two errors as written. In Step 1, the factor that remains when -5 is removed from the second group should be x + 3, not x - 3. If Step 1 were correct, then there would be no common factor to remove in Step 2.

Exercises 6.3

1. $x^2 + 3x = x(x + 3)$ 3. $x^2 + 3x + 2 = (x + 1)(x + 2)$

5. $x^2 - 3x + 2 = (x - 1)(x - 2)$ 7. $x^2 + 3x - 2$ is not factorable

9. $x^2 + x - 2 = (x - 1)(x + 2)$ 11. $x^2 - x - 2 = (x + 1)(x - 2)$

13. $a^2 + 8a + 12 = (a + 2)(a + 6)$

15. $a^2 - a - 12 = (a - 4)(a + 3)$

17. $a^2 - a + 12$ is not factorable

19. $a^2 - 12a = a(a - 12)$

21. $a - 12 + a^2 = a^2 + a - 12 = (a + 4)(a - 3)$

23. $x^2 - 3xy + 2y^2 = (x - y)(x - 2y)$

25. $a^2 + 10a + 24 = (a + 4)(a + 6)$

27. $y^2 + 12y + 36 = (y + 6)(y + 6)$ or $(y + 6)^2$

29. $y^2 - 36 = (y - 6)(y + 6)$

31. $x^2 - 7x - 18 = (x - 9)(x + 2)$

33. $r^2 - 3rs - 10s^2 = (r - 5s)(r + 2s)$

35. $c^2 - 6c + 5 = (c - 1)(c - 5)$

37. $4x^2 + 8x + 4 = 4(x^2 + 2x + 1) = 4(x + 1)(x + 1)$ or $4(x + 1)^2$

39. $x^2 - 30 + x = x^2 + x - 30 = (x + 6)(x - 5)$

41. $2x^2 - 50 = 2(x^2 - 25) = 2(x - 5)(x + 5)$

43. $x^2 - x - 20 = (x - 5)(x + 4)$

45. $x^2 - x + 20$ is not factorable.

47. $y^2 + 11y + 28 = (y + 4)(y + 7)$

49. $2y^2 + 2y - 84 = 2(y^2 + y - 42) = 2(y + 7)(y - 6)$

51. $49 - d^2 = (7 - d)(7 + d)$

53. $49 + d^2$ is not factorable.

55. $10x^2 - 40xy - 120y^2 = 10(x^2 - 4xy - 12y^2) = 10(x - 6y)(x + 2y)$

57. The factors of 10 are 1 and 10 and 2 and 5. Since the last term is positive, the signs in the parentheses must be the same. Possibilities:

$(x + 1)(x + 10) = x^2 + 11x + 10$

$(x - 1)(x - 10) = x^2 - 11x + 10$

$(x + 2)(x + 5) = x^2 + 7x + 10$

$(x - 2)(x - 5) = x^2 - 7x + 10$

Therefore, the possible values of k are 11, -11, 7, and -7.

58. As in (57), the factors of 10 are 1 and 10 and 2 and 5.   Since
the last term is negative, the signs in the parentheses must
be opposite. Possibilities:

$$(x + 1)(x - 10) = x^2 \underline{- 9x} - 10$$
$$(x - 1)(x + 10) = x^2 \underline{+ 9x} - 10$$
$$(x + 2)(x - 5) = x^2 \underline{- 3x} - 10$$
$$(x - 2)(x + 5) = x^2 \underline{+ 3x} - 10$$

Therefore, the possible values of b are -9, 9, -3, and 3.

59. There are infinitely many such integers. We can always find
such a "c" by choosing two integers that differ by 5 and
forming the product

$$(x + \text{larger integer})(x - \text{smaller integer})$$

For example, since 9 and 4 differ by 5, $(x + 9)(x - 4) =$
$x^2 + 5x - 36$ will give the value c = -36. Clearly, we can
find two integers that differ by 5 in infinitely many ways.
(Interestingly, if we ask for all <u>positive</u> integers c with
this property, there are only two answers: c = 4 and c = 6.)

Exercises 6.4

1. $x^2 + 3x = x(x + 3)$ 3. $x^2 + 3x + 2 = (x + 1)(x + 2)$

5. $x^2 + 3x - 2$ is not factorable.

7. $3x^2 + 8x + 4 = (3x + 2)(x + 2)$

9. $2x^2 + 11x + 12 = (2x + 3)(x + 4)$

11. $2x^2 + 10x + 12 = 2(x^2 + 5x + 6) = 2(x + 2)(x + 3)$

13. $5x^2 - 27x + 10 = (5x - 2)(x - 5)$

15. $5x^2 - 15x + 10 = 5(x^2 - 3x + 2) = 5(x - 1)(x - 2)$

17. $2y^2 - y - 6 = (2y + 3)(y - 2)$

19. $5a^2 + 9a - 18 = (5a - 6)(a + 3)$

21. $2t^2 + 7t + 6 = (2t + 3)(t + 2)$

23. $2t^2 + 6t + 6 = 2(t^2 + 3t + 3)$

25. $3w^2 - 6w - 30 = 3(w^2 - 2w - 10)$

27. $3x^2 - 4x + 2$ is not factorable.

29. $3x^2 - 14xy + 15y^2 = (3x - 5y)(x - 3y)$

31. $6a^2 + 17a + 10 = (6a + 5)(a + 2)$

33. $6a^2 + 17a - 10 = (3a + 10)(2a - 1)$

35. $6a^2 - 18a - 24 = 6(a^2 - 3a - 4) = 6(a - 4)(a + 1)$

37. $x^2 - 36y^2 = (x - 6y)(x + 6y)$

39. $4x^2 - 36y^2 = 4(x^2 - 9y^2) = 4(x - 3y)(x + 3y)$

41. $x^3 + 5x^2 - 24x = x(x^2 + 5x - 24) = x(x + 8)(x - 3)$

43. $x^2 + 5x^2 - 24x = 6x^2 - 24x = 6x(x - 4)$

45. $4x^4 - 24x^3 + 32x^2 = 4x^2(x^2 - 6x + 8) = 4x^2(x - 2)(x - 4)$

47. $6x^2y - 8xy^2 + 12xy = 2xy(3x - 4y + 6)$

49. $3x^2 - 7x - 48 = (3x - 16)(x + 3)$

51. $8x^2 - 32x = 8x(x - 4)$

53. $2x - x^2 + 15 = -x^2 + 2x + 15 = -(x^2 - 2x - 15) = -(x - 5)(x + 3)$

55. $84xy - 16x^2y - 4x^3y = 4xy(21 - 4x - x^2)$
$$= -4xy(x^2 + 4x - 21) = -4xy(x + 7)(x - 3)$$

57. $-x^2 + 25 = 25 - x^2 = (5 - x)(5 + x)$

59. The proposed factor $2x + 2$ has a common factor of 2, which would imply that the original trinomial $6x^2 - 5x - 4$ has a common factor of 2. This is not the case. We can eliminate eight possible factorizations of $6x^2 - 5x - 4$ in this way: In addition to $(3x - 2)(2x + 2)$, we can eliminate

    $(3x - 1)(2x + 4)$ $(3x + 1)(2x - 4)$
    $(3x + 2)(2x - 2)$ $(6x - 2)(x + 2)$
    $(6x + 2)(x - 2)$ $(6x - 4)(x + 1)$
    $(6x + 4)(x - 1)$

This leaves four possibilities: $(6x - 1)(x + 4)$, $(6x + 1)(x - 4)$, $(3x + 4)(2x - 1)$, and $(3x - 4)(2x + 1)$, the last of which is the correct one.

Exercises 6.5

1. $\dfrac{3x + 12}{6} = \dfrac{\cancel{3x}^{1}}{\cancel{6}_{2}} + \dfrac{\cancel{12}^{2}}{\cancel{6}_{1}} = \dfrac{x}{2} + 2 = \dfrac{x + 4}{2}$

3. $\dfrac{t^2 - 6t}{6t} = \dfrac{t\cancel{t}^{?}}{\cancel{6t}} - \dfrac{\cancel{6t}^{1}}{\cancel{6t}_{1}} = \dfrac{t}{6} - 1 = \dfrac{t - 6}{6}$

5. $\dfrac{3x^2 y - 9xy^2}{3xy} = \dfrac{\cancel{3x^2 y}^{x}}{\cancel{3xy}_{1}} - \dfrac{{}^{3}\cancel{9xy}^{y}}{\cancel{3xy}_{1}} = x - 3y$

7. $\dfrac{3x^2 y - 9xy^2}{6x^2 y^2} = \dfrac{{}^{1}\cancel{3x^2 y}}{\underset{2}{\cancel{6x^2 y^2}}_{y}} - \dfrac{{}^{3}\cancel{9xy^2}}{\underset{2x}{\cancel{6x^2 y^2}}} = \dfrac{1}{2y} - \dfrac{3}{2x} = \dfrac{x - 3y}{2xy}$

9. $\dfrac{10a^2 b^3 c - 15ab^2 c^2 - 20a^3 b^2 c^3}{5ab^2 c} = \dfrac{{}^{2a\,b}\cancel{10a^2 b^3 c}}{\underset{1}{\cancel{5ab^2 c}}} - \dfrac{{}^{3}\cancel{15ab^2 c^2}{}^{c}}{\underset{1}{\cancel{5ab^2 c}}} - \dfrac{{}^{4a^2}\cancel{20a^3 b^2 c^3}{}^{c^2}}{\underset{1}{\cancel{5ab^2 c}}}$

$$= 2ab - 3c - 4a^2 c^2$$

11.
```
              x -  5
      _____
x + 2 )x² -  3x +  2
      -(x² +  2x)
      _____
            -5x +  2
           -(-5x - 10)
           _____
                   12
```

13.
```
              t +  2
      _____
t - 5 )t² -  3t - 10
      -(t² -  5t)
      _____
            2t - 10
          -(2t - 10)
          _____
                  0
```

15.
```
              w +  1
      _____
w + 3 )w² +  4w - 21
      -(w² +  3w)
      _____
             w - 21
           -(w +  3)
           _____
                -24
```

17.
```
              2x   -  1
      _____
x - 1 )2x² -  3x +  7
      -(2x² -  2x)
      _____
             -x +  7
            -(-x +  1)
            _____
                    6
```

19.
```
              y² +  3y +  7
      _____
y - 2 )y³ +  y² +  y - 14
      -(y³ -2y²)
      _____
            3y² +  y
          -(3y² -6y)
          _____
                 7y - 14
               -(7y - 14)
               _____
                       0
```

21.
```
              2a² -  a -  2
      _____
a + 1 )2a³ +  a² -  3a +  2
      -(2a³ +2a²)
      _____
             -a² -  3a
           -(-a² -   a)
           _____
                  -2a +  2
                -(-2a -  2)
                _____
                        4
```

23.

$$
\begin{array}{r}
x^2 - 4x + 12 \\
x + 3 \overline{\smash{\big)}\ x^3 - x^2 + 0x + 36} \\
\underline{-(x^3 + 3x^2)} \\
-4x^2 + 0x \\
\underline{-(-4x^2 - 12x)} \\
12x + 36 \\
\underline{-(12x + 36)} \\
0
\end{array}
$$

25.

$$
\begin{array}{r}
x^3 + 2x^2 + 4x + 8 \\
x - 2 \overline{\smash{\big)}\ x^4 + 0x^3 + 0x^2 + 0x - 16} \\
\underline{-(x^4 - 2x^3)} \\
2x^3 + 0x^2 \\
\underline{-(2x^3 - 4x^2)} \\
4x^2 + 0x \\
\underline{-(4x^2 - 8x)} \\
8x - 16 \\
\underline{-(8x - 16)} \\
0
\end{array}
$$

27.

$$
\begin{array}{r}
x^2 + 4x - 2 \\
3x + 2 \overline{\smash{\big)}\ 3x^3 + 14x^2 + 2x - 4} \\
\underline{-(3x^3 + 2x^2)} \\
12x^2 + 2x \\
\underline{-(12x^2 + 8x)} \\
-6x - 4 \\
\underline{-(-6x - 4)} \\
0
\end{array}
$$

29.

$$
\begin{array}{r}
2t^2 + 5t - 4 \\
2t - 5 \overline{\smash{\big)}\ 4t^3 + 0t^2 - 33t + 24} \\
\underline{-(4t^3 - 10t^2)} \\
10t^2 - 33t \\
\underline{-(10t^2 - 25t)} \\
-8t + 24 \\
\underline{-(-8t + 20)} \\
4
\end{array}
$$

Chapter 6 Review Exercises

1. $(x + 5)(x + 7) = x^2 + 7x + 5x + 35 = x^2 + 12x + 35$

3. $(x - 5)(x - 7) = x^2 - 7x - 5x + 35 = x^2 - 12x + 35$

5. $(x + 5)(x - 7) = x^2 - 7x + 5x - 35 = x^2 - 2x - 35$

7. $(x - 5)(x + 7) = x^2 + 7x - 5x - 35 = x^2 + 2x - 35$

9. $(x - 5)(x - 5) = x^2 - 5x - 5x + 25 = x^2 - 10x + 25$

11. $(x - 5)(x + 5) = x^2 + 5x - 5x - 25 = x^2 - 25$

13. $(x + 9y)(x - 9y) = x^2 - 9xy + 9xy - 81y^2 = x^2 - 81y^2$

15. $(2x + 3)(x - 7) = 2x^2 - 14x + 3x - 21 = 2x^2 - 11x - 21$

17. $(5x - 2)(3x + 4) = 15x^2 + 20x - 6x - 8 = 15x^2 + 14x - 8$

19. $x^2 + 7x + 12 = (x + 3)(x + 4)$

21. $x^2 + 7x = x(x + 7)$

23. $x^2 - 13x + 12 = (x - 1)(x - 12)$

25. $x^2 - 6xy - 27y^2 = (x + 3y)(x - 9y)$

27. $x^2 - 64 = (x - 8)(x + 8)$

29. $2x^2 + 9x + 10 = (2x + 5)(x + 2)$

31. $3x^2 - 6x - 24 = 3(x^2 - 2x - 8) = 3(x - 4)(x + 2)$

33. $6a^2 + 36a + 48 = 6(a^2 + 6a + 8) = 6(a + 2)(a + 4)$

35. $5x^3y - 80xy^3 = 5xy(x^2 - 16y^2) = 5xy(x - 4y)(x + 4y)$

37. $x^2 + 9x = x(x + 9)$

39. $25t^2 - 1 = (5t - 1)(5t + 1)$

41. $30 - x^2 + x = -x^2 + x + 30 = -(x^2 - x - 30) = -(x - 6)(x + 5)$

43. $12x - 3x^2 - 9 = -3x^2 + 12x - 9 = -3(x^2 - 4x + 3)$
$$= -3(x - 1)(x - 3)$$

45. $\dfrac{x^2y - xy^2}{xy} = \dfrac{\cancel{x^2y}^{x}}{\cancel{xy}_1} - \dfrac{\cancel{xy^2}^{y}}{\cancel{xy}_1} = x - y$

47.
$$
\begin{array}{r}
x - 3 \\
x - 1\overline{)x^2 - 4x - 5} \\
\underline{-(x^2 - x)} \\
-3x - 5 \\
\underline{-(-3x + 3)} \\
-8
\end{array}
$$

49.
$$
\begin{array}{r}
2x^2 + 6x + 14 \\
x - 3\overline{)2x^3 + 0x^2 - 4x - 4} \\
\underline{-(2x^3 - 6x^2)} \\
6x^2 - 4x \\
\underline{-(6x^2 - 18x)} \\
14x - 4 \\
\underline{-(14x - 42)} \\
38
\end{array}
$$

51.
$$
\begin{array}{r}
x^2 - 2x + 4 \\
x + 2\overline{)x^3 + 0x^2 + 0x + 8} \\
\underline{-(x^3 + 2x^2)} \\
-2x^2 + 0x \\
\underline{-(-2x^2 - 4x)} \\
4x + 8 \\
\underline{-(4x + 8)} \\
0
\end{array}
$$

Chapter 6 Practice Test

1. $6x^3 + 12x^2 - 15x = 3x(2x^2 + 4x - 5)$

3. $x^2 + 9x + 8 = (x + 1)(x + 8)$

5. $4x^2 - 20x = 4x(x - 5)$

7. $6x^2 + 24x + 18 = 6(x^2 + 4x + 3) = 6(x + 1)(x + 3)$

9. $x^2 + 4x + 4 = (x + 2)(x + 2)$

11. $x^2y^2 - 9 = (xy - 3)(xy + 3)$

13.
$$
\begin{array}{r}
2x^2 + 4x + 3 \\
x - 2 \overline{)\,2x^3 + 0x^2 - 5x + 6} \\
\underline{-(2x^3 - 4x^2)} \\
4x^2 - 5x \\
\underline{-(4x^2 - 8x)} \\
3x + 6 \\
\underline{-(3x - 6)} \\
12
\end{array}
$$

Cumulative Review: Chapters 4-6

1. $\dfrac{-24}{42} = \dfrac{(-4)\cancel{(6)}}{(7)\cancel{(6)}} = \dfrac{-4}{7} = -\dfrac{4}{7}$

3. $\dfrac{\cancel{36s}^{\,9}\,\cancel{s}\,\cancel{t}^{\,8t9}}{\cancel{20s}^{\,9}\,\cancel{t}^{\,8}}_{5\ s} = \dfrac{9t}{5s}$

5. $\dfrac{\cancel{6x}}{\cancel{25}}_5 \cdot \dfrac{\cancel{10}^{\,2}}{\cancel{x}_1} = \dfrac{12}{5}$

7. $\dfrac{6x}{25} + \dfrac{10}{x} = \dfrac{6x(x)}{25(x)} + \dfrac{10(25)}{x(25)} = \dfrac{6x^2}{25x} + \dfrac{250}{25x} = \dfrac{6x^2 + 250}{25x}$

9. $\dfrac{3t - 5}{6t^2} + \dfrac{9t + 5}{6t^2} = \dfrac{3t - 5 + 9t + 5}{6t^2} = \dfrac{\cancel{12t}^{\,2}}{\cancel{6t}^{\,2}_{\,t}}_{\,1} = \dfrac{2}{t}$

11. $(x + 8)(x - 5) = x^2 - 5x + 8x - 40 = x^2 + 3x - 40$

13. $(a + b + c)(a + b - c) = a(a + b - c) + b(a + b - c)$
$$+ c(a + b - c)$$
$$= a^2 + ab - ac + ab + b^2 - bc + ac$$
$$+ bc - c^2$$
$$= a^2 + 2ab + b^2 - c^2$$

15. $\dfrac{12x^3y^2}{35z^2} \div \dfrac{20xy}{14z} = \dfrac{\cancel{12x^3y^2}^{\,3x^2y^2}}{\cancel{35z^2}_{\,5z}} \cdot \dfrac{\cancel{14z}^{\,2}}{\cancel{20xy}_{\,5}} = \dfrac{6x^2y}{25z}$

17. $(5a - 3c)(4a + 3c) = 20a^2 + 15ac - 12ac - 9c^2 = 20a^2 + 3ac - 9c^2$

19. $\dfrac{5}{3x} - \dfrac{7}{2x} = \dfrac{5(2)}{3x(2)} - \dfrac{7(3)}{2x(3)} = \dfrac{10}{6x} - \dfrac{21}{6x} = \dfrac{10 - 21}{6x} = \dfrac{-11}{6x} = -\dfrac{11}{6x}$

21. $\dfrac{5}{6x^2y} - \dfrac{9}{10xy^3} = \dfrac{5(5y^2)}{6x^2y(5y^2)} - \dfrac{9(3x)}{10xy^3(3x)} = \dfrac{25y^2}{30x^2y^3} - \dfrac{27x}{30x^2y^3}$

$= \dfrac{25y^2 - 27x}{30x^2y^3}$

23. $(x + 3)(x - 12) + (x + 6)^2 = (x + 3)(x - 12) + (x + 6)(x + 6)$

$= x^2 - 12x + 3x - 36 + x^2 + 6x$

$+ 6x + 36$

$= 2x^2 + 3x$

25. $(8 \cdot \dfrac{4}{x}) \div \dfrac{16}{x^2} = \dfrac{32}{x} \div \dfrac{16}{x^2} = \dfrac{\cancel{32}^2}{\cancel{x}_1} \cdot \dfrac{\cancel{x^2}^{x}}{\cancel{16}_1} = 2x$

27. $(a - 3)(2a + 3)(2a - 3) = (a - 3)(4a^2 - 6a + 6a - 9)$

$= (a - 3)(4a^2 - 9)$

$= 4a^3 - 9a - 12a^2 + 27$

$= 4a^3 - 12a^2 - 9a + 27$

29. $2 + \dfrac{3}{x} - \dfrac{1}{x^2} = \dfrac{2}{1} + \dfrac{3}{x} - \dfrac{1}{x^2} = \dfrac{2(x^2)}{1(x^2)} + \dfrac{3(x)}{x(x)} - \dfrac{1}{x^2}$

$= \dfrac{2x^2}{x^2} + \dfrac{3x}{x^2} - \dfrac{1}{x^2} = \dfrac{2x^2 + 3x - 1}{x^2}$

31. $(x^2 - xy + 3y^2) + (5x^2 - 8y^2) + (y^2 - 6x^2)$

$= x^2 + 5x^2 - 6x^2 - xy + 3y^2 - 8y^2 + y^2$

$= -xy - 4y^2$

33. (a) degree of $5x^4 - 3x^2 + 6x - 1$ is 4.

(b) coefficient of second degree term is -3.

35. $\dfrac{x^2 + 8x}{2x} = \dfrac{\cancel{x^2}^{x}}{2\cancel{x}} + \dfrac{\cancel{8x}^4}{\cancel{2x}_1} = \dfrac{x}{2} + 4 = \dfrac{x + 8}{2}$

37.

$$
\begin{array}{r}
y - 1 \\
y - 2 \overline{) y^2 - 3y + 4} \\
\underline{-(y^2 - 2y)} \\
-y + 4 \\
\underline{-(-y + 2)} \\
2
\end{array}
$$

39.

$$
\begin{array}{r}
6x^2 + 8x + 9 \\
3x - 4 \overline{) 18x^3 + 0x^2 - 5x - 28} \\
\underline{-(18x^3 - 24x^2)} \\
24x^2 - 5x \\
\underline{-(24x^2 - 32x)} \\
27x - 28 \\
\underline{-(27x - 36)} \\
8
\end{array}
$$

41. $5^0 + 2^{-3} + 2^{-4} = 1 + \dfrac{1}{2^3} + \dfrac{1}{2^4} = 1 + \dfrac{1}{8} + \dfrac{1}{16} = \dfrac{16}{16} + \dfrac{2}{16} + \dfrac{1}{16}$

$$= \dfrac{16 + 2 + 1}{16} = \dfrac{19}{16}$$

43. $\dfrac{(x^2)^3}{x^2 x^3} = \dfrac{x^6}{x^5} = x^{6-5} = x$

45. $\dfrac{(2x^3)^4}{4(x^5)^3} = \dfrac{2^4(x^3)^4}{4(x^5)^3} = \dfrac{16x^{12}}{4x^{15}} = \dfrac{16}{4} \cdot \dfrac{x^{12}}{x^{15}} = \dfrac{4}{1} \cdot x^{-3} = \dfrac{4}{1} \cdot \dfrac{1}{x^3} = \dfrac{4}{x^3}$

47. $\dfrac{(3a^{-3}t^2)^{-3}}{(a^{-1}t^{-2})^2} = \dfrac{3^{-3}(a^{-3})^{-3}(t^2)^{-3}}{(a^{-1})^2(t^{-2})^2} = \dfrac{3^{-3}a^9 t^{-6}}{a^{-2}t^{-4}} = \dfrac{1}{3^3} \cdot \dfrac{a^9}{a^{-2}} \cdot \dfrac{t^{-6}}{t^{-4}}$

$$= \dfrac{1}{27}a^{11}t^{-2} = \dfrac{1}{27} \cdot \dfrac{a^{11}}{1} \cdot \dfrac{1}{t^2} = \dfrac{a^{11}}{27t^2}$$

49. $.000439 = 4.39 \times 10^{-4}$

51. $\dfrac{(4 \times 10^{-3})(5 \times 10^4)}{2 \times 10^{-3}} = \dfrac{\overset{2}{\cancel{(4)}}(5)}{\underset{1}{\cancel{2}}} \times \dfrac{10^{-3} 10^4}{10^{-3}} = 10 \times \dfrac{10^1}{10^{-3}}$

$$= 10 \times 10^4 = 1 \times 10^5$$

53. $\dfrac{x}{3} - \dfrac{x}{4} = \dfrac{x - 4}{6}$ $\qquad$ LCD = 12

$$12\left(\dfrac{x}{3} - \dfrac{x}{4}\right) = 12 \cdot \dfrac{x - 4}{6}$$

$$\dfrac{\overset{4}{\cancel{12}}}{1} \cdot \dfrac{x}{\underset{1}{\cancel{3}}} - \dfrac{\overset{3}{\cancel{12}}}{1} \cdot \dfrac{x}{\underset{1}{\cancel{4}}} = \dfrac{\overset{2}{\cancel{12}}}{1} \cdot \dfrac{x - 4}{\underset{1}{\cancel{6}}}$$

$$4x - 3x = 2(x - 4)$$
$$x = 2x - 8$$
$$-x = -8$$
$$x = 8$$

55. $\dfrac{a}{5} - \dfrac{a}{6} = \dfrac{a}{30}$ LCD = 30

$30\left(\dfrac{a}{5} - \dfrac{a}{6}\right) = 30 \cdot \dfrac{a}{30}$

$\dfrac{\cancel{30}^{6}}{1} \cdot \dfrac{a}{\cancel{5}_{1}} - \dfrac{\cancel{30}^{5}}{1} \cdot \dfrac{a}{\cancel{6}_{1}} = \dfrac{\cancel{30}^{1}}{1} \cdot \dfrac{a}{\cancel{30}_{1}}$

6a - 5a = a

a = a   identity

57. $\dfrac{7 - 2y}{4} - \dfrac{5 - 4y}{6} = \dfrac{8y + 5}{9}$ LCD = 36

$36\left(\dfrac{7 - 2y}{4} - \dfrac{5 - 4y}{6}\right) = 36 \cdot \dfrac{8y + 5}{9}$

$\dfrac{\cancel{36}^{9}}{1} \cdot \dfrac{7 - 2y}{\cancel{4}_{1}} - \dfrac{\cancel{36}^{6}}{1} \cdot \dfrac{5 - 4y}{\cancel{6}_{1}} = \dfrac{\cancel{36}^{4}}{1} \cdot \dfrac{8y + 5}{\cancel{9}_{1}}$

9(7 - 2y) - 6(5 - 4y) = 4(8y + 5)

63 - 18y - 30 + 24y = 32y + 20

6y + 33 = 32y + 20

33 = 26y + 20

13 = 26y

$\dfrac{\cancel{13}^{1}}{\cancel{26}_{2}} = y$

$\dfrac{1}{2} = y$

59. .8x - .07(x - 5) = 58.75   LCD = 100

100(.8x - .07(x - 5)) = 100(58.75)

100(.8x) - 100(.07(x - 5)) = 100(58.75)

80x - 7(x - 5) = 5875

80x - 7x + 35 = 5875

73x + 35 = 5875

73x = 5840

x = 80

61. $x^2 + 6x + 5 = (x + 1)(x + 5)$

63. $x^2 - 5x + 6 = (x - 2)(x - 3)$

65. $6x^3 y - 12xy^2 - 9x^2 y = 3xy(2x^2 - 4y - 3x)$

67. $u^2 - 49 = (u - 7)(u + 7)$

69. $2r^2 + r - 15 = (2r - 5)(r + 3)$

71. $5t^2 + 10t + 15 = 5(t^2 + 2t + 3)$

73. $6x^2 - 17xy + 12y^2 = (3x - 4y)(2x - 3y)$

75. $x^2 + 16x = x(x + 16)$

77. $x^2 + ax + xy + ay = (x^2 + ax) + (xy + ay)$
$$= x(x + a) + y(x + a) = (x + a)(x + y)$$

79. $x^2 - 4x - ax + 4a = (x^2 - 4x) + (-ax + 4a)$
$$= x(x - 4) - a(x - 4) = (x - 4)(x - a)$$

81. Let x = # of cheaper tickets sold
    360-x = # of more expensive tickets sold

    $6.25x + 8.75(360 - x) = 2850$

    $100(6.25x + 8.75(360 - x)) = 100 \cdot 2850$

    $100(6.25x) + 100(8.75(360 - x)) = 100 \cdot 2850$

    $625x + 875(360 - x) = 285000$

    $625x + 315000 - 875x = 285000$

    $-250x + 315000 = 285000$

    $-250x = -30000$

    $x = 120$

    Then 360 - x = 360 - 120 = 240. Thus, 120 tickets at $6.25
    each and 240 tickets at $8.75 were sold.

83. Let x = # of votes that Party A received.

    $$\frac{x}{15700} = \frac{8}{5}$$

    $$15700 \cdot \frac{x}{15700} = 15700 \cdot \frac{8}{5}$$

    $$\frac{\cancel{15700}^{1}}{1} \cdot \frac{x}{\cancel{15700}_{1}} = \frac{\overset{3140}{\cancel{15700}}}{1} \cdot \frac{8}{\cancel{5}_{1}}$$

    $$x = 25,120$$

    Thus, Party A received 25,120 votes.

85.   Let t = # of hours needed for the faster car to overtake the
          slower one.

$$80t = 65(t + \frac{1}{4})$$

$$80t = 65t + 65 \cdot \frac{1}{4}$$

$$15t = \frac{65}{4}$$

$$t = \frac{\frac{65}{4}}{15} = \frac{65}{4} \cdot \frac{1}{15} = \frac{65}{60} = 1\frac{5}{60}$$

Thus, the faster car overtakes the slower one after 1 hour
and 5 minutes.

Cumulative Practice Test: Chapters 4-6

1. $(x - 2y)(x^2 - 3xy - y^2) = x(x^2 - 3xy - y^2) - 2y(x^2 - 3xy - y^2)$

$$= x^3 - 3x^2y - xy^2 - 2x^2y + 6xy^2 + 2y^3$$

$$= x^3 - 3x^2y - 2x^2y - xy^2 + 6xy^2 + 2y^3$$

$$= x^3 - 5x^2y + 5xy^2 + 2y^3$$

3. $\dfrac{\overset{4s}{\cancel{12s^2t^3}}}{\underset{1}{\cancel{5d^2}}} \cdot \dfrac{\overset{\frac{1}{\cancel{3}}d^3}{\cancel{15d^5}}}{\underset{\underset{1}{\frac{1}{\cancel{3}}t}}{\cancel{9st^4}}} = \dfrac{4sd^3}{t}$

5. $(x - 5)^2 - (x + 5)^2 = (x - 5)(x - 5) - (x + 5)(x + 5)$

$$= x^2 - 10x + 25 - (x^2 + 10x + 25)$$

$$= x^2 - 10x + 25 - x^2 - 10x - 25$$

$$= x^2 - x^2 - 10x - 10x + 25 - 25$$

$$= -20x$$

7. $\dfrac{3x - 7}{2y} - \dfrac{9x - 7}{2y} = \dfrac{3x - 7 - (9x - 7)}{2y} = \dfrac{3x - 7 - 9x + 7}{2y}$

$$= \dfrac{\overset{3}{\cancel{-6}}x}{\cancel{2}y} = \dfrac{-3x}{y} = -\dfrac{3x}{y}$$

9. $\dfrac{5}{6ab^2} + \dfrac{4}{9b} = \dfrac{5(3)}{6ab^2(3)} + \dfrac{4(2ab)}{9b(2ab)} = \dfrac{15}{18ab^2} + \dfrac{8ab}{18ab^2} = \dfrac{15 + 8ab}{18ab^2}$

11.

$$\require{enclose}
\begin{array}{r}
4x^2 + 5x + 15 \\
x - 2 \enclose{longdiv}{4x^3 - 3x^2 + 5x - 20} \\
\end{array}$$

$$
\begin{array}{r}
-(4x^3 - 8x^2) \\
\hline
5x^2 + 5x \\
-(5x^2 - 10x) \\
\hline
15x - 20 \\
-(15x - 30) \\
\hline
10
\end{array}
$$

13. $\dfrac{16x^3y^5}{9z^4} \div 36xyz = \dfrac{\cancel{16x^3y^5}^{\,4x^2y^4}}{9z^4} \cdot \dfrac{1}{\cancel{36xyz}_{9}} = \dfrac{4x^2y^4}{81z^5}$

15. $\dfrac{(.008)(25000)}{(6000)(.00015)} = \dfrac{(8 \times 10^{-3})(2.5 \times 10^4)}{(6 \times 10^3)(1.5 \times 10^{-4})} = \dfrac{\cancel{(8)}^4 \cancel{(2.5)}^5}{\cancel{(6)}_3 \cancel{(1.5)}_3} \times \dfrac{10^{-3}10^4}{10^3 10^{-4}}$

$$= \dfrac{20}{9} \times \dfrac{10^1}{10^{-1}} = 2.22 \times 10^2 \text{ (rounded off)}$$

17. $\dfrac{a}{6} - \dfrac{a}{9} = 18$

$18(\dfrac{a}{6} - \dfrac{a}{9}) = 18(18)$

$\dfrac{\cancel{18}^3}{1} \cdot \dfrac{a}{\cancel{6}_1} - \dfrac{\cancel{18}^2}{1} \cdot \dfrac{a}{\cancel{9}_1} = 324$

$3a - 2a = 324$

$a = 324$

19. $x^2 - 10x - 24 = (x - 12)(x + 2)$

21. $2t^2 + 5t - 12 = (2t - 3)(t + 4)$

23. $3x^3y - 12xy^3 = 3xy(x^2 - 4y^2) = 3xy(x - 2y)(x + 2y)$

25. $x^2 - 3x - xy + 3y = x(x - 3) - y(x - 3) = (x - 3)(x - y)$

27. Let L = length of the rectangle

$\frac{1}{3}$L + 5 = width of the rectangle

$2L + 2(\frac{1}{3}L + 5) = 34$

$2L + \frac{2}{3}L + 10 = 34$

$3(2L + \frac{2}{3}L + 10) = 3(34)$

$3(2L) + \dfrac{\cancel{3}}{1} \cdot \dfrac{2}{\cancel{3}_1}L + 3(10) = 3(34)$

CHECK: 8 is 5 more than
$\frac{1}{3}(9) = 3$.   2(9) +
$2(8) = 18 + 16 \overset{\checkmark}{=} 34.$

$$6L + 2L + 30 = 102$$
$$8L + 30 = 102$$
$$8L = 72$$
$$L = 9$$

Then $\frac{1}{3}L + 5 = \frac{1}{3}(9) + 5 = 3 + 5 = 8$. Thus, the length of the rectangle is 9 meters and the width is 8 meters.

29.   Let x = # of hours that the two work together.

$$24(x + 4) + 40x = 480$$
$$24x + 96 + 40x = 480$$
$$64x + 96 = 480$$
$$64x = 384$$
$$x = 6$$

CHECK: The assistant works for 10 hours at $24 per hour, for a bill of 10(24) = $240. The consultant works for 6 hours at $40 per hour, for a bill of 6(40) = $240.
$240 + $240 $\overset{?}{=}$ $480

Thus, the consultant and her assistant work together for 6 hours.

Chapter 7

MORE RATIONAL EXPRESSIONS

1. $\dfrac{\cancel{8x^3y^{10}}^{\,4\;\;y^5}}{\cancel{10x^6y^5}_{\,5x^3}} = \dfrac{4y^5}{5x^3}$

3. $\dfrac{5x - 7x}{x^2 - 7x^2} = \dfrac{\cancel{-2x}^{\,1}}{\cancel{-6x^2}_{\,3x}} = \dfrac{1}{3x}$

5. $\dfrac{\cancel{6x^2(x+4)^5}^{\,2\;\;(x+4)^4}}{\cancel{9x^3(x+4)}_{\,3x}} = \dfrac{2(x+4)^4}{3x}$

7. $\dfrac{12a^2b + 6c^3}{8a^2b + 4c^3} = \dfrac{\cancel{6(2a^2b + c^3)}^{\,3}}{\cancel{4(2a^2b + c^3)}_{\,2}} = \dfrac{3}{2}$

9. $\dfrac{3x - 6}{5x - 10} = \dfrac{3\cancel{(x - 2)}}{5\cancel{(x - 2)}} = \dfrac{3}{5}$

11. $\dfrac{3x - 6}{6x - 12} = \dfrac{\cancel{3}^{\,1}\cancel{(x - 2)}}{\cancel{6}_{\,2}\cancel{(x - 2)}} = \dfrac{1}{2}$

13. $\dfrac{3x - 6}{6x + 12} = \dfrac{\cancel{3}^{\,1}(x - 2)}{\cancel{6}_{\,2}(x + 2)} = \dfrac{x - 2}{2(x + 2)}$

15. $\dfrac{5y}{10y + 20} = \dfrac{\cancel{5}^{\,1}y}{\cancel{10}_{\,2}(y + 2)} = \dfrac{y}{2(y + 2)}$

17. $\dfrac{6x + 18}{x^2 - 9} = \dfrac{6\cancel{(x + 3)}}{(x - 3)\cancel{(x + 3)}} = \dfrac{6}{x - 3}$

19. $\dfrac{6x^2 + 18}{x^2 - 9} = \dfrac{6(x^2 + 3)}{x^2 - 9}$ (cannot be reduced)

137

21. $\dfrac{t^2 + 3t}{t^2 + 3t - 10} = \dfrac{t(t + 3)}{(t + 5)(t - 2)}$ (cannot be reduced)

23. $\dfrac{2x^2 + x + x}{4x^3 + 4x^2} = \dfrac{2x^2 + 2x}{4x^3 + 4x^2} = \dfrac{\overset{1}{\cancel{2x(x + 1)}}}{\underset{2x}{\cancel{4x^2(x + 1)}}} = \dfrac{1}{2x}$

25. $\dfrac{y^2 - 5y - 6}{y^2 - 12y + 36} = \dfrac{\cancel{(y - 6)}(y + 1)}{\cancel{(y - 6)}(y - 6)} = \dfrac{y + 1}{y - 6}$

27. $\dfrac{s^2 - 2s - 15}{s^2 - 6s + 5} = \dfrac{\cancel{(s - 5)}(s + 3)}{\cancel{(s - 5)}(s - 1)} = \dfrac{s + 3}{s - 1}$

29. $\dfrac{x^2(x + 3)(x - 4)}{x^4 - 4x^3} = \dfrac{x^2(x + 3)\cancel{(x - 4)}}{\underset{x}{\cancel{x^3(x - 4)}}} = \dfrac{x + 3}{x}$

31. $\dfrac{3a^2 + a - 2}{a^2 - a - 2} = \dfrac{(3a - 2)\cancel{(a + 1)}}{(a - 2)\cancel{(a + 1)}} = \dfrac{3a - 2}{a - 2}$

33. $\dfrac{4x^2 + 7x - 2}{x^2 + 4x + 4} = \dfrac{(4x - 1)\cancel{(x + 2)}}{(x + 2)\cancel{(x + 2)}} = \dfrac{4x - 1}{x + 2}$

35. $\dfrac{x^2 - x + 3x - 8}{x^2 + 4x} = \dfrac{x^2 + 2x - 8}{x^2 + 4x} = \dfrac{(x - 2)\cancel{(x + 4)}}{x\cancel{(x + 4)}} = \dfrac{x - 2}{x}$

37. $\dfrac{6x^2 - 12x - 18}{3x^2 - 9x - 30} = \dfrac{6(x^2 - 2x - 3)}{3(x^2 - 3x - 10)} = \dfrac{\overset{2}{\cancel{6}}(x - 3)(x + 1)}{\underset{1}{\cancel{3}}(x - 5)(x + 2)} = \dfrac{2(x - 3)(x + 1)}{(x - 5)(x + 2)}$

39. $\dfrac{6x^2 - 5x^2 - 4}{x^2 - 6x + 8} = \dfrac{x^2 - 4}{x^2 - 6x + 8} = \dfrac{\cancel{(x - 2)}(x + 2)}{\cancel{(x - 2)}(x - 4)} = \dfrac{x + 2}{x - 4}$

41. $\dfrac{x^2 - 7x + 10}{x^2 - 7x + 12} = \dfrac{(x - 2)(x - 5)}{(x - 3)(x - 4)}$ (cannot be reduced)

43. $\dfrac{y^3 - y^2 - 2y}{6y^2 - 24} = \dfrac{y(y^2 - y - 2)}{6(y^2 - 4)} = \dfrac{y\cancel{(y - 2)}(y + 1)}{6\cancel{(y - 2)}(y + 2)} = \dfrac{y(y + 1)}{6(y + 2)}$

45. $\dfrac{c^2 - 9c}{c^3 - 9c^2} = \dfrac{\overset{1}{\cancel{c(c - 9)}}}{\underset{c}{\cancel{c^2(c - 9)}}} = \dfrac{1}{c}$

47. The student was incorrect in each case, because he or she
     tried to cancel terms instead of factors. Neither of the
     fractions can be reduced because neither contains a common
     factor in its numerator and denominator . (In part (a), we
     could write $\dfrac{x^2 + 5}{x} = \dfrac{x\cancel{x}}{\cancel{x}_1} + \dfrac{5}{x} = \dfrac{x}{1} + \dfrac{5}{x}$ if we wished.)

Exercises 7.2

1. $\dfrac{\overset{4}{\cancel{8}}x^{2}\overset{2}{y}}{\underset{3}{\cancel{9}}y\underset{z^{2}}{\cancel{z^{3}}}} \cdot \dfrac{\overset{4a}{\cancel{12a^{2}}}z}{\underset{1}{\cancel{2ax}}^{2}} = \dfrac{16ay^{2}}{3z^{2}}$

3. $\dfrac{3st^{2}}{5p} \div \dfrac{15t^{2}}{s^{2}} = \dfrac{\cancel{3st}^{2}}{5p} \cdot \dfrac{s^{2}}{\underset{5}{\cancel{15t}}^{2}} = \dfrac{s^{3}}{25p}$

5. $\dfrac{12x^{2}y^{3}}{5z} \cdot 30xyz = \dfrac{12x^{2}y^{3}}{\underset{1}{\cancel{5z}}} \cdot \dfrac{\overset{6}{\cancel{30xyz}}}{1} = 72x^{3}y^{4}$

7. $28a^{2}b^{3}z \div \dfrac{4a}{7b} = \dfrac{\overset{7a}{\cancel{28a^{2}}}b^{3}z^{4}}{1} \cdot \dfrac{7b}{\underset{1}{\cancel{4a}}} = 49ab^{4}z^{4}$

9. $\dfrac{x^{2}+4x}{x^{2}} \cdot \dfrac{x}{x^{2}+6x+5} = \dfrac{x(x+4)}{\underset{x_{1}}{\cancel{x^{2}}}} \cdot \dfrac{\overset{1}{\cancel{x}}}{(x+1)(x+5)} = \dfrac{x+4}{(x+1)(x+5)}$

11. $\dfrac{x^{2}+4x}{x^{2}+4x+4} \cdot \dfrac{x^{2}-4}{x^{2}-4x+4} = \dfrac{x(x+4)}{(x+2)\cancel{(x+2)}} \cdot \dfrac{\overset{1}{\cancel{(x-2)}}(x+2)}{\cancel{(x-2)}(x-2)}$

$= \dfrac{x(x+4)}{(x+2)(x-2)}$

13. $\dfrac{r^{2}-4r-5}{2r-10} \div \dfrac{r^{2}-3r+2}{4r^{2}} = \dfrac{r^{2}-4r-5}{2r-10} \cdot \dfrac{4r^{2}}{r^{2}-3r+2}$

$= \dfrac{\cancel{(r-5)}(r+1)}{\underset{1}{\cancel{2(r-5)}}} \cdot \dfrac{\overset{2}{\cancel{4}}r^{2}}{(r-1)(r-2)}$

$= \dfrac{2r^{2}(r+1)}{(r-1)(r-2)}$

15. $\dfrac{m^{2}}{m^{2}+3m} \div \dfrac{3m^{2}}{m^{2}+6m} = \dfrac{m^{2}}{m^{2}+3m} \cdot \dfrac{m^{2}+6m}{3m^{2}} = \dfrac{\overset{1}{\cancel{m^{2}}}}{\cancel{m}(m+3)} \cdot \dfrac{\cancel{m}(m+6)}{3\cancel{m^{2}}}$

$= \dfrac{m+6}{3(m+3)}$

17. $\dfrac{x^{2}+3x+2}{x^{2}+2x} \cdot \dfrac{x}{x^{2}+2} = \dfrac{(x+1)\cancel{(x+2)}}{\underset{1}{\cancel{x(x+2)}}} \cdot \dfrac{\overset{1}{\cancel{x}}}{x^{2}+2} = \dfrac{x+1}{x^{2}+2}$

19. $\dfrac{y^{2}-3y-4}{y^{2}-2y-8} \cdot \dfrac{y^{2}+4y+4}{y^{2}-8y+16} = \dfrac{\cancel{(y-4)}(y+1)}{\underset{1}{\cancel{(y-4)}\cancel{(y+2)}}} \cdot \dfrac{\cancel{(y+2)}(y+2)}{(y-4)(y-4)}$

$= \dfrac{(y+1)(y+2)}{(y-4)(y-4)}$

21. $\dfrac{x^2 + 2x}{x^2 - x - 2} \cdot \dfrac{x - 2}{x} = \dfrac{\cancel{x}(x + 2)}{\cancel{(x - 2)}(x + 1)} \cdot \dfrac{\cancel{x - 2}^{\,1}}{\cancel{x}_1} = \dfrac{x + 2}{x + 1}$

23. $\dfrac{2x^2 + x - 15}{x^2 - 9} \cdot \dfrac{6x^2 + 7x + 1}{2x^2 - 3x - 5} = \dfrac{\cancel{(2x - 5)}\cancel{(x + 3)}}{(x - 3)\cancel{(x + 3)}} \cdot \dfrac{(6x + 1)\cancel{(x + 1)}}{\cancel{(2x - 5)}\cancel{(x + 1)}}$

$= \dfrac{6x + 1}{x - 3}$

25. $\dfrac{4a}{a + 4} \cdot \dfrac{a + 5}{5a} \div \dfrac{a^2 + 6a + 5}{a^2 + 5a + 4} = (\dfrac{4\cancel{a}}{a + 4} \cdot \dfrac{a + 5}{5\cancel{a}}) \div \dfrac{a^2 + 6a + 5}{a^2 + 5a + 4}$

$= \dfrac{4(a + 5)}{5(a + 4)} \cdot \dfrac{a^2 + 5a + 4}{a^2 + 6a + 5}$

$= \dfrac{4\cancel{(a + 5)}}{5\cancel{(a + 4)}} \cdot \dfrac{\cancel{(a + 1)}^{1}\cancel{(a + 4)}}{\cancel{(a + 1)}\cancel{(a + 5)}_1} = \dfrac{4}{5}$

27. $\dfrac{x}{2} \div \dfrac{2}{x} \cdot \dfrac{x^2 - 16}{x^2 - 4x} = (\dfrac{x}{2} \div \dfrac{2}{x}) \cdot \dfrac{x^2 - 16}{x^2 - 4x} = (\dfrac{x}{2} \cdot \dfrac{x}{2}) \cdot \dfrac{x^2 - 16}{x^2 - 4x}$

$= \dfrac{x^2}{4} \cdot \dfrac{\cancel{(x - 4)}(x + 4)}{\cancel{x}(x - 4)_1} = \dfrac{x(x + 4)}{4}$

29. $\dfrac{t^2 + 2t}{t^2 + 2t + 1} \cdot \dfrac{2t^2 + 7t + 6}{t^2 + t} = \dfrac{t^2 + 2t}{t^2 + 2t + 1} \cdot \dfrac{t^2 + t}{2t^2 + 7t + 6}$

$= \dfrac{t\cancel{(t + 2)}}{(t + 1)\cancel{(t + 1)}} \cdot \dfrac{t\cancel{(t + 1)}}{(2t + 3)\cancel{(t + 2)}}$

$= \dfrac{t^2}{(t + 1)(2t + 3)}$

31. $\dfrac{2x^2 + 6x + 4x}{x^2 - 25} \cdot \dfrac{(x + 5)^2}{4x - 2x} = \dfrac{2x^2 + 10x}{x^2 - 25} \cdot \dfrac{(x + 5)^2}{2x}$

$= \dfrac{2x\cancel{(x + 5)}^{1}}{(x - 5)\cancel{(x + 5)}} \cdot \dfrac{(x + 5)(x + 5)}{2x_1}$

$= \dfrac{(x + 5)(x + 5)}{x - 5}$

33. $\dfrac{x^3 y - xy^3}{8x^2 y + 4xy^2} \div \dfrac{(x - y)^2}{2x^2 + 3xy + y^2} = \dfrac{x^3 y - xy^3}{8x^2 y + 4xy^2} \cdot \dfrac{2x^2 + 3xy + y^2}{(x - y)^2}$

$= \dfrac{xy(x^2 - y^2)}{4xy(2x + y)} \cdot \dfrac{(2x + y)(x + y)}{(x - y)^2}$

$= \dfrac{\cancel{xy}\cancel{(x - y)}(x + y)}{{}^1 4\cancel{xy}\cancel{(2x + y)}} \cdot \dfrac{\cancel{(2x + y)}(x + y)}{\cancel{(x - y)}(x - y)}$

$= \dfrac{(x + y)(x + y)}{4(x - y)}$

35. $(\frac{x}{3} \cdot \frac{x}{4}) \cdot \frac{12}{x^2 - 3x} = \frac{x^2}{12} \cdot \frac{12}{x^2 - 3x} = \frac{\cancel{x^2}^x}{\cancel{12}_1} \cdot \frac{\cancel{12}^1}{\cancel{x}(x - 3)} = \frac{x}{x - 3}$

37. $(\frac{c}{2} + \frac{c}{5}) \div \frac{c^2 + 7c}{10} = (\frac{c(5)}{2(5)} + \frac{c(2)}{5(2)}) \div \frac{c^2 + 7c}{10}$

$= (\frac{5c}{10} + \frac{2c}{10}) \div \frac{c^2 + 7c}{10} = \frac{7c}{10} \div \frac{c^2 + 7c}{10}$

$= \frac{7c}{10} \cdot \frac{10}{c^2 + 7c} = \frac{7\cancel{c}}{\cancel{10}_1} \cdot \frac{\cancel{10}^1}{\cancel{c}(c + 7)} = \frac{7}{c + 7}$

39. $(\frac{w}{4} - \frac{9}{w}) \cdot (\frac{w + 10}{2w} - \frac{5}{w}) = (\frac{w(w)}{4(w)} - \frac{9(4)}{w(4)}) \cdot (\frac{w + 10}{2w} - \frac{5(2)}{w(2)})$

$= (\frac{w^2}{4w} - \frac{36}{4w}) \cdot (\frac{w + 10}{2w} - \frac{10}{2w})$

$= (\frac{w^2 - 36}{4w}) \cdot (\frac{w + 10 - 10}{2w})$

$= \frac{(w - 6)(w + 6)}{4w} \cdot \frac{\cancel{w}^1}{\cancel{2w}} = \frac{(w - 6)(w + 6)}{8w}$

Exercises 7.3

1. $\frac{5x - 2}{4x + 8} + \frac{3x + 2}{4x + 8} = \frac{5x - 2 + 3x + 2}{4x + 8} = \frac{8x}{4x + 8} = \frac{\cancel{8x}^{2x}}{\cancel{4}(x + 2)} = \frac{2x}{x + 2}$

3. $\frac{5x - 2}{4x + 8} - \frac{3x + 2}{4x + 8} = \frac{5x - 2 - (3x + 2)}{4x + 8} = \frac{5x - 2 - 3x - 2}{4x + 8}$

$= \frac{2x - 4}{4x + 8} = \frac{\cancel{2}^1(x - 2)}{\cancel{4}^2(x + 2)} = \frac{x - 2}{2(x + 2)}$

7. $\frac{x + 7}{x + 2} - \frac{x + 3}{x + 2} + \frac{x - 2}{x + 2} = \frac{(x + 7) - (x + 3) + (x - 2)}{x + 2}$

$= \frac{x + 7 - x - 3 + x - 2}{x + 2} = \frac{\cancel{x + 2}^1}{\cancel{x + 2}_1} = \frac{1}{1} = 1$

11. $\frac{5}{2x} + \frac{4}{x + 2} = \frac{5(x + 2)}{2x(x + 2)} + \frac{4(2x)}{(x + 2)(2x)} = \frac{5x + 10}{2x(x + 2)} + \frac{8x}{2x(x + 2)}$

$= \frac{5x + 10 + 8x}{2x(x + 2)} = \frac{13x + 10}{2x(x + 2)}$

13. $\frac{5}{\cancel{2}x} \cdot \frac{\cancel{x}^2}{x + 2} = \frac{10}{x(x + 2)}$

17.
$$\frac{7}{a+7} - \frac{5}{a+5} = \frac{7(a+5)}{(a+7)(a+5)} - \frac{5(a+7)}{(a+5)(a+7)}$$

$$= \frac{7a+35}{(a+7)(a+5)} - \frac{5a+35}{(a+7)(a+5)}$$

$$= \frac{7a+35-(5a+35)}{(a+7)(a+5)} = \frac{7a+35-5a-35}{(a+7)(a+5)}$$

$$= \frac{2a}{(a+7)(a+5)}$$

19.
$$\frac{4}{3x^2} - \frac{2}{x^2+3x} = \frac{4}{3x^2} - \frac{2}{x(x+3)} = \frac{4(x+3)}{3x^2(x+3)} - \frac{2(3x)}{x(x+3)(3x)}$$

$$= \frac{4x+12}{3x^2(x+3)} - \frac{6x}{3x^2(x+3)} = \frac{4x+12-6x}{3x^2(x+3)}$$

$$= \frac{-2x+12}{3x^2(x+3)} = \frac{2(-x+6)}{3x^2(x+3)}$$

23.
$$\frac{4}{x^2+4x} - \frac{2}{x^2-4x} = \frac{4}{x(x+4)} - \frac{2}{x(x-4)}$$

$$= \frac{4(x-4)}{x(x+4)(x-4)} - \frac{2(x+4)}{x(x-4)(x+4)}$$

$$= \frac{4x-16}{x(x+4)(x-4)} - \frac{2x+8}{x(x+4)(x-4)}$$

$$= \frac{4x-16-(2x+8)}{x(x+4)(x-4)} = \frac{4x-16-2x-8}{x(x+4)(x-4)}$$

$$= \frac{2x-24}{x(x+4)(x-4)} = \frac{2(x-12)}{x(x+4)(x-4)}$$

25.
$$2 - \frac{x}{x-1} = \frac{2}{1} - \frac{x}{x-1} = \frac{2(x-1)}{1(x-1)} - \frac{x}{x-1} = \frac{2x-2}{x-1} - \frac{x}{x-1}$$

$$= \frac{2x-2-x}{x-1} = \frac{x-2}{x-1}$$

29.
$$\frac{3}{x^2-16} - \frac{3}{2x^2+8x} = \frac{3}{(x-4)(x+4)} - \frac{3}{2x(x+4)}$$

$$= \frac{3(2x)}{(x-4)(x+4)(2x)} - \frac{3(x-4)}{2x(x+4)(x-4)}$$

$$= \frac{6x}{2x(x+4)(x-4)} - \frac{3x-12}{2x(x+4)(x-4)}$$

$$= \frac{6x-(3x-12)}{2x(x+4)(x-4)} = \frac{6x-3x+12}{2x(x+4)(x-4)}$$

$$= \frac{3x+12}{2x(x+4)(x-4)} = \frac{3\cancel{(x+4)}}{2x\cancel{(x+4)}(x-4)}$$

$$= \frac{3}{2x(x-4)}$$

33.
$$\frac{x}{x^2 + 6x + 9} + \frac{1}{x^2 + 4x + 3} = \frac{x}{(x+3)(x+3)} + \frac{1}{(x+1)(x+3)}$$

$$= \frac{x(x+1)}{(x+3)(x+3)(x+1)} + \frac{1(x+3)}{(x+1)(x+3)(x+3)}$$

$$= \frac{x^2 + x}{(x+1)(x+3)(x+3)} + \frac{x+3}{(x+1)(x+3)(x+3)}$$

$$= \frac{x^2 + x + x + 3}{(x+1)(x+3)(x+3)} = \frac{x^2 + 2x + 3}{(x+1)(x+3)(x+3)}$$

37.
$$5 - \frac{1}{3x - 6} + \frac{3}{x^2 - 2x} = \frac{5}{1} - \frac{1}{3(x-2)} + \frac{3}{x(x-2)}$$

$$= \frac{5(3x(x-2))}{1(3x(x-2))} - \frac{1(x)}{3(x-2)(x)} + \frac{3(3)}{x(x-2)(3)}$$

$$= \frac{15x^2 - 30x}{3x(x-2)} - \frac{x}{3x(x-2)} + \frac{9}{3x(x-2)}$$

$$= \frac{15x^2 - 30x - x + 9}{3x(x-2)} = \frac{15x^2 - 31x + 9}{3x(x-2)}$$

39.
$$\frac{5}{x^2 + x - 6} - \frac{3}{x^2 + 3x} + \frac{2}{x^2 - 2x} = \frac{5}{(x+3)(x-2)} - \frac{3}{x(x+3)} + \frac{2}{x(x-2)}$$

$$= \frac{5(x)}{(x+3)(x-2)(x)} - \frac{3(x-2)}{x(x+3)(x-2)} + \frac{2(x+3)}{x(x-2)(x+3)}$$

$$= \frac{5x}{x(x+3)(x-2)} - \frac{3x - 6}{x(x+3)(x-2)} + \frac{2x + 6}{x(x+3)(x-2)}$$

$$= \frac{5x - (3x - 6) + 2x + 6}{x(x+3)(x-2)} = \frac{5x - 3x + 6 + 2x + 6}{x(x+3)(x-2)}$$

$$= \frac{4x + 12}{x(x+3)(x-2)} = \frac{4(x+3)}{x(x+3)(x-2)} = \frac{4}{x(x-2)}$$

45.
$$\frac{1 - \frac{1}{a}}{\frac{1}{a} - \frac{1}{a^2}} = \frac{a^2(1 - \frac{1}{a})}{a^2(\frac{1}{a} - \frac{1}{a^2})} = \frac{a^2 \cdot 1 - \frac{a^2}{1} \cdot \frac{1}{a}}{\frac{a^2}{1} \cdot \frac{1}{a} - \frac{a^2}{1} \cdot \frac{1}{a^2}} = \frac{a^2 - a}{a - 1}$$

$$= \frac{a(a-1)}{a-1} = \frac{a}{1} = a$$

47. $\dfrac{\dfrac{a}{2} - \dfrac{b}{4}}{\dfrac{4}{b^2} - \dfrac{1}{a^2}} = \dfrac{4a^2b^2(\dfrac{a}{2} - \dfrac{b}{4})}{4a^2b^2(\dfrac{4}{b^2} - \dfrac{1}{a^2})} = \dfrac{\dfrac{\overset{2}{\cancel{4a^2b^2}}}{1} \cdot \dfrac{a}{\underset{1}{\cancel{2}}} - \dfrac{\cancel{4a^2b^2}}{1} \cdot \dfrac{b}{\underset{1}{\cancel{4}}}}{\dfrac{4a^2\cancel{b}}{\underset{1}{1}} \cdot \dfrac{4}{\cancel{b^2}} - \dfrac{4a^2b^2}{1} \cdot \dfrac{1}{\underset{1}{\cancel{a^2}}}}$

$$= \dfrac{2a^3b^2 - a^2b^3}{16a^2 - 4b^2} = \dfrac{a^2b^2(2a - b)}{4(4a^2 - b^2)}$$

$$= \dfrac{a^2b^2\cancel{(2a - b)}}{4\cancel{(2a - b)}(2a + b)} = \dfrac{a^2b^2}{4(2a + b)}$$

49. (a) $(x + \dfrac{2}{x})(x - \dfrac{3}{x}) = x^2 - \dfrac{\cancel{x}}{1}(\dfrac{3}{\cancel{x}}) + \dfrac{\cancel{x}}{1}(\dfrac{2}{\cancel{x}}) - (\dfrac{2}{x})(\dfrac{3}{x})$

$$x^2 - 3 + 2 - \dfrac{6}{x^2} = x^2 - 1 - \dfrac{6}{x^2}$$

(b) $x + \dfrac{2}{x} = \dfrac{x}{1} + \dfrac{2}{x} = \dfrac{x(x)}{1(x)} + \dfrac{2}{x} = \dfrac{x^2}{x} + \dfrac{2}{x} = \dfrac{x^2 + 2}{x}$

$$= x - \dfrac{3}{x} = \dfrac{x}{1} - \dfrac{3}{x} = \dfrac{x(x)}{1(x)} - \dfrac{3}{x} = \dfrac{x^2}{x} - \dfrac{3}{x} = \dfrac{x^2 - 3}{x}$$

Then $(x + \dfrac{2}{x})(x - \dfrac{3}{x}) = \dfrac{x^2 + 2}{x} \cdot \dfrac{x^2 - 3}{x} = \dfrac{(x^2 + 2)(x^2 - 3)}{x^2}$

The second method is easier. If the instructions ask for the
answer in the form of a single fraction, we get such an answer
directly in part (b). In part (a), there would be further
work to do.

Exercises 7.4

1. $\dfrac{x}{5} + \dfrac{x - 1}{4} + \dfrac{x - 3}{2} = 3$

$$20(\dfrac{x}{5} + \dfrac{x - 1}{4} + \dfrac{x - 3}{2}) = 20 \cdot 3$$

$\dfrac{\overset{4}{\cancel{20}}}{1} \cdot \dfrac{x}{\underset{1}{\cancel{5}}} + \dfrac{\overset{5}{\cancel{20}}}{1} \cdot \dfrac{x - 1}{\underset{1}{\cancel{4}}} + \dfrac{\overset{10}{\cancel{20}}}{1} \cdot \dfrac{x - 3}{\underset{1}{\cancel{2}}} = 60$

$4x + 5(x - 1) + 10(x - 3) = 60$ CHECK: $x = 5$

$\quad 4x + 5x - 5 + 10x - 30 = 60$ $\dfrac{(5)}{5} + \dfrac{(5) - 1}{4} + \dfrac{(5) - 3}{2} \overset{?}{=} 3$

$\qquad\qquad\qquad 19x - 35 = 60$ $\dfrac{5}{5} + \dfrac{4}{4} + \dfrac{2}{2} \overset{?}{=} 3$

$\qquad\qquad\qquad\quad 19x = 95$ $1 + 1 + 1 \overset{?}{=} 3$

$\qquad\qquad\qquad\qquad x = 5$ $3 \overset{\checkmark}{=} 3$

7. $\dfrac{2r + 1}{3} - \dfrac{r + 1}{5} = \dfrac{r + 8}{6}$

$30\left(\dfrac{2r + 1}{3} - \dfrac{r + 1}{5}\right) = 30\left(\dfrac{r + 8}{6}\right)$

$\dfrac{\cancel{30}^{10}}{1} \cdot \dfrac{2r + 1}{\cancel{3}_1} - \dfrac{\cancel{30}^6}{1} \cdot \dfrac{r + 1}{\cancel{5}_1} = \dfrac{\cancel{30}^5}{1} \cdot \dfrac{r + 8}{\cancel{6}_1}$

$10(2r + 1) - 6(r + 1) = 5(r + 8)$ CHECK: $r = 4$

$\qquad\qquad 20r + 10 - 6r - 6 = 5r + 40 \qquad\qquad \dfrac{2(4)+1}{3} - \dfrac{(4)+1}{5} \overset{?}{=} \dfrac{(4)+8}{6}$

$\qquad\qquad\qquad\quad 14r + 4 = 5r + 40 \qquad\qquad\qquad\qquad \dfrac{9}{3} - \dfrac{5}{5} \overset{?}{=} \dfrac{12}{6}$

$\qquad\qquad\qquad\qquad 9r + 4 = 40 \qquad\qquad\qquad\qquad\qquad 3 - 1 \overset{?}{=} 2$

$\qquad\qquad\qquad\qquad\qquad 9r = 36 \qquad\qquad\qquad\qquad\qquad\quad 2 \overset{\checkmark}{=} 2$

$\qquad\qquad\qquad\qquad\qquad\quad r = 4$

9. $\dfrac{3}{x} - \dfrac{2}{3} = \dfrac{2}{x}$

$3x\left(\dfrac{3}{x} - \dfrac{2}{3}\right) = 3x\left(\dfrac{2}{x}\right)$ CHECK: $x = \dfrac{3}{2}$

$\dfrac{3\cancel{x}}{1} \cdot \dfrac{3}{\cancel{x}_1} - \dfrac{\cancel{3}x}{1} \cdot \dfrac{2}{\cancel{3}_1} = \dfrac{3\cancel{x}}{1} \cdot \dfrac{2}{\cancel{x}_1} \qquad\qquad \dfrac{3}{\left(\dfrac{3}{2}\right)} - \dfrac{2}{3} \overset{?}{=} \dfrac{2}{\left(\dfrac{3}{2}\right)}$

$\qquad\qquad 9 - 2x = 6 \qquad\qquad\qquad\qquad \dfrac{3}{1} \cdot \dfrac{2}{3} - \dfrac{2}{3} \overset{?}{=} \dfrac{2}{1} \cdot \dfrac{2}{3}$

$\qquad\qquad\quad -2x = -3 \qquad\qquad\qquad\qquad\quad 2 - \dfrac{2}{3} \overset{?}{=} \dfrac{4}{3}$

$\qquad\qquad\qquad x = \dfrac{3}{2} \qquad\qquad\qquad\qquad\qquad\quad \dfrac{4}{3} \overset{\checkmark}{=} \dfrac{4}{3}$

13. $\dfrac{4}{x - 1} - \dfrac{5}{8} = \dfrac{3}{2x - 2}$

$\dfrac{4}{x - 1} - \dfrac{5}{8} = \dfrac{3}{2(x - 1)}$

$8(x - 1)\left(\dfrac{4}{x - 1} - \dfrac{5}{8}\right) = 8(x - 1)\left(\dfrac{3}{2(x - 1)}\right)$

$\dfrac{8\cancel{(x - 1)}}{1} \cdot \dfrac{4}{\cancel{x - 1}_1} - \dfrac{\cancel{8}(x - 1)}{1} \cdot \dfrac{5}{\cancel{8}_1} = \dfrac{^4\cancel{8}\cancel{(x - 1)}}{1} \cdot \dfrac{3}{\cancel{2(x - 1)}_1}$

$32 - 5(x - 1) = 12 \qquad\qquad\qquad$ CHECK: $x = 5$

$\qquad 32 - 5x + 5 = 12 \qquad\qquad\qquad\qquad \dfrac{4}{(5)-1} - \dfrac{5}{8} \overset{?}{=} \dfrac{3}{2(5)-2}$

$\qquad\quad -5x + 37 = 12 \qquad\qquad\qquad\qquad\qquad \dfrac{4}{4} - \dfrac{5}{8} \overset{?}{=} \dfrac{3}{8}$

$\qquad\qquad\quad -5x = -25 \qquad\qquad\qquad\qquad\qquad \dfrac{8}{8} - \dfrac{5}{8} \overset{?}{=} \dfrac{3}{8}$

$\qquad\qquad\qquad x = 5 \qquad\qquad\qquad\qquad\qquad\qquad \dfrac{3}{8} \overset{\checkmark}{=} \dfrac{3}{8}$

15. $\dfrac{8}{x - 2} + 3 = \dfrac{x + 6}{x - 2}$

$(x - 2)(\dfrac{8}{x - 2} + 3) = (x - 2)(\dfrac{x + 6}{x - 2})$

$\dfrac{\cancel{x - 2}^{1}}{1} \cdot \dfrac{8}{\cancel{x - 2}_{1}} + \dfrac{x - 2}{1} \cdot \dfrac{3}{1} = \dfrac{\cancel{x - 2}^{1}}{1} \cdot \dfrac{x + 6}{\cancel{x - 2}_{1}}$

$8 + 3(x - 2) = x + 6$ CHECK: x = 2

$8 + 3x - 6 = x + 6$

$3x + 2 = x + 6$ $\dfrac{8}{(2) - 2} + 3 \overset{?}{=} \dfrac{(2) + 6}{(2) - 2}$

$2x + 2 = 6$ $\dfrac{8}{0} + 3 \overset{?}{=} \dfrac{8}{0}$

$2x = 4$

$x = 2$ $\dfrac{8}{0}$ is not defined, so

                        x = 2 is not a solution.

Since x = 2 does not satisfy the original equation, no solution can be found.

19. $\dfrac{5}{x^2 - x} - \dfrac{1}{2x - 2} = \dfrac{1}{x}$

$\dfrac{5}{x(x - 1)} - \dfrac{1}{2(x - 1)} = \dfrac{1}{x}$

$2x(x - 1)(\dfrac{5}{x(x - 1)} - \dfrac{1}{2(x - 1)}) = 2x(x - 1)(\dfrac{1}{x})$

$\dfrac{\cancel{2x(x - 1)}}{1} \cdot \dfrac{5}{\cancel{x(x - 1)}_{1}} - \dfrac{\cancel{2x(x - 1)}}{1} \cdot \dfrac{1}{\cancel{2(x - 1)}_{1}} = \dfrac{2\cancel{x}(x - 1)}{1} \cdot \dfrac{1}{\cancel{x}_{1}}$

$10 - x = 2(x - 1)$ CHECK: x = 4

$10 - x = 2x - 2$

$10 = 3x - 2$ $\dfrac{5}{(4)^2 - (4)} - \dfrac{1}{2(4) - 2} \overset{?}{=} \dfrac{1}{(4)}$

$12 = 3x$ $\dfrac{5}{16 - 4} - \dfrac{1}{8 - 2} \overset{?}{=} \dfrac{1}{4}$

$4 = x$ $\dfrac{5}{12} - \dfrac{1}{6} \overset{?}{=} \dfrac{1}{4}$

                          $\dfrac{5}{12} - \dfrac{2}{12} \overset{?}{=} \dfrac{1}{4}$

                             $\dfrac{3}{12} \overset{?}{=} \dfrac{1}{4}$

                             $\dfrac{1}{4} \overset{\checkmark}{=} \dfrac{1}{4}$

25.
$$\frac{5}{x^2 - 2x - 3} = \frac{4}{x^2 - 3x - 4}$$

$$\frac{5}{(x - 3)(x + 1)} = \frac{4}{(x - 4)(x + 1)}$$

$$\frac{\cancel{(x - 3)}(x - 4)\cancel{(x + 1)}}{1}\left(\frac{5}{\cancel{(x - 3)}\cancel{(x + 1)}}\right) = \frac{(x - 3)\cancel{(x - 4)}\cancel{(x + 1)}}{1}\left(\frac{4}{\cancel{(x - 4)}\cancel{(x + 1)}}\right)$$

$$5(x - 4) = 4(x - 3)$$
$$5x - 20 = 4x - 12$$
$$x - 20 = -12$$
$$x = 8$$

CHECK: x = 8

$$\frac{5}{(8)^2 - 2(8) - 3} \overset{?}{=} \frac{4}{(8)^2 - 3(8) - 4}$$

$$\frac{5}{64 - 16 - 3} \overset{?}{=} \frac{4}{64 - 24 - 4}$$

$$\frac{5}{45} \overset{?}{=} \frac{4}{36}$$

$$\frac{1}{9} \overset{\checkmark}{=} \frac{1}{9}$$

27.
$$\frac{9}{x^2 - 3x + 2} - \frac{2}{x - 1} = \frac{1}{x - 2}$$

$$\frac{9}{(x - 1)(x - 2)} - \frac{2}{x - 1} = \frac{1}{x - 2}$$

$$(x - 1)(x - 2)\left(\frac{9}{(x - 1)(x - 2)} - \frac{2}{x - 1}\right) = (x - 1)(x - 2)\left(\frac{1}{x - 2}\right)$$

$$\frac{\cancel{(x - 1)}\cancel{(x - 2)}^1}{1} \cdot \frac{9}{\cancel{(x - 1)}\cancel{(x - 2)}} - \frac{\cancel{(x - 1)}(x - 2)}{1} \cdot \frac{2}{\cancel{x - 1}_1}$$

$$= \frac{(x - 1)\cancel{(x - 2)}}{1} \cdot \frac{1}{\cancel{x - 2}_1}$$

$$9 - 2(x - 2) = x - 1$$
$$9 - 2x + 4 = x - 1$$
$$13 - 2x = x - 1$$
$$13 = 3x - 1$$
$$14 = 3x$$
$$\frac{14}{3} = x$$

29.
$$\frac{x}{2} + \frac{x}{3} + \frac{x}{4} \qquad \text{LCD} = 12$$

$$= \frac{x(6)}{2(6)} + \frac{x(4)}{3(4)} + \frac{x(3)}{4(3)} = \frac{6x}{12} + \frac{4x}{12} + \frac{3x}{12} = \frac{6x + 4x + 3x}{12} = \frac{13x}{12}$$

33. $\dfrac{x + 1}{2} - \dfrac{3}{x} = \dfrac{x}{2}$

$2x\left(\dfrac{x + 1}{2} - \dfrac{3}{x}\right) = 2x\left(\dfrac{x}{2}\right)$

$\dfrac{2x}{1} \cdot \dfrac{x + 1}{2}_1 - \dfrac{2x}{1} \cdot \dfrac{3}{x}_1 = \dfrac{2x}{1} \cdot \dfrac{x}{2}_1$

$x(x + 1) - 6 = x^2$ CHECK: $x = 6$

$\quad x^2 + x - 6 = x^2$ $\dfrac{(6)+1}{2} - \dfrac{3}{(6)} \overset{?}{=} \dfrac{(6)}{2}$

$\qquad\qquad x - 6 = 0$ $\dfrac{7}{2} - \dfrac{3}{6} \overset{?}{=} \dfrac{6}{2}$

$\qquad\qquad\quad x = 6$ $\dfrac{7}{2} - \dfrac{1}{2} \overset{?}{=} \dfrac{6}{2}$

$\qquad\qquad\qquad\qquad\qquad\qquad\qquad \dfrac{6}{2} \overset{\checkmark}{=} \dfrac{6}{2}$

Exercises 7.5

3. $3x + 6y = 18$

$\quad \underline{-3x \qquad\qquad\quad - 3x}$

$\qquad\quad 6y = 18 - 3x$

$\qquad \dfrac{6y}{6} = \dfrac{18 - 3x}{6}$

$\qquad\quad y = \dfrac{18 - 3x}{6} = \dfrac{3(6 - x)}{6_2} = \dfrac{6 - x}{2}$

7. $3(m + 2p) = 4(p - m)$

$\qquad 3m + 6p = 4p - 4m$

$\quad \underline{+\ 4m \qquad\qquad\quad + 4m}$

$\qquad 7m + 6p = 4p$

$\qquad\quad \underline{-\ 6p\ \ = -6p}$

$\qquad 7m \qquad = -2p$

$\qquad \dfrac{7m}{7} \qquad = \dfrac{-2p}{7}$

$\qquad\ m \qquad\quad = \dfrac{-2p}{7} = -\dfrac{2p}{7}$

11. $\dfrac{x}{2} + \dfrac{y}{3} = \dfrac{x}{3} + \dfrac{y}{4} - \dfrac{1}{6}$

$12\left(\dfrac{x}{2} + \dfrac{y}{3}\right) = 12\left(\dfrac{x}{3} + \dfrac{y}{4} - \dfrac{1}{6}\right)$

$\dfrac{12^6}{1} \cdot \dfrac{x}{2}_1 + \dfrac{12^4}{1} \cdot \dfrac{y}{3}_1 = \dfrac{12^4}{1} \cdot \dfrac{x}{3}_1 + \dfrac{12^3}{1} \cdot \dfrac{y}{4}_1 - \dfrac{12^2}{1} \cdot \dfrac{1}{6}_1$

$$6x + 4y = 4x + 3y - 2$$
$$-4x \qquad -4x$$
$$\overline{2x + 4y = \qquad 3y - 2}$$
$$- 4y \qquad - 4y$$
$$\overline{2x = \qquad -y - 2}$$
$$\frac{\cancel{2}x}{\cancel{2}} = \frac{-y - 2}{2}$$
$$x = \frac{-y - 2}{2}$$

17. $$2pn - \frac{y}{3} = 3n + ay + p$$

$$3(2pn - \frac{y}{3} = 3(3n + ay + p)$$

$$6pn - \frac{\cancel{3}}{1} \cdot \frac{y}{\cancel{3}_1} = 9n + 3ay + 3p$$

$$6pn - y \qquad = 9n + 3ay + 3p$$
$$+ y \qquad \qquad + y$$
$$\overline{6pn \qquad = 9n + 3ay + 3p + y}$$
$$- 9n \qquad -9n$$
$$\overline{6pn - 9n \qquad = \qquad 3ay + 3p + y}$$
$$- 3p \qquad - 3p$$
$$\overline{6pn - 9n - 3p = \qquad 3ay}$$
$$6pn - 9n - 3p = (3a + 1)y$$
$$\frac{6pn - 9n - 3p}{3a + 1} = \frac{\cancel{(3a + 1)}y}{\cancel{3a + 1}}$$
$$\frac{6pn - 9n - 3p}{3a + 1} = y$$

19. $$y = \frac{u + 1}{u - 1}$$

$$(u - 1)y = \frac{\cancel{(u - 1)}}{1}(\frac{u + 1}{\cancel{u - 1}_1})$$

$$(u - 1)y = u + 1$$

$$uy - y \qquad = u + 1$$
$$- u \qquad -u$$
$$\overline{uy - y - u = 1}$$
$$+ y \qquad + y$$
$$\overline{uy \qquad - u = 1 + y}$$
$$u(y - 1) = 1 + y$$

$$\frac{u\cancel{(y - 1)}}{\cancel{y - 1}_1} = \frac{1 + y}{y - 1}$$

$$u = \frac{1 + y}{y - 1}$$

25. $A = \frac{1}{2}h(b_1 + b_2)$

$2A = 2(\frac{1}{2}h(b_1 + b_2)$

$2A = h(b_1 + b_2)$

$\dfrac{2A}{b_1 + b_2} = h$

29. $C = \frac{5}{9}(F - 32)$

$9C = 9(\frac{5}{9}(F - 32))$

$9C = 5(F - 32)$

$\dfrac{9C}{5} = F - 32$

$\dfrac{9C}{5} + 32 = F$

33. $\dfrac{x - \mu}{s} < 2$

$\cancel{s}(\dfrac{x - \mu}{\cancel{s}}) < s(2)$ (since s is positive)

$x - \mu < 2s$

$x < 2s + \mu$

35. $\dfrac{1}{f} = \dfrac{1}{f_1} + \dfrac{1}{f_2}$

$ff_1f_2(\frac{1}{f}) = ff_1f_2(\frac{1}{f_1} + \frac{1}{f_2})$

$\dfrac{\cancel{f}f_1f_2}{1} \cdot \dfrac{1}{\cancel{f_1}} = \dfrac{f\cancel{f_1}f_2}{1} \cdot \dfrac{1}{\cancel{f_1}} + \dfrac{ff_1\cancel{f_2}}{1} \cdot \dfrac{1}{\cancel{f_2}}$

$f_1f_2 = ff_2 + ff_1$

$f_1f_2 = f(f_2 + f_1)$

$\dfrac{f_1f_2}{f_2 + f_1} = f$

Exercises 7.6

3. Let x = # of people who preferred Brand X
    200-x = # of people who did not.

$$\frac{x}{200 - x} = \frac{13}{12}$$

$$\frac{12(200 - x)}{1} \cdot \frac{x}{200 - x} = \frac{12(200 - x)}{1} \cdot \frac{13}{12}$$

12x = 13(200 - x)   CHECK: $\frac{104}{96} = \frac{8(13)}{8(12)} = \frac{13}{12}$,

12x = 2600 - 13x   and 104 + 96 = 200.

25x = 2600

  x = 104

Then 200 - x = 200 - 104 = 96. Thus, 104 people preferred Brand X.

5. Let x = # of hits Joe must get in his next 50 at-bats.

$$\frac{120 + x}{400 + 50} = .400 = \frac{400}{1000} = \frac{2}{5}$$

$$\frac{120 + x}{450} = \frac{2}{5}$$

$$\frac{450}{1} \cdot \frac{120 + x}{450} = \frac{450^{90}}{1} \cdot \frac{2}{5_1}$$

120 + x = 180

      x = 60

This is impossible, since the largest possible value of x is 50. Therefore, Joe cannot raise his average to .400 in his next 50 at-bats.

9. Let x = # of hours that the electrician needs to complete the job working alone.
      2x = # of hours that the apprentice needs to complete the job working alone

$$6\left(\frac{1}{x}\right) + 6\left(\frac{1}{2x}\right) = 1$$

$$\frac{6}{1} \cdot \frac{1}{x} + \frac{6^3}{1} \cdot \frac{1}{2x} = 1$$

$$\frac{6}{x} + \frac{3}{x} = 1$$

$$\frac{9}{x} = 1$$

$$\frac{x}{1} \cdot \frac{9}{x} = x \cdot 1$$

$$9 = x$$

CHECK: In one hour, the electrician completes $\frac{1}{9}$ of the job, so in 6 hours he completes $\frac{6}{9} = \frac{2}{3}$ of the job. In one hour, the apprentice completes $\frac{1}{18}$ of the job, so in 6 hours he completes $\frac{6}{18} = \frac{1}{3}$ of the job. $\frac{2}{3} + \frac{1}{3} = 1$ (the entire job).

11. Let r = rate of the train (in kph)
     r+100 = rate of the plane (in kph)

$$\frac{300}{r} = \frac{500}{r + 100}$$

$$\frac{r(r + 100)}{1} \cdot \frac{300}{r_1} = \frac{r(r + 100)}{1} \cdot \frac{500}{r + 100_1}$$

300(r + 100) = 500r   CHECK: At the rate of 150 kph, the

300r + 30000 = 500r   train covers 300 kilometers

     30000 = 200r   in $\frac{300}{150}$ = 2 hours. At the

       150 = r   rate of 250 kph, the plane

                                     covers 500 kilometers in

                                     $\frac{500}{250}$ = 2 hours, the same

                                     amount of time.

Then 250 = r + 100. Thus, the train travels at the rate of 150
kph and the plane travels at the rate of 250 kph.

15. Let t = # of hours that Ronnie walks
     3 - t = # of hours that Ronnie jogs

     6t = 14(3 - t)   CHECK: Ronnie walks 6(2.1) =

     6t = 42 - 14t   12.6 kilometers to his
                                     friend's house and jogs
     20t = 42   14(3 - 2.1) = 14(.9) =
                                     12.6 kilometers back, the
     $t = \frac{42}{20} = \frac{21}{10} = 2.1$ same distance.

Then the distance to Ronnie's friend's house is 6(2.1) = 12.6
kilometers.

17. Let x = smaller number
       3x = larger number

$\frac{1}{x} + \frac{1}{3x} = \frac{5}{3}$ CHECK: $\frac{12}{5}$ is three times $\frac{4}{5}$,

$3x(\frac{1}{x} + \frac{1}{3x}) = 3x(\frac{5}{3})$ and $\frac{1}{(\frac{12}{5})} + \frac{1}{(\frac{4}{5})} = \frac{5}{12} + \frac{5}{4}$

$\frac{3x}{1} \cdot \frac{1}{x_1} + \frac{3x^1}{1} \cdot \frac{1}{3x_1} = \frac{3x}{1} \cdot \frac{5}{3_1}$ $= \frac{5}{12} + \frac{15}{12} = \frac{20}{12} = \frac{5}{3}$.

3 + 1 = 5x

   4 = 5x

$\frac{4}{5} = x$

Then, $3(\frac{4}{5}) = \frac{12}{5} = 3x$. Thus, the numbers are $\frac{4}{5}$ and $\frac{12}{5}$.

19. Let x = number to be added

$$\frac{3 + x}{5 + x} = \frac{5}{6}$$

$$\frac{6(5 + x)}{1}(\frac{3 + x}{5 + x}) = \frac{6(5 + x)}{1} \cdot \frac{5}{6}$$

$6(3 + x) = 5(5 + x)$ CHECK: $\frac{3 + (7)}{5 + (7)} = \frac{10}{12} = \frac{5}{6}$

$18 + 6x = 25 + 5x$

$18 + x = 25$

$x = 7$

Thus, the number to be added to both the numerator and denominator is 7.

21. Let x = numerator of the fraction
x + 2 = denominator of the traction

$$\frac{x + 2}{x} = \frac{x}{x + 2}$$

$$\frac{x(x + 2)}{1} \cdot \frac{x + 2}{x} = \frac{x(x + 2)}{1} \cdot \frac{x}{x + 2}$$

$(x + 2)(x + 2) = x^2$

$x^2 + 4x + 4 = x^2$ CHECK: 1 is two more than -1, and the reciprocal of

$4x + 4 = 0$ $\frac{-1}{1}$ is $\frac{1}{-1}$, which is equal

$4x = -4$ to the original fraction.

$x = -1$

Then x + 2 = -1 + 2 = 1. Thus, the fraction is $\frac{-1}{1}$.

Chapter 7 - Review Exercises

1. $\dfrac{x^2}{x^2 + 2}$ cannot be reduced.

3. $\dfrac{x^2 + 3x - 4}{x^2 - 16} = \dfrac{(x + 4)(x - 1)}{(x - 4)(x + 4)} = \dfrac{x - 1}{x - 4}$

5. $\dfrac{a^2 + 8a + 16}{a^2 + 6a + 8} = \dfrac{(a + 4)(a + 4)}{(a + 2)(a + 4)} = \dfrac{a + 4}{a + 2}$

7. $\dfrac{3z^2 - 12}{3z^2 + 9z + 6} = \dfrac{3(z^2 - 4)}{3(z^2 + 3z + 2)} = \dfrac{3(z - 2)(z + 2)}{3(z + 1)(z + 2)} = \dfrac{z - 2}{z + 1}$

9. $\dfrac{x}{x+2} + \dfrac{x}{2} = \dfrac{x(2)}{(x+2)(2)} + \dfrac{x(x+2)}{2(x+2)} = \dfrac{2x}{2(x+2)} + \dfrac{x^2+2x}{2(x+2)}$

$= \dfrac{2x+x^2+2x}{2(x+2)} = \dfrac{x^2+4x}{2(x+2)} = \dfrac{x(x+4)}{2(x+2)}$

11. $\dfrac{3}{2x+4} + \dfrac{6}{x^2+2x} = \dfrac{3}{2(x+2)} + \dfrac{6}{x(x+2)}$

$= \dfrac{3(x)}{2(x+2)(x)} + \dfrac{6(2)}{x(x+2)(2)}$

$= \dfrac{3x}{2x(x+2)} + \dfrac{12}{2x(x+2)}$

$= \dfrac{3x+12}{2x(x+2)} = \dfrac{3(x+4)}{2x(x+2)}$

13. $\dfrac{x^2-5x-6}{2x-12} \div \dfrac{x^2+2x+1}{8x^2} = \dfrac{x^2-5x-6}{2x-12} \cdot \dfrac{8x^2}{x^2+2x+1}$

$= \dfrac{\cancel{(x-6)}(x+1)}{\cancel{2(x-6)}\,_1} \cdot \dfrac{\overset{4}{\cancel{8}}x^2}{\cancel{(x+1)}(x+1)}$

$= \dfrac{4x^2}{x+1}$

15. $\dfrac{5}{z^2+z-6} - \dfrac{3}{z^2+3z} = \dfrac{5}{(z+3)(z-2)} - \dfrac{3}{z(z+3)}$

$= \dfrac{5(z)}{(z+3)(z-2)(z)} - \dfrac{3(z-2)}{z(z+3)(z-2)}$

$= \dfrac{5z}{z(z+3)(z-2)} - \dfrac{3z-6}{z(z+3)(z-2)}$

$= \dfrac{5z-(3z-6)}{z(z+3)(z-2)} = \dfrac{5z-3z+6}{z(z+3)(z-2)}$

$= \dfrac{2z+6}{z(z+3)(z-2)} = \dfrac{2\cancel{(z+3)}}{z\cancel{(z+3)}(z-2)}$

$= \dfrac{2}{z(z-2)}$

17. $2 + \dfrac{3}{x+2} - \dfrac{1}{x} = \dfrac{2}{1} + \dfrac{3}{x+2} - \dfrac{1}{x}$

$= \dfrac{2(x(x+2))}{1(x(x+2))} + \dfrac{3(x)}{(x+2)(x)} - \dfrac{1(x+2)}{x(x+2)}$

$= \dfrac{2x^2+4x}{x(x+2)} + \dfrac{3x}{x(x+2)} - \dfrac{x+2}{x(x+2)}$

$= \dfrac{2x^2+4x+3x-(x+2)}{x(x+2)} = \dfrac{2x^2+4x+3x-x-2}{x(x+2)}$

$= \dfrac{2x^2+6x-2}{x(x+2)} = \dfrac{2(x^2+3x-1)}{x(x+2)}$

19. $\dfrac{5}{x} - \dfrac{2}{3x} = \dfrac{13}{6}$

$6x\left(\dfrac{5}{x} - \dfrac{2}{3x}\right) = 6x\left(\dfrac{13}{6}\right)$

$\dfrac{6x}{1} \cdot \dfrac{5}{x}_1 - \dfrac{{}^2 6x}{1} \cdot \dfrac{2}{3x}_1 = \dfrac{6x}{1} \cdot \dfrac{13}{6}_1$

$30 - 4 = 13x$

$\qquad 26 = 13x$

$\qquad\; 2 = x$

21. $\dfrac{y + 2}{y} + \dfrac{4}{y + 2} = \dfrac{y}{y + 2}$

$y(y + 2)\left(\dfrac{y + 2}{y} + \dfrac{4}{y + 2}\right) = y(y + 2)\left(\dfrac{y}{y + 2}\right)$

$\dfrac{y(y + 2)}{1} \cdot \dfrac{y + 2}{y}_1 + \dfrac{y(y + 2)}{1} \cdot \dfrac{4}{y + 2}_1 = \dfrac{y(y + 2)}{1} \cdot \dfrac{y}{y + 2}_1$

$(y + 2)(y + 2) + 4y = y^2$

$y^2 + 4y + 4 + 4y = y^2$

$y^2 + 8y + 4 = y^2$

$8y + 4 = 0$

$8y = -4$

$y = -\dfrac{4}{8} = -\dfrac{1}{2}$

23. $\dfrac{x + 2}{x - 3} + \dfrac{4}{3} = \dfrac{5}{x - 3}$

$3(x - 3)\left(\dfrac{x + 2}{x - 3} + \dfrac{4}{3}\right) = 3(x - 3)\left(\dfrac{5}{x - 3}\right)$

$\dfrac{3(x - 3)}{1} \cdot \dfrac{x + 2}{x - 3}_1 + \dfrac{3(x - 3)}{1} \cdot \dfrac{4}{3}_1 = \dfrac{3(x - 3)}{1} \cdot \dfrac{5}{x - 3}_1$

$3(x + 2) + 4(x - 3) = 15$

$3x + 6 + 4x - 12 = 15$

$7x - 6 = 15$

$7x = 21$

$x = 3$

This value does not check in the original equation, since it produces fractions with denominators of 0. Thus, the equation has no solution.

25. $\begin{array}{rcl} 3x - 4y + 7 &=& 8x - 7y + 3 \\ -8x && -8x \end{array}$

$\begin{array}{rcl} \overline{-5x - 4y + 7} &=& \overline{ - 7y + 3} \\ + 4y && + 4y \end{array}$

$\begin{array}{rcl} \overline{-5x + 7} &=& \overline{ - 3y + 3} \\ - 7 && - 7 \end{array}$

$\begin{array}{rcl} \overline{-5x} &=& \overline{ - 3y - 4} \end{array}$

$\dfrac{-5x}{-5} = \dfrac{-3y - 4}{-5}$

$x = \dfrac{-3y - 4}{-5} \quad \text{or} \quad \dfrac{3y + 4}{5}$

27. Let x = # of black marbles in the bag
    x + 80 = # of red marbles in the bag

$\dfrac{x + 80}{x} = \dfrac{7}{5}$

$\dfrac{5x}{1} \cdot \dfrac{x + 80}{x_{\,1}} = \dfrac{5x}{1} \cdot \dfrac{7}{5_{\,1}}$ CHECK: 280 is 80 more than 200,

  $5(x + 80) = 7x$ and $\dfrac{280}{200} = \dfrac{7}{5}$.

  $5x + 400 = 7x$

  $400 = 2x$

  $200 = x$

Then 280 = x + 80. Thus, there are 200 black marbles and 280 red marbles in the bag, or 480 marbles altogether.

29. Let x = # of hours John needs to do the job alone.

$4\left(\dfrac{1}{x}\right) + 4\left(\dfrac{1}{6}\right) = 1$

$\dfrac{4}{x} + \dfrac{4}{6} = 1$ CHECK: In 4 hours, Susan does

$6x\left(\dfrac{4}{x} + \dfrac{4}{6}\right) = 6x \cdot 1$ $4\left(\dfrac{1}{6}\right) = \dfrac{4}{6} = \dfrac{2}{3}$ of the job;

$\dfrac{6x}{1} \cdot \dfrac{4}{x_{\,1}} + \dfrac{6x}{1} \cdot \dfrac{4}{6_{\,1}} = 6x$ in 4 hours, John does

$24 + 4x = 6x$ $4\left(\dfrac{1}{12}\right) = \dfrac{4}{12} = \dfrac{1}{3}$ of the

$24 = 2x$ job.

$12 = x$ $\dfrac{2}{3} + \dfrac{1}{3} = 1$ (the entire job)

Thus, John needs 12 hours to do the job alone.

Chapter 7 Practice Test

1. $\dfrac{4x^2}{x^2 - 4x} = \dfrac{4x^2}{x(x - 4)} = \dfrac{4x}{x - 4}$

3. $\dfrac{3}{x+3} + \dfrac{2}{x+2} = \dfrac{3(x+2)}{(x+3)(x+2)} + \dfrac{2(x+3)}{(x+2)(x+3)}$

$$= \dfrac{3x+6}{(x+3)(x+2)} + \dfrac{2x+6}{(x+3)(x+2)}$$

$$= \dfrac{3x+6+2x+6}{(x+3)(x+2)} = \dfrac{5x+12}{(x+3)(x+2)}$$

5. $\dfrac{5}{2x} - \dfrac{10}{x^2+4x} = \dfrac{5}{2x} - \dfrac{10}{x(x+4)} = \dfrac{5(x+4)}{2x(x+4)} - \dfrac{10(2)}{x(x+4)(2)}$

$$= \dfrac{5x+20}{2x(x+4)} - \dfrac{20}{2x(x+4)} = \dfrac{5x+20-20}{2x(x+4)}$$

$$= \dfrac{5\cancel{x}}{2\cancel{x}(x+4)} = \dfrac{5}{2(x+4)}$$

7. $\dfrac{2x-5}{x^2-3x} - \dfrac{3x+7}{x^2-3x} + \dfrac{6x-3}{x^2-3x} = \dfrac{2x-5-(3x+7)+6x-3}{x^2-3x}$

$$= \dfrac{2x-5-3x-7+6x-3}{x^2-3x}$$

$$= \dfrac{5x-15}{x^2-3x} = \dfrac{5\cancel{(x-3)}}{x\cancel{(x-3)}} = \dfrac{5}{x}$$

9. $at + b = \dfrac{3t}{2} + 7$

$2(at+b) = 2\left(\dfrac{3t}{2}+7\right)$

$2at + 2b = 3t + 14$

$\underline{-3t-3t}$

$\overline{2at - 3t + 2b = 14}$

$\underline{-2b-2b}$

$\overline{2at - 3t = 14 - 2b}$

$(2a-3)t = 14 - 2b$

$t = \dfrac{14-2b}{2a-3}$

11. Let t = # of hours needed to go from A to B

14 - t = # of hours needed to go from B to A

$45t = 60(14 - t)$ CHECK: Time going $= \dfrac{360}{45} = 8$

$45t = 840 - 60t$

$105t = 840$ hours. Time returning

$t = 8$ $= \dfrac{360}{60} = 6$ hours.

$8 + 6 \overset{\checkmark}{=} 14$ hours.

Thus, the distance between the towns is 45(8) = 360 kilometers.

Chapter 8

GRAPHING AND SYSTEMS OF LINEAR EQUATIONS

Exercises 8.1

1-19. (odd)

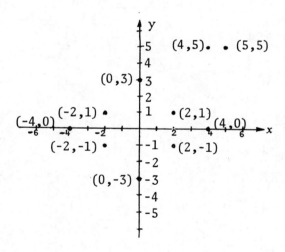

21. Quadrant I

23. Quadrant III

25. on y-axis

27. Quadrant II

29. on both x-axis and y-axis

31. Quadrant IV

33. $\{(x,y)\,|\,y = x + 2$ and $x = -3,\ 0,\ 4\}$

x	y	(x,y)
-3	-1	(-3,-1)
0	2	(0,2)
4	6	(4,6)

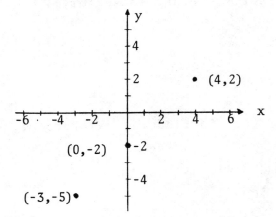

34. $\{(x,y)\,|\,x = y + 2$ and $x = -3,\ 0,\ 4\}$

x	y	(x,y)
-3	-5	(-3,-5)
0	-2	(0,-2)
4	2	(4,2)

35. (2,3), (0,6), (6,-3), (4,0)

36. (-2,-16), (0, -8), (3,4), (2,0)

37. An ordered pair (x,y) is a pair of numbers in which the order of appearance matters. For instance (3,4) and (4,3) would be different as ordered pairs, even though both involve the same two numbers.

38. The notation {x,y} stands for the set containing the two elements x and y. Here, order does not matter. That is, {3,4} and {4,3} are equal as sets. When we write (x,y), we mean that x comes first and y second.

Exercises 8.2

1. To find the x-intercept, we set y = 0 and solve for x.

$$x - y = 7$$
$$x - (0) = 7$$
$$x - 0 = 7$$
$$x = 7$$

Therefore, the x-intercept is 7. To find the y-intercept, we set x = 0 and solve for y.

$$x - y = 7$$
$$(0) - y = 7$$
$$0 - y = 7$$
$$-y = 7$$
$$y = -7$$

Therefore, the y-intercept is -7.

5. To find the x-intercept, we set y = 0 and solve for x.

$$2x + 3y = 12$$
$$2x + 3(0) = 12$$
$$2x + 0 = 12$$
$$2x = 12$$
$$x = 6$$

Therefore, the x-intercept is 6. To find the y-intercept, we set x = 0 and solve for y.

$$2x + 3y = 12$$
$$2(0) + 3y = 12$$
$$0 + 3y = 12$$
$$3y = 12$$
$$y = 4$$

Therefore, the y-intercept is 4.

9. To find the x-intercept, we set y = 0 and solve for x.

$$2x = 5y$$
$$2x = 5(0)$$
$$2x = 0$$
$$x = 0$$

Therefore, the x-intercept is 0. To find the y-intercept, we set x = 0 and solve for y.

$$2x = 5y$$
$$2(0) = 5y$$
$$0 = 5y$$
$$0 = y$$

Therefore, the y-intercept is 0.

11. To find the x-intercept, we set y = 0 and solve for x. Since the equation x = 5 does not contain y, its solution is just x = 5. So the x-intercept is 5. To find the y-intercept, we set x = 0 and solve for y. But this gives 0 = 5, which is a contradiction. So the equation x = 5 has no y-intercept.

15. x + y = 5

x-intercept:	y-intercept:	check point: choose x = 1
x + (0) = -5	(0) + y = -5	(1) + y = -5
x + 0 = -5	0 + y = -5	1 + y = -5
x = -5	y = -5	y = -6
Plot (-5,0)	Plot (0,-5)	Plot (1,-6)

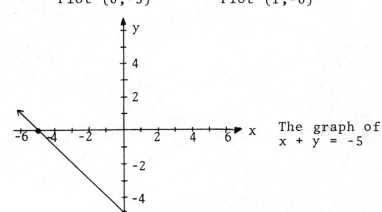

The graph of
x + y = -5

19. 3x - 4y = 12

x-intercept:	y-intercept:	check point: choose x = 8
3x - 4(0) = 12	3(0) - 4y = 12	3(8) - 4y = 12
3x - 0 = 12	0 - 4y = 12	24 - 4y = 12
3x = 12	-4y = 12	-4y = -12
x = 4	y = -3	y = 3
Plot (4,0)	Plot (0,-3)	Plot (8,3)

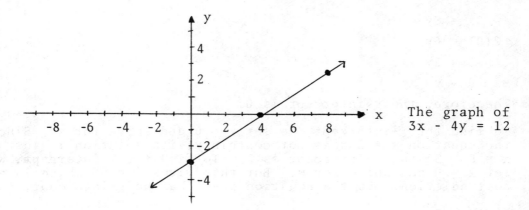

The graph of
3x - 4y = 12

23. y = -4x

x-intercept: second point: choose x = 1   check point: choose
   (0) = -4x   y = -4(1)   x = -1
    0 = -4x   y = -4
    0 = x   y = -4(-1)
                                                   y = 4
Plot (0,0)   Plot (1,-4)   Plot (-1,4)

(As noted in the text, the y-intercept of this equation will
also be equal to 0.)

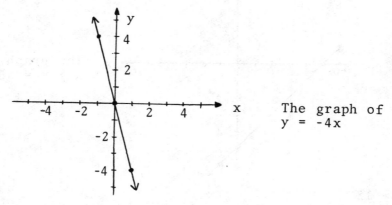

The graph of
y = -4x

27. y = 5

Its graph is a line parallel
to the x-axis and 5 units
above it.

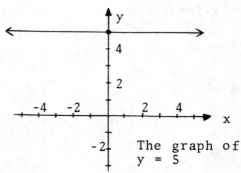

The graph of
y = 5

29. x = -4

Its graph is a line
parallel to the y-
axis and 4 units to
the left of it.

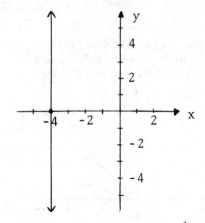

The graph of
x = -4

33. 2(x - 3) = 4(y + 2)

x-intercept:	y-intercept:	check point: choose x = 1
2(x - 3) = 4((0) + 2)	2((0) - 3) = 4(y + 2)	2((1) - 3) = 4(y + 2)
2(x - 3) = 4(0 + 2)	2(0 - 3) = 4(y + 2)	2(1 - 3) = 4(y + 2)
2x - 6 = 8	-6 = 4y + 8	2(-2) = 4(y + 2)
2x = 14	-14 = 4y	-4 = 4y + 8
x = 7	$-\frac{7}{2}$ = y	-12 = 4y
		-3 = y

Plot (7,0)   Plot $(0, -\frac{7}{2})$ Plot (1,-3)

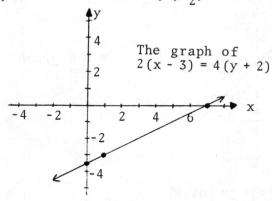

The graph of
2(x - 3) = 4(y + 2)

37.

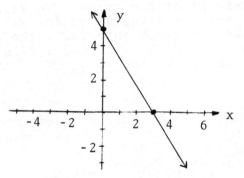

38. Some points on this line are (-4,-4), (-3,-3), (0,0), (2,2), and (5,5). Since the y-coordinate of any such point is equal to its x-coordinate, an equation of this line would be y = x.

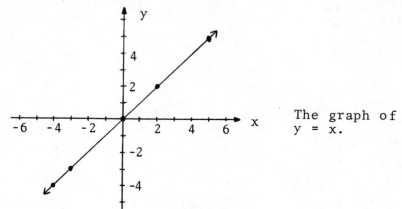

The graph of
y = x.

39. Some points on this line are (-4,4), (-3,3), (0,0), (2,-2), and (5,-5). Since the y-coordinate of any such point is equal to the negative of its x-coordinate, an equation of this line would be y = -x.

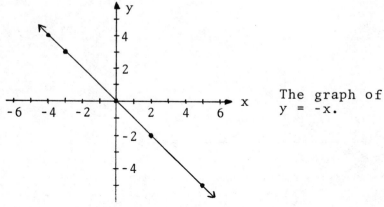

The graph of
y = -x.

40. The x-coordinate of the point where a graph intersects the x-axis is called an x-intercept of the graph. To find an x-intercept of an equation, set y = 0 and solve for x. The y-coordinate of the point where a graph intersects the y-axis is called a y-intercept of the graph. To find a y-intercept of an equation, set x = 0 and solve for y.

Exercises 8.3

1. $m = \dfrac{y_2 - y_1}{x_2 - x_1} = \dfrac{9 - 5}{6 - 3} = \dfrac{4}{3}$

5. $m = \dfrac{y_2 - y_1}{x_2 - x_1} = \dfrac{-4 - (-2)}{-3 - (-1)} = \dfrac{-4 + 2}{-3 + 1} = \dfrac{-2}{-2} = 1$

9. $m = \dfrac{y_2 - y_1}{x_2 - x_1} = \dfrac{7 - 7}{-3 - 4} = \dfrac{0}{-7} = 0$

11. m is undefined. (If we tried to use the formula, we would have obtained $m = \dfrac{9 - 6}{2 - 2} = \dfrac{3}{0}$, and division by zero is undefined.)

13. $m = \dfrac{y_2 - y_1}{x_2 - x_1} = \dfrac{0 - a}{a - 0} = \dfrac{-a}{a} = -1$

17.

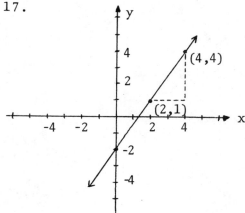

21.

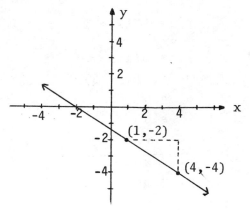

23. A slope of 0 means that the line is horizontal.

25. No slope means that the line is vertical.

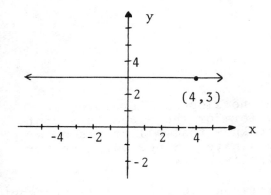

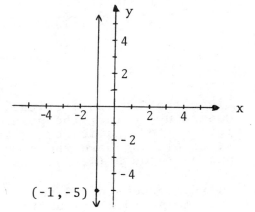

27. $y - y_1 = m(x - x_1)$
     $y - 5 = 3(x - 1)$ or
     $y = 3x + 2$

$(x_1, y_1) = (1, 5)$, $m = 3$

31. $y - y_1 = m(x - x_1)$ $(x_1,y_1) = (-3,-5)$, $m = -\frac{2}{3}$

$y - (-5) = -\frac{2}{3}(x - (-3))$

$y + 5 = -\frac{2}{3}(x + 3)$ or $y = -\frac{2}{3}x - 7$

35. $y = mx + b$ $m = \frac{1}{4}$, $b = -2$

$y = \frac{1}{4}x + (-2)$

$y = \frac{1}{4}x - 2$

37. $y - y_1 = m(x - x_1)$ $(x_1,y_1) = (-2,0)$, $m = -\frac{3}{4}$

$y - 0 = -\frac{3}{4}(x - (-2))$

$y = -\frac{3}{4}(x + 2)$ or $y = -\frac{3}{4}x - \frac{3}{2}$

41. $y - y_1 = m(x - x_1)$ $(x_1,y_1) = (5,6)$, $m = 0$

$y - 6 = 0(x - 5)$

$y - 6 = 0$

$y = 6$

45. $m = \dfrac{y_2 - y_1}{x_2 - x_1} = \dfrac{-2 - 4}{2 - (-1)} = \dfrac{-6}{3} = -2$ $(x_1,y_1) = (-1,4)$

$y - y_1 = m(x - x_1)$

$y - 4 = -2(x - (-1))$

$y - 4 = -2(x + 1)$ or $y = -2x + 2$

49. $m = \dfrac{y_2 - y_1}{x_2 - x_1} = \dfrac{-1 - 0}{0 - (-1)} = \dfrac{-1}{1} = -1$ $b = -1$

$y = mx + b$
$y = (-1)x + (-1)$
$y = -x - 1$

53. Since the line is vertical, it has no slope. Therefore, we
cannot use either the point-slope form or the slope-intercept
form of an equation of a line. We know that all points on a
vertical line have the same x-coordinate. Since our line
passes through $(4,-3)$, its equation is $x = 4$.

57. An x-intercept of -3 means $(-3,0)$ is on the line. A y-intercept
of 4 means $(0,4)$ is on the line. Then

$$m = \frac{y_2 - y_1}{x_2 - x_1} = \frac{4 - 0}{0 - (-3)} = \frac{4}{3}$$

and $b = 4$, so that an equation (in slope-intercept form) is
$y = \frac{4}{3}x + 4$.

59. $y = 5x + 7$

$y = mx + b$. So $m = 5$.

63. $x + y = 7$
$\underline{-x -x }$
$y = -x + 7$

$y = mx + b$. So $m = -1$.

67. $2x - 5y + 7 = 0$
$\underline{-2x -2x}$
$-5y + 7 = -2x$
$\underline{ - 7 - 7}$
$-5y = -2x - 7$

$-5y = -2x - 7$

$\dfrac{-5y}{-5} = \dfrac{-2x - 7}{-5}$

$y = \dfrac{-2x}{-5} + \dfrac{-7}{-5}$

$y = \dfrac{2}{5}x + \dfrac{7}{5}$

$y = mx + b$. So $m = \dfrac{2}{5}$.

69. If two lines are parallel, then they should have the same steepness. This suggests that parallel lines have equal slopes.

70. First, compute the slope of the line through $(-1,-2)$ and $(2,0)$: $m = \dfrac{0 - (-2)}{2 - (-1)} = \dfrac{2}{3}$. Next, compute the slope of the line through $(2,0)$ and $(5,2)$: $m = \dfrac{2 - 0}{5 - 2} = \dfrac{2}{3}$. Since these two lines have equal slopes, they are either parallel or actually one line. But the two lines in question cannot be parallel, since $(2,0)$ is a point on each and parallel lines have no point in common. We can then conclude that the three points $(-1,-2)$, $(2,0)$, and $(5,2)$ all lie on a straight line. (Points with this property are called collinear.)

Exercises 8.4

1. $x + y = 4$

Set $y = 0$ and solve for x to get an x-intercept of 4.
Set $x = 0$ and solve for y to get a y-intercept of 4.

$x - y = 2$

Set $y = 0$ and solve for x to get an x-intercept of 2.
Set $x = 0$ and solve for y to get a y-intercept of -2.

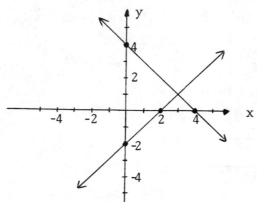

The lines cross at the point (3,1). So the system $\{\begin{array}{l} x + y = 4 \\ x - y = 2 \end{array}$
is satisfied by the point (3,1).

5.   3x + y = 6

Set y = 0 and solve for x to get an x-intercept of 2.
Set x = 0 and solve for y to get a y-intercept of 6.

6x + 2y = 12

Set y = 0 and solve for x to get an x-intercept of 2.
Set x = 0 and solve for y to get a y-intercept of 6.

Since these lines have the same x-intercept and the same y-
intercept, the lines coincide. Therefore there are infinitely
many solutions to the system $\{\begin{array}{l} 3x + y = 6 \\ 6x + 2y = 12 \end{array}$: $\{(x,y)\,|\,3x + y = 6\}$

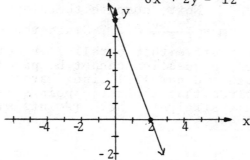

9.   3x - 2y = 6

Set y = 0 and solve for x to get an x-intercept of 2.
Set x = 0 and solve for y to get a y-intercept of -3.

x + y = 2

Set y = 0 and solve for x to get an x-intercept of 2.
Set x = 0 and solve for y to get a y-intercept of 2.

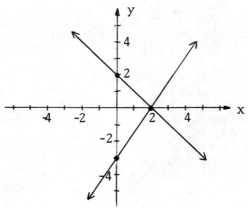

The lines cross at the point (2,0). So the system $\{\begin{matrix} 3x - 2y = 6 \\ x + y = 2 \end{matrix}$
is satisfied by the point (2,0).

13.   5x - 3y = 15

Set y = 0 and solve for x to get an x-intercept of 3.
Set x = 0 and solve for y to get a y-intercept of -5.

2x - y = 4

Set y = 0 and solve for x to get an x-intercept of 2.
Set x = 0 and solve for y to get a y-intercept of -4.

The lines cross at the point
(-3,-10). So the system

$\{\begin{matrix} 5x - 3y = 15 \\ 2x - y = 4 \end{matrix}$ is satisfied

by the point (-3,-10).

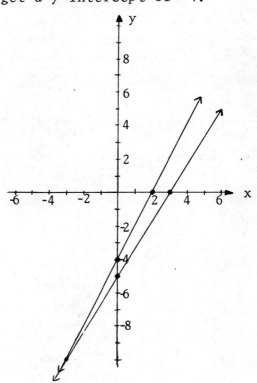

17.   y = x - 3

Set y = 0 and solve for x to get an x-intercept of 3.
Set x = 0 and solve for y to get a y-intercept of -3.

y = x + 4

Set y = 0 and solve for x to get an x-intercept of -4.
Set x = 0 and solve for y to get a y-intercept of 4.

These lines appear to be
parallel. Therefore, the
system $\{\begin{smallmatrix} y = x - 3 \\ y = x + 4 \end{smallmatrix}$ has no
solutions.

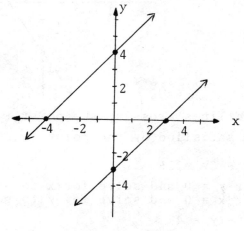

21.   3x + y = 3

Set y = 0 and solve for x to get an x-intercept of 1.
Set x = 0 and solve for y to get a y-intercept of 3.

y = x + 5

Set y = 0 and solve for x to get an x-intercept of -5.
Set x = 0 and solve for y to get a y-intercept of 5.

The lines cross at the point
$(-\frac{1}{2},\frac{9}{2})$. So the system
$\{\begin{smallmatrix} 3x + y = 3 \\ y = x + 5 \end{smallmatrix}$ is satisfied
by the point $(-\frac{1}{2},\frac{9}{2})$.

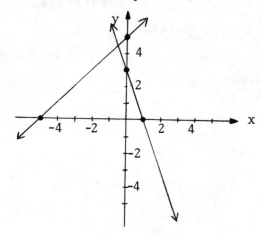

25.   2x + y = 10

Set y = 0 and solve for x to get an x-intercept of 5.
Set x = 0 and solve for y to get a y-intercept of 10.

2y = 20 - 4x

Set y = 0 and solve for x to get an x-intercept of 5.
Set x = 0 and solve for y to get a y-intercept of 10.

Since these lines have the same
x-intercept and the same y-
intercept, the lines coincide.
Therefore, there are infinitely
many solutions to the system
$\{^{2x\ +\ y\ =\ 10}_{\ \ \ 2y\ =\ 20\ -\ 4x}$: $\{(x,y)\,|\,2x + y = 10\}$

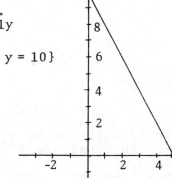

29.   x + y = 6

Set y = 0 and solve for x to get an x-intercept of 6.
Set x = 0 and solve for y to get a y-intercept of 6.

y = -2

This is a horizontal line two units below the x-axis.

The lines cross at the point
(8,-2). So the system
$\{^{x\ +\ y\ =\ 6}_{\ \ \ \ \ y\ =-2}$ is satisfied by the
point (8,-2).

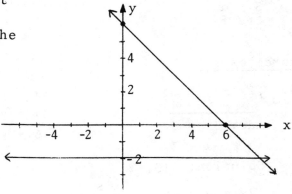

33.   y = 4

This is a horizontal line four units above the x-axis.

x = -1

This is a vertical line one unit to the left of the y-axis.

The lines cross at the point
(-1,4). So the system
$\{\begin{matrix} y = 4 \\ x = -1 \end{matrix}$ is satisfied by the
point (-1,4).

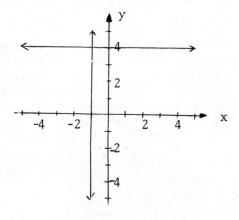

35.   A solution to a system of equations is an ordered pair that
satisfies both equations simultaneously.

36.   It is impossible for a system of two linear equations to have
exactly two solutions. If this were possible, then we would
be able to draw two straight lines that intersect exactly
twice. But two straight lines either do not intersect at all
(when they are parallel), intersect in one point, or intersect
in infinitely many points (when they coincide).

37.   1 - b
2 - e
3 - a
4 - c
5 - d
6 - f

Exercises 8.5

3. $\{\begin{matrix} 2x + y = 5 \\ x - y = 4 \end{matrix}$

Add: 3x = 9

x = 3

Solution: (3,-1)

2x + y = 5

2(3) + y = 5

6 + y = 5

y = -1

CHECK:

x - y = 4

(3) - (1) $\overset{?}{=}$ 4

3 + 1 $\overset{?}{=}$ 4

4 $\overset{\checkmark}{=}$ 4

7. $\{\begin{matrix} 2x + y = 15 \\ x - 2y = 0 \end{matrix}$ $\xrightarrow{\text{as is}}$ 2x + y = 15

$\xrightarrow{\text{multiply by -2}}$ -2x + 4y = 0

Add: 5y = 15

y = 3

2x + y = 15

2x + (3) = 15

2x + 3 = 15

2x = 12

x = 6

Solution: $(6,3)$

CHECK:

$$x - 2y = 0$$
$$(6) - 2(3) \overset{?}{=} 0$$
$$6 - 6 \overset{?}{=} 0$$
$$0 \overset{\checkmark}{=} 0$$

11. $\begin{cases} r + 2t = 10 \\ 3r + t = -15 \end{cases}$
$\xrightarrow{\text{as is}}$
$\xrightarrow{\text{multiply by -2}}$

$$\begin{array}{r} r + 2t = 10 \\ -6r - 2t = 30 \\ \hline \text{Add: } -5r = 40 \\ r = -8 \end{array}$$

$$\begin{array}{r} r + 2t = 10 \\ (-8) + 2t = 10 \\ -8 + 2t = 10 \\ 2t = 18 \\ t = 9 \end{array}$$

Solution: $(-8,9)$

CHECK:

$$3r + t = -15$$
$$3(-8) + (9) \overset{?}{=} -15$$
$$-24 + 9 \overset{?}{=} -15$$
$$-15 \overset{\checkmark}{=} -15$$

13. $\begin{cases} 6x + y = 6 \\ 4x + 1 = y \end{cases}$

Rewrite the second equation in the system as $4x - y = -1$.

CHECK:

$$4x + 1 = y$$
$$4\left(\tfrac{1}{2}\right) + 1 \overset{?}{=} (3)$$
$$2 + 1 \overset{?}{=} 3$$
$$3 \overset{\checkmark}{=} 3$$

$$\begin{array}{r} 6x + y = 6 \\ 4x - y = -1 \\ \hline \text{Add: } 10x = 5 \\ x = \tfrac{5}{10} = \tfrac{1}{2} \end{array}$$

$$6x + y = 6$$
$$6\left(\tfrac{1}{2}\right) + y = 6$$
$$3 + y = 6$$
$$y = 3$$

Solution: $(\tfrac{1}{2},3)$

17. $\begin{cases} 11a - 2b = 30 \\ 3a + 3b = -6 \end{cases}$
$\xrightarrow{\text{multiply by 3}}$
$\xrightarrow{\text{multiply by 2}}$

$$\begin{array}{r} 33a - 6b = 90 \\ 6a + 6b = -12 \\ \hline \text{Add: } 39a = 78 \\ a = 2 \end{array}$$

$$\begin{array}{r} 11a - 2b = 30 \\ 11(2) - 2b = 30 \\ 22 - 2b = 30 \\ -2b = 8 \\ b = -4 \end{array}$$

Solution: $(2,-4)$

CHECK:

$$3a + 3b = -6$$
$$3(2) + 3(-4) \overset{?}{=} -6$$
$$6 + (-12) \overset{?}{=} -6$$
$$-6 \overset{\checkmark}{=} -6$$

21. $\begin{cases} 5x + 2y = 4y + 9 \\ \quad\quad y = x - 3 \end{cases}$

$5x + 2y = 4y + 9 \xrightarrow[\text{from both sides}]{\text{subtract } 4y} 5x - 2y = 9$

$y = x - 3 \xrightarrow[\text{from both sides}]{\text{subtract } x} -x + y = -3$

$5x - 2y = 9 \xrightarrow{\text{as is}} 5x - 2y = 9$

$-x + y = -3 \xrightarrow{\text{multiply by } 2} -2x + 2y = -6$

$\text{Add: } 3x = 3$

$x = 1$

$y = x - 3$
$y = (1) - 3$
$y = 1 - 3$
$y = -2$

Solution: $(1, -2)$

CHECK:

$5x + 2y = 4y + 9$

$5(1) + 2(-2) \overset{?}{=} 4(-2) + 9$

$5 + (-4) \overset{?}{=} -8 + 9$

$1 \overset{\checkmark}{=} 1$

23. $\begin{cases} \dfrac{x}{2} + \dfrac{y}{3} = 1 \\ \dfrac{x}{4} - y = 11 \end{cases}$

$\dfrac{x}{2} + \dfrac{y}{3} = 1 \xrightarrow{\text{multiply by } 6} 3x + 2y = 6$

$\dfrac{x}{4} - y = 11 \xrightarrow{\text{multiply by } 4} x - 4y = 44$

$3x + 2y = 6 \xrightarrow{\text{multiply by } 2} 6x + 4y = 12$

$x - 4y = 44 \xrightarrow{\text{as is}} x - 4y = 44$

$\text{Add: } 7x = 56$

$x = 8$

$\dfrac{x}{2} + \dfrac{y}{3} = 1$

$\dfrac{(8)}{2} + \dfrac{y}{3} = 1$

$4 + \dfrac{y}{3} = 1$

$\dfrac{y}{3} = -3$

$y = -9$

Solution: $(8, -9)$

CHECK:

$\dfrac{x}{4} - y = 11$

$\dfrac{(8)}{4} - (-9) \overset{?}{=} 11$

$2 + 9 \overset{?}{=} 11$

$11 \overset{\checkmark}{=} 11$

27. $\begin{cases} .4x + .2y = 8 \\ .7x - .3y = 1 \end{cases}$

$.4x + .2y = 8 \xrightarrow{\text{multiply by } 10} 4x + 2y = 80$

$.7x - .3y = 1 \xrightarrow{\text{multiply by } 10} 7x - 3y = 10$

$4x + 2y = 80 \xrightarrow{\text{multiply by } 3} 12x + 6y = 240$

$7x - 3y = 10 \xrightarrow{\text{multiply by } 2} 14x - 6y = 20$

$\text{Add: } 26x = 260$

$x = 10$

$.4x + .2y = 8$
$.4(10) + .2y = 8$
$4 + .2y = 8$
$.2y = 4$
$2y = 40$
$y = 20$

Solution: (10,20)   CHECK:

$$.7x - .3y = 1$$
$$.7(10) - .3(20) \overset{?}{=} 1$$
$$7 - 6 \overset{?}{=} 1$$
$$1 \overset{\checkmark}{=} 1$$

31. The student forgot to multiply the right hand side of the second equation by 2.

32. The student mistakenly multiplied 0 times 2 in the second equation and got a product of 2 rather than 0.

Exercises 8.6

3. Let n = # of nickels that Sam has
    Let q = # of quarters that Sam has.

$\begin{cases} n + q = 80 \\ 5n + 25q = 1360 \end{cases}$ $\xrightarrow{\text{multiply by -5}}$ $\quad -5n - 5q = -400$ $\qquad n + q = 80$
$\xrightarrow{\text{as is}}$ $\quad \underline{5n + 25q = 1360}$ $\qquad n + 48 = 80$
$\qquad\qquad\qquad\qquad$ Add: $20q = 960$ $\qquad\qquad n = 32$
$\qquad\qquad\qquad\qquad\qquad\quad q = 48$

Thus, Sam has 32 nickels and 48 quarters.

CHECK: $32 + 48 \overset{\checkmark}{=} 80$

$\qquad\qquad 32(5) + 48(25) = 160 + 1200 \overset{\checkmark}{=} 1360$

5. Let x = speed of the slower car.
    Let y = speed of the faster car.

$\begin{cases} y = x + 15 \\ 5x + 5y = 275 \\ -x + y = 15 \\ 5x + 5y = 275 \end{cases}$ $\xrightarrow[\text{from both sides}]{\text{subtract } x}$ $\quad -x + y = 15$
$\xrightarrow{\text{as is}}$ $\quad 5x + 5y = 275$ $\qquad 35 = x + 15$
$\xrightarrow{\text{multiply by 5}}$ $\quad -5x + 5y = 75$ $\qquad 20 = x$
$\xrightarrow{\text{as is}}$ $\quad \underline{5x + 5y = 275}$
$\qquad\qquad\qquad\qquad$ Add: $10y = 350$
$\qquad\qquad\qquad\qquad\qquad\quad y = 35$

Thus, the speed of the slower car is 20 kph and the speed of the faster car is 35 kph.

CHECK: The difference of the speeds is 35 - 20 = 15 kph.
          The slower car travels 5(20) = 100 km and the faster car travels 5(35) = 175 km. The distance between the cars after 5 hours is 100 + 175 = 275 km.

7. Let x = amount of money that Carmen invested at 6%.
   Let y = amount of money that Carmen invested at 7%.

$$\begin{cases} x + y = 1700 \\ .06x + .07y = 110 \end{cases}$$

$\xrightarrow{\text{as is}}$ $x + y = 1700$

$\xrightarrow{\text{multiply by 100}}$ $6x + 7y = 11000$

$\begin{aligned} x + y &= 1700 \\ 6x + 7y &= 11000 \end{aligned}$

$\xrightarrow{\text{multiply by -6}}$ $-6x - 6y = -10200$

$\xrightarrow{\text{as is}}$ $\underline{6x + 7y = 11000}$

Add: $y = 800$

$x + y = 1700$

$x + 800 = 1700$

$x = 900$

Thus, Carmen invested \$900 at 6% and \$800 at 7%.

CHECK: $\$900 + \$800 \overset{\checkmark}{=} \$1700$

$.06(\$900) + .07(\$800) = \$54 + \$56 \overset{\checkmark}{=} \$110$

9. Let x = price of a cassette.
   Let y = price of an LP.

$$\begin{cases} 4x + 6y = 48.80 \\ 5x + 3y = 32.65 \end{cases}$$

$\xrightarrow{\text{as is}}$ $4x + 6y = 48.80$

$\xrightarrow{\text{multiply by -2}}$ $\underline{-10x - 6y = -65.30}$

Add: $-6x = -16.50$

$x = 2.75$

$4x + 6y = 48.80$

$4(2.75) + 6y = 48.80$

$11.00 + 6y = 48.80$

$6y = 37.80$

$y = 6.30$

Thus, a cassette costs \$2.75 and an LP costs \$6.30.

CHECK: $4(\$2.75) + 6(\$6.30) = \$11.00 + \$37.80 \overset{\checkmark}{=} \$48.80$

$5(\$2.75) + 3(\$6.30) = \$13.75 + \$18.90 \overset{\checkmark}{=} \$32.65$

11. Let L = length of the rectangle.
    Let W = width of the rectangle.

$L = 2W$

$2L + 2W = 28$

Substitute the value of L from the first equation into the second to get $2(2W) + 2W = 28$

$4W + 2W = 28$

$6W = 28$

$W = \dfrac{28}{6} = \dfrac{14}{3}$

So $L = 2W = 2\left(\dfrac{14}{3}\right) = \dfrac{28}{3}$.

Thus, the width of the rectangle is $\frac{14}{3}$ inches and the length is $\frac{28}{3}$ inches.

CHECK: $\frac{28}{3}$ is twice as large as $\frac{14}{3}$.   The perimeter of the rectangle is $2(\frac{28}{3}) + 2(\frac{14}{3}) = \frac{56}{3} + \frac{28}{3} = \frac{84}{3} = 28$, as required.

15.   Let x = larger number.
Let y = smaller number.
$$\frac{x}{y} = \frac{6}{5}$$
$$x - y = 8$$

Solve the second equation for x, obtaining $x = y + 8$.   Then substitute this result into the first equation:

$$\frac{y + 8}{y} = \frac{6}{5}$$

$$\frac{5\!\!\!/}{1} \cdot \frac{y + 8}{\cancel{y}_1} = \frac{\cancel{5}y}{1} \cdot \frac{6}{\cancel{5}_1}$$

$$5(y + 8) = 6y$$
$$5y + 40 = 6y$$
$$40 = y$$

Then $x = y + 8 = 40 + 8 = 48$.   Thus, the numbers are 48 and 40.

CHECK: $\frac{48}{40} = \frac{6\cancel{(8)}}{5\cancel{(8)}} \overset{\vee}{=} \frac{6}{5}$ and $48 - 40 \overset{\vee}{=} 8$.

19.   Let x = cost of a receiver.
Let y = cost of a turntable.

$8x + 4y = 2060$ $\xrightarrow{\text{multiply by 3}}$ $24x + 12y = 6180$

$5x + 6y = 1690$ $\xrightarrow{\text{multiply by -2}}$ $\underline{-10x - 12y = -3380}$

$\qquad\qquad\qquad\qquad\qquad\qquad$ Add: $14x = 2800$

$\qquad\qquad\qquad\qquad\qquad\qquad\qquad\quad x = 200$

$$8(200) + 4y = 2060$$
$$1600 + 4y = 2060$$
$$4y = 460$$
$$y = 115$$

Thus, a receiver costs $200 and a turntable costs $115.

CHECK: $8(\$200) + 4(\$115) = \$1600 + \$460 \overset{\vee}{=} \$2060$

$\qquad\qquad 5(\$200) + 6(\$115) = \$1000 + \$690 \overset{\vee}{=} \$1690$

23. Let x = # of $7 books bought.
     Let y = # of $9 books bought.

$x + y = 35$ $\xrightarrow{\text{multiply by -7}}$ $-7x - 7y = -245$

$7x + 9y = 271$ $\xrightarrow{\text{as is}}$ $7x + 9y = \underline{271}$

Add: $2y = 26$

$y = 13$

$x + y = 35$
$x + 13 = 35$
$x = 22$

Thus, the bookstore bought 22 books at $7 each and 13 books at $9 each.

CHECK: $22 + 13 \overset{\checkmark}{=} 35$

$22(\$7) + 13(\$9) = \$154 + \$117 \overset{\checkmark}{=} \$271$

27. Let p = speed (in mph) of the plane in still air.
     Let w = speed (in mph) of the wind.

$p + w = 150$ $p + w = 150$

$\underline{p - w = 90}$ $120 + w = 150$

Add: $2p = 240$ $w = 30$

$p = 120$

Thus, the speed of the plane in still air is 120 mph and the speed of the wind is 30 mph.

CHECK: With the tailwind, the speed of the plane is increased by the speed of the wind, giving 120 + 30 = 150. With the headwind, the speed of the plane is decreased by the speed of the wind, giving 120 - 30 = 90.

Chapter 8 Review Exercises

1, 3, 5.

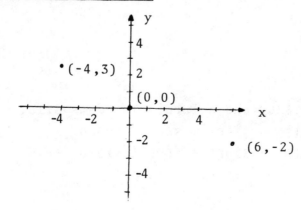

7. $2x + 4y = 14$
    $2(3) + 4y = 14$
      $6 + 4y = 14$
          $4y = 8$
           $y = 2$
Therefore, the ordered
pair is (3,2).

9. $x + 2y = 4$
   $x + 2(-3) = 4$
     $x - 6 = 4$
       $x = 10$
Therefore, the ordered
pair is (10,-3).

11. $x - y = 0$
  $(0) - y = 0$
    $0 - y = 0$
     $-y = 0$
      $y = 0$
Therefore, the ordered
pair is (0,0).

13. $x - y = 8$

x-intercept:
  $x - (0) = 8$
    $x - 0 = 8$
      $x = 8$
Plot (8,0)

y-intercept:
  $(0) - y = 8$
   $0 - y = 8$
    $-y = 8$
     $y = -8$
Plot (0,-8)

check point: choose $x = 4$
  $(4) - y = 8$
   $4 - y = 8$
    $-y = 4$
     $y = -4$
Plot (4,-4)

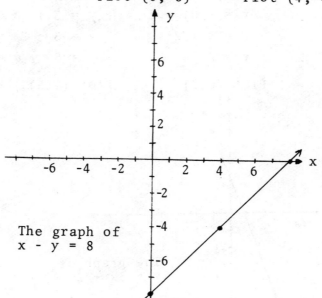

The graph of
$x - y = 8$

15.   3x + 7y = 21

   x-intercept: y-intercept: check point: choose y = 6

     3x + 7(0) = 21   3(0) + 7y = 21   3x + 7(6) = 21

       3x + 0 = 21   0 + 7y = 21   3x + 42 = 21

         3x = 21   7y = 21   3x = -21

          x = 7   y = 3   x = -7

  Plot (7,0)   Plot (0,3)   Plot (-7,6)

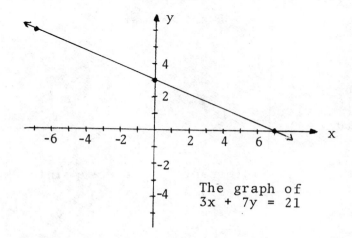

The graph of
3x + 7y = 21

17.   y = 3x + 2

   x-intercept: y-intercept: check point: choose x = 1

    0 = 3x + 2   y = 3(0) + 2   y = 3(1) + 2

   -2 = 3x   y = 0 + 2   y = 3 + 2

  $-\dfrac{2}{3}$ = x   y = 2   y = 5

  Plot $(-\dfrac{2}{3},0)$ Plot (0,2)   Plot (1,5)

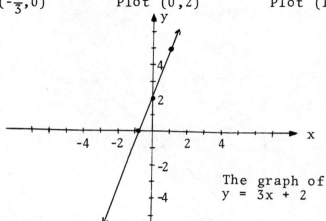

The graph of
y = 3x + 2

19.   x - 2y = 4

    x-intercept: y-intercept: check point: choose y = -1

      x - 2(0) = 4   (0) - 2y = 4   x - 2(-1) = 4

         x - 0 = 4   0 - 2y = 4   x + 2 = 4

            x = 4   -2y = 4   x = 2

    Plot (4,0)   y =-2   Plot (2,-1)

                   Plot (0,-2)

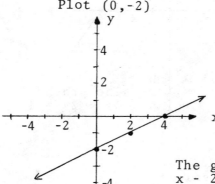

The graph of
x - 2y = 4

21.   x = 4

Its graph is a line parallel
to the y-axis and 4 units to
the right of it.

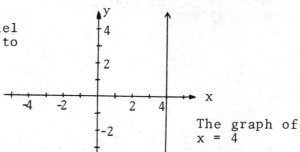

The graph of
x = 4

23.   3x + 2y = 12

    x-intercept: y-intercept: check point: choose x = 2

     3x + 2(0) = 12   3(0) + 2y = 12   3(2) + 2y = 12

       3x + 0 = 12   0 + 2y = 12   6 + 2y = 12

          3x = 12   2y = 12   2y = 6

           x = 4   y = 6   y = 3

    Plot (4,0)   Plot (0,6)   Plot (2,3)

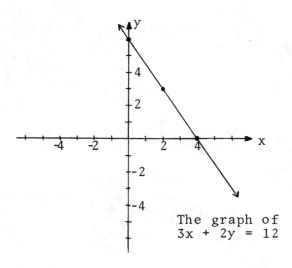

The graph of
3x + 2y = 12

25.   3y = 6

This equation is equivalent
to y = 2 (divide both sides
by 3), whose graph is a line
parallel to the x-axis and 2
units above it.

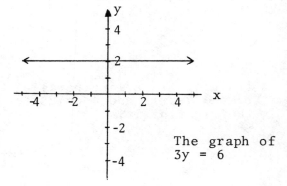

The graph of
3y = 6

27. $m = \dfrac{y_2 - y_1}{x_2 - x_1} = \dfrac{7 - 5}{1 - 2} = \dfrac{2}{-1} = -2$

29. $m = \dfrac{y_2 - y_1}{x_2 - x_1} = \dfrac{2 - (-2)}{3 - (-3)} = \dfrac{2 + 2}{3 + 3} = \dfrac{4}{6} = \dfrac{2}{3}$

31. $m = \dfrac{y_2 - y_1}{x_2 - x_1} = \dfrac{8 - 8}{-1 - 1} = \dfrac{0}{-2} = 0$

33. $(x_1, y_1) = (3,2)$, $m = 4$
       $y - y_1 = m(x - x_1)$
       $y - 2 = 4(x - 3)$ or $y = 4x - 10$

35. $m = \dfrac{y_2 - y_1}{x_2 - x_1} = \dfrac{0 - (-6)}{1 - 2} = \dfrac{0 + 6}{1 - 2} = \dfrac{6}{-1} = -6$

$(x_1, y_1) = (2, -6)$

$y - y_1 = m(x - x_1)$

$y - (-6) = -6(x - 2)$

$y + 6 = -6(x - 2)$ or $y = -6x + 6$

37.   All points on a horizontal line have the same y-coordinate. Since the point (3,8) is on our line, an equation for this horizontal line must be y = 8.

39.   x + y = 4

To find x-intercept, set y = 0 and solve for x. We get x = 4.
To find y-intercept, set x = 0 and solve for y. We get y = 4.

x - y = 0

Here, both the x and y intercepts are 0. To find a second point on this line, choose y = 1 and find x = 1. This gives (1,1).

The lines cross at the point
(2,2). So the system
$\{\begin{array}{l} x + y = 4 \\ x - y = 0 \end{array}$ is satisfied by the
point (2,2).

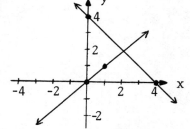

41.   x - 2y = 8

To find x-intercept, set y = 0 and solve for x. We get x = 8.
To find y-intercept, set x = 0 and solve for y. We get y = -4.

y = x - 5

To find x-intercept, set y = 0 and solve for x. We get x = 5.
To find y-intercept, set x = 0 and solve for y. We get y = -5.

The lines cross at the
point (2,-3). So the
system $\{\begin{array}{l} x - 2y = 8 \\ y = x - 5 \end{array}$ is
satisfied by the point
(2,-3).

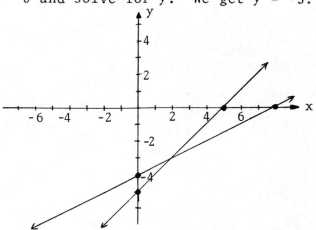

43. $\begin{cases} x + y = 4 \\ x - y = 6 \end{cases}$

Add: $2x = 10$

$x = 5$

$\begin{aligned} x + y &= 4 \\ 5 + y &= 4 \\ y &= -1 \end{aligned}$

CHECK: $\begin{aligned} x - y &= 6 \\ (5) - (-1) &\overset{?}{=} 6 \\ 5 + 1 &\overset{?}{=} 6 \\ 6 &\overset{\checkmark}{=} 6 \end{aligned}$

Solution: (5,-1)

45. $\begin{cases} x - 5y = 1 \\ 3x - 2y = 3 \end{cases}$ $\xrightarrow{\text{multiply by } -3}$ $\xrightarrow{\text{as is}}$

$\begin{aligned} -3x + 15y &= -3 \\ 3x - 2y &= 3 \end{aligned}$

Add: $13y = 0$

$y = 0$

$\begin{aligned} x - 5y &= 1 \\ x - 5(0) &= 1 \\ x - 0 &= 1 \\ x &= 1 \end{aligned}$

Solution: (1,0)

CHECK: $\begin{aligned} 3x - 2y &= 3 \\ 3(1) - 2(0) &\overset{?}{=} 3 \\ 3 - 0 &\overset{?}{=} 3 \\ 3 &\overset{\checkmark}{=} 3 \end{aligned}$

47. $\begin{cases} 4x - 3y = 10 \\ 9x + 2y = 5 \end{cases}$ $\xrightarrow{\text{multiply by } 2}$ $\xrightarrow{\text{multiply by } 3}$

$\begin{aligned} 8x - 6y &= 20 \\ 27x + 6y &= 15 \end{aligned}$

Add: $35x = 35$

$x = 1$

$\begin{aligned} 4x - 3y &= 10 \\ 4(1) - 3y &= 10 \\ 4 - 3y &= 10 \\ -3y &= 6 \\ y &= -2 \end{aligned}$

Solution: (1,-2)

CHECK: $\begin{aligned} 9x + 2y &= 5 \\ 9(1) + 2(-2) &\overset{?}{=} 5 \\ 9 + (-4) &\overset{?}{=} 5 \\ 9 - 4 &\overset{?}{=} 5 \\ 5 &\overset{\checkmark}{=} 5 \end{aligned}$

49. $\begin{cases} \dfrac{x}{2} + y = 5 \\ 2y = 8 - x \end{cases}$ $\xrightarrow{\text{multiply by } 2}$ $\xrightarrow[\text{to both sides}]{\text{add } x}$

$\begin{aligned} x + 2y &= 10 \\ x + 2y &= 8 \end{aligned}$

Subtract: $0 = 2$, a contradiction.

Therefore, the system of equations has no solution.

51. $\begin{cases} x + y - 8 = 2x - 4 \\ 2(y - x) = 8 \end{cases}$ $\xrightarrow[\text{from both sides}]{\text{subtract } 2x}$ $\xrightarrow[\text{sides by } 2]{\text{divide both}}$

$\begin{aligned} y - x - 8 &= -4 \\ \\ y - x &= 4 \end{aligned}$

$$\xrightarrow[\text{to both sides}]{\text{add 8}} \quad y - x = 4$$

$$\xrightarrow{\text{as is}} \qquad y - x = 4$$

Subtract: $0 = 0$, an identity.

Therefore, the system of equations has infinitely many solutions: $\{(x,y) \mid y - x = 4\}$.

53. Let x = # of gallons of pure water in the mixture.
     Let y = # of gallons of 30% alcohol solution in the mixture.

$$x + y = 30 \qquad \xrightarrow{\text{as is}} \qquad x + y = 30$$

$$0x + .30y = .25(30) \xrightarrow{\text{multiply by 100}} 30y = 750$$

From the second equation, find $y = 25$. Then $30 = x + y = x + 25$, so $x = 5$. Thus, 5 gallons of water should be added to 25 gallons of a 30% alcohol solution to produce 30 gallons of a 25% alcohol solution.

CHECK: $.30(25) = 7.5$ gallons of pure alcohol
        $.25(30) = 7.5$ gallons of pure alcohol

55. Let x = walking speed (in kph).
     Let y = jogging speed (in kph).

$$x + y = 17 \qquad \xrightarrow{\text{as is}} \qquad x + y = 17$$

$$2x + \tfrac{1}{2}y = 16 \xrightarrow{\text{multiply by -2}} -4x - y = -32$$

$$\text{Add: } -3x = -15$$

$$x = 5$$

$$x + y = 17$$
$$5 + y = 17$$
$$y = 12$$

Thus, their walking speed is 5 kph and their jogging speed is 12 kph.

CHECK: $1(5) + 1(12) \overset{\checkmark}{=} 17$

        $2(5) + \tfrac{1}{2}(12) = 10 + 6 \overset{\checkmark}{=} 16$

Chapter 8 Practice Test

1. $\dfrac{2y - x}{5} = x - y$

$\dfrac{2(-4) - (-3)}{5} \overset{?}{=} (-3) - (-4)$

$\dfrac{-8 + 3}{5} \overset{?}{=} -3 + 4$

$\dfrac{-5}{5} \overset{?}{=} 1$

$-1 \neq 1$

So the point $(-3,-4)$ does not satisfy the given equation.

3. (a) $3x - 5y = 15$

x-intercept:	y-intercept:	check point: choose x = -
$3x - 5(0) = 15$	$3(0) - 5y = 15$	$3(-5) - 5y = 15$
$3x - 0 = 15$	$0 - 5y = 15$	$-15 - 5y = 15$
$3x = 15$	$-5y = 15$	$-5y = 30$
$x = 5$	$y = -3$	$y = -6$
Plot $(5,0)$	Plot $(0,-3)$	Plot $(-5,-6)$

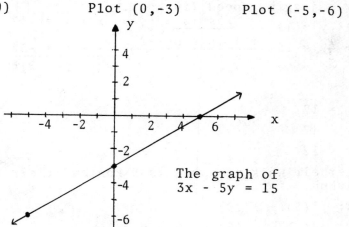

The graph of
$3x - 5y = 15$

(b) $y = 3x - 12$

x-intercept:	y-intercept:	check point: choose x = 2
$0 = 3x - 12$	$y = 3(0) - 12$	$y = 3(2) - 12$
$12 = 3x$	$y = 0 - 12$	$y = 6 - 12$
$4 = x$	$y = -12$	$y = -6$
Plot $(4,0)$	Plot $(0,-12)$	Plot $(2,-6)$

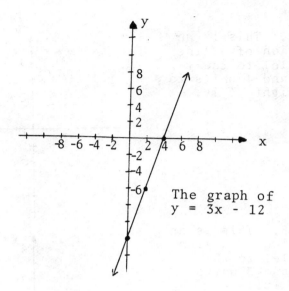

The graph of
y = 3x - 12

(c) y + 2x = 0

x-intercept:

0 + 2x = 0

2x = 0

x = 0

Plot (0,0)

(This implies
that y = 0 is
the y-intercept.)

second point:
choose x = 1

y + 2(1) = 0

y + 2 = 0

y = -2

Plot(1,-2)

check point:
choose x = -1

y + 2(-1) = 0

y - 2 = 0

y = 2

Plot (-1,2)

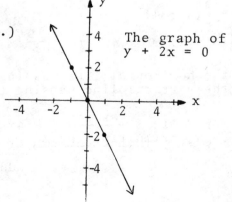

The graph of
y + 2x = 0

(d) x = 4. This is an
    equation of a line
    parallel to the y-
    axis and 4 units to
    the right of it.

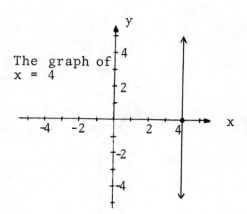

The graph of x = 4

(e) y = -3. This is an
    equation of a line
    parallel to the x-
    axis and 3 units
    below it.

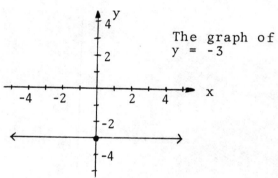

The graph of y = -3

5. $m = \frac{4}{3}$, $(x_1, y_1) = (4, -1)$

$y - y_1 = m(x - x_1)$

$y - (-1) = \frac{4}{3}(x - 4)$

$y + 1 = \frac{4}{3}(x - 4)$ or $y = \frac{4}{3}x - \frac{19}{3}$

7. y = 5 is the horizontal line passing through (3,5).
    x = 3 is the vertical line passing through (3,5).

9. (a) $\begin{cases} 4x - 3y = 11 \\ 3x + y = 5 \end{cases}$ $\xrightarrow{\text{as is}}$ $\xrightarrow{\text{multiply by 3}}$

$4x - 3y = 11$
$\underline{9x + 3y = 15}$
Add: $13x = 26$
$x = 2$

$4x - 3y = 11$
$4(2) - 3y = 11$
$8 - 3y = 11$
$-3y = 3$
$y = -1$

Solution: (2,-1)

CHECK: $3x + y = 5$

$3(2) + (-1) \overset{?}{=} 5$

$6 - 1 \overset{?}{=} 5$

$5 \overset{\checkmark}{=} 5$

(b) $2x - 7y = 4$ $\xrightarrow{\text{multiply by -5}}$ $-10x + 35y = -20$ $2x - 7y = 4$

$5x - 4y = 10$ $\xrightarrow{\text{multiply by 2}}$ $\underline{10x - 8y = 20}$ $2x - 7(0) = 4$

Add: $27y = 0$ $2x - 0 = 4$

$y = 0$ $2x = 4$

$x = 2$

Solution: (2,0)

CHECK: $5x - 4y = 10$

$5(2) - 4(0) \overset{?}{=} 10$

$10 - 0 \overset{?}{=} 10$

$10 \overset{\checkmark}{=} 10$

(c) $\dfrac{3x}{2} - y = 6$ $\xrightarrow{\text{multiply by 2}}$ $3x - 2y = 12$

$x - \dfrac{2y}{3} = 5$ $\xrightarrow{\text{multiply by 3}}$ $\underline{3x - 2y = 15}$

Subtract: $0 = -3$, a contradiction.

So the system has no solution.

Chapter 9

RADICAL EXPRESSIONS

Exercises 9.1

1. $\sqrt{4} = 2$ because $2 \cdot 2 = 4$ 3. $-\sqrt{4} = -2$

5. $\sqrt{-4}$ does not exist   11. $\sqrt{64} = 8$ because $8 \cdot 8 = 64$

15. $\sqrt{169} = 13$ because $13 \cdot 13 = 169$

19. $\sqrt{289} = 17$ because $17 \cdot 17 = 289$

23. $\sqrt{3}\sqrt{3} = 3$ 27. $(\sqrt{11})^2 = 11$

31. $\sqrt{x}\sqrt{x} = x$

35. $(\sqrt{7})^5 = \underbrace{\sqrt{7} \cdot \sqrt{7}} \cdot \underbrace{\sqrt{7} \cdot \sqrt{7}} \cdot \sqrt{7}$

$= \quad 7 \quad \cdot \quad 7 \quad \cdot \quad \sqrt{7} = 49\sqrt{7}$

37. $\sqrt{25 - 9} = \sqrt{16} = 4$

39. $\sqrt{25} - \sqrt{9} = 5 - 3 = 2$

41. $(\sqrt{25} - \sqrt{9})^2 = 2^2 = 4$

43. $(\sqrt{25 - 9})^2 = (\sqrt{16})^2 = 16$

45. $\sqrt{17} = 4.12$ correct to 1 place

$= 4.123$ correct to 2 places

$= 4.1231$ correct to 3 places

46. $\sqrt{23}$ = 4.80   correct to 1 place

        = 4.796   correct to 2 places

        = 4.7958   correct to 3 places

47. $\sqrt{110}$ = 10.49   correct to 1 place

          = 10.488   correct to 2 places

          = 10.4881   correct to 3 places

48. $\sqrt{260}$ = 16.12   correct to 1 place

          = 16.125   correct to 2 places

          = 16.1245   correct to 3 places

49. Since 20^2 = 400, 30^2 = 900, and 648 is between 400 and 900, $\sqrt{648}$ must be between 20 and 30. Consider the following table:

$$0^2 = \underline{0} \qquad\qquad 5^2 = 2\underline{5}$$
$$1^2 = \underline{1} \qquad\qquad 6^2 = 3\underline{6}$$
$$2^2 = \underline{4} \qquad\qquad 7^2 = 4\underline{9}$$
$$3^2 = \underline{9} \qquad\qquad 8^2 = 6\underline{4}$$
$$4^2 = 1\underline{6} \qquad\qquad 9^2 = 8\underline{1}$$

This implies that any perfect square must end in one of the digits underlined: 0, 1, 4, 9, 6, or 5. Therefore, any number that ends in either 2, 3, 7, or 8 cannot be a perfect square. So 648 cannot be a perfect square.

50. Using the same argument as in (49), $\sqrt{841}$ must be between 20 and 30. Since 841 ends in the digit 1, there are only two possibilities, if 841 is a perfect square: $(21)^2$ = 841 or $(29)^2$ = 841. Since 841 is closer to 900 than it is to 400, try $(29)^2$ first, since 29 is closer to 30 than it is to 20. Since 29 · 29 = 841, conclude that 841 <u>is</u> a perfect square, and that $\sqrt{841}$ = 29.

51. It is incorrect to claim that $\sqrt{1+1} = \sqrt{1} + \sqrt{1}$. In fact, if a and b are positive, it is <u>never</u> true that $\sqrt{a+b} = \sqrt{a} + \sqrt{b}$. That is, the square root of the sum of two positive numbers is never equal to the sum of the square roots of those numbers.

52. For any non-negative number a, $\sqrt{a}\sqrt{a}$ = a tells us that $\sqrt{a}$ is the non-negative quantity whose square is equal to a.

<u>Exercises 9.2</u>

3. $\sqrt{18} = \sqrt{9 \cdot 2} = \sqrt{9}\sqrt{2} = 3\sqrt{2}$

7. $\sqrt{50} = \sqrt{25 \cdot 2} = \sqrt{25}\sqrt{2} = 5\sqrt{2}$

11. $\sqrt{x^6} = x^3$, because $x^3 x^3 = x^6$

13. $\sqrt{x^7} = \sqrt{x^6 \cdot x} = \sqrt{x^6}\sqrt{x} = x^3\sqrt{x}$

15. $\sqrt{16x^{16}} = \sqrt{16}\sqrt{x^{16}} = 4x^8$

19. $\sqrt{40x^8} = \sqrt{4x^8}\sqrt{10} = \sqrt{4}\sqrt{x^8}\sqrt{10} = 2x^4\sqrt{10}$

23. $\sqrt{12x^5} = \sqrt{4x^4}\sqrt{3x} = \sqrt{4}\sqrt{x^4}\sqrt{3x} = 2x^2\sqrt{3x}$

27. $\sqrt{x^6 + y^8}$ cannot be simplified.

31. $\sqrt{28x^9y^6} = \sqrt{4x^8y^6}\sqrt{7x} = \sqrt{4}\sqrt{x^8}\sqrt{y^6}\sqrt{7x} = 2x^4y^3\sqrt{7x}$

37. $\sqrt{48x^6y^8z^9} = \sqrt{16x^6y^8z^8}\sqrt{3z} = \sqrt{16}\sqrt{x^6}\sqrt{y^8}\sqrt{z^8}\sqrt{3z} = 4x^3y^4z^4\sqrt{3z}$

39. $\sqrt{\dfrac{4}{9}} = \dfrac{\sqrt{4}}{\sqrt{9}} = \dfrac{2}{3}$

41. $\sqrt{\dfrac{7}{25}} = \dfrac{\sqrt{7}}{\sqrt{25}} = \dfrac{\sqrt{7}}{5}$

43. $\sqrt{\dfrac{5}{6}} = \dfrac{\sqrt{5}}{\sqrt{6}} = \dfrac{\sqrt{5} \cdot \sqrt{6}}{\sqrt{6} \cdot \sqrt{6}} = \dfrac{\sqrt{30}}{6}$

47. $\dfrac{1}{\sqrt{2}} = \dfrac{1 \cdot \sqrt{2}}{\sqrt{2} \cdot \sqrt{2}} = \dfrac{\sqrt{2}}{2}$

49. $\dfrac{18}{\sqrt{10}} = \dfrac{18 \cdot \sqrt{10}}{\sqrt{10} \cdot \sqrt{10}} = \dfrac{\overset{9}{\cancel{18}}\sqrt{10}}{\underset{5}{\cancel{10}}} = \dfrac{9\sqrt{10}}{5}$

53. $\dfrac{15}{2\sqrt{7}} = \dfrac{15 \cdot \sqrt{7}}{2\sqrt{7} \cdot \sqrt{7}} = \dfrac{15\sqrt{7}}{2 \cdot 7} = \dfrac{15\sqrt{7}}{14}$

57. $\dfrac{8x}{\sqrt{2x}} = \dfrac{8x\sqrt{2x}}{\sqrt{2x}\sqrt{2x}} = \dfrac{\overset{4}{\cancel{8x}}\sqrt{2x}}{\underset{1}{\cancel{2x}}} = 4\sqrt{2x}$

61. $\dfrac{x^2}{\sqrt{xy}} = \dfrac{x^2\sqrt{xy}}{\sqrt{xy}\sqrt{xy}} = \dfrac{\overset{x}{\cancel{x^2}}\sqrt{xy}}{\cancel{xy}} = \dfrac{x\sqrt{xy}}{y}$

63. $\dfrac{\sqrt{8}}{\sqrt{6}} = \dfrac{\sqrt{8} \cdot \sqrt{6}}{\sqrt{6} \cdot \sqrt{6}} = \dfrac{\sqrt{48}}{6} = \dfrac{\sqrt{16}\sqrt{3}}{6} = \dfrac{\overset{2}{\cancel{4}}\sqrt{3}}{\underset{3}{\cancel{6}}} = \dfrac{2\sqrt{3}}{3}$

65. When we square a real number other than 0 or 1, we get an answer that is different from the original number. So it

is incorrect to say that $\dfrac{2}{\sqrt{5}} = \dfrac{2^2}{(\sqrt{5})^2}$. When we rationalize the denominator properly, we multiply $\dfrac{2}{\sqrt{5}}$ by $\dfrac{\sqrt{5}}{\sqrt{5}}$. This means that we multiply by 1, which does <u>not</u> change the value of the original number.

66. $\dfrac{1}{\sqrt{5}} = \dfrac{1 \cdot \sqrt{5}}{\sqrt{5} \cdot \sqrt{5}} = \dfrac{\sqrt{5}}{5}$

$\dfrac{1}{\sqrt{5}} = \dfrac{1}{2.2360} = .4472$ correct to 3 places

$\dfrac{\sqrt{5}}{5} = \dfrac{2.2360}{5} = .4472$ correct to 3 places

It is easier to compute $\dfrac{\sqrt{5}}{5}$ than to compute $\dfrac{1}{\sqrt{5}}$, since $\dfrac{1}{\sqrt{5}}$ involves division by a decimal quantity, whereas $\dfrac{\sqrt{5}}{5}$ does not.

67. $\dfrac{\sqrt{3}}{\sqrt{7}} = \dfrac{1.7321}{2.6458} = .6547$ correct to 3 places

$\dfrac{\sqrt{3}}{\sqrt{7}} = \dfrac{\sqrt{3} \cdot \sqrt{7}}{\sqrt{7} \cdot \sqrt{7}} = \dfrac{\sqrt{21}}{7} = \dfrac{4.5828}{7} = .6547$ correct to 3 places

Exercises 9.3

3. $\sqrt{5} + 2\sqrt{5} + 3\sqrt{5} = (1 + 2 + 3)\sqrt{5} = 6\sqrt{5}$

7. $4\sqrt{6} - \sqrt{6} = (4 - 1)\sqrt{6} = 3\sqrt{6}$

11. $3\sqrt{5} + 5\sqrt{3}$ cannot be simplified.

15. $\sqrt{5}\sqrt{5} = 5$

19. $\sqrt{5} + \sqrt{5} = 2\sqrt{5}$

21. $\sqrt{5} + 3\sqrt{7} - 4\sqrt{5} - 5\sqrt{7} = \sqrt{5} - 4\sqrt{5} + 3\sqrt{7} - 5\sqrt{7} = -3\sqrt{5} - 2\sqrt{7}$

27. $2(\sqrt{5} - \sqrt{3}) + 3(\sqrt{3} - \sqrt{5}) = 2\sqrt{5} - 2\sqrt{3} + 3\sqrt{3} - 3\sqrt{5}$
$= 2\sqrt{5} - 3\sqrt{5} - 2\sqrt{3} + 3\sqrt{3}$
$= -\sqrt{5} + \sqrt{3}$

31. $6(\sqrt{m} - \sqrt{n}) - (3\sqrt{m} + 6\sqrt{n}) = 6\sqrt{m} - 6\sqrt{n} - 3\sqrt{m} - 6\sqrt{n}$
$= 6\sqrt{m} - 3\sqrt{m} - 6\sqrt{n} - 6\sqrt{n} = 3\sqrt{m}\ 12\sqrt{n}$

33. $\sqrt{8} + \sqrt{18} = \sqrt{4}\sqrt{2} + \sqrt{9}\sqrt{2} = 2\sqrt{2} + 3\sqrt{2} = 5\sqrt{2}$

35. $\sqrt{25} + \sqrt{24} = 5 + \sqrt{4}\sqrt{6} = 5 + 2\sqrt{6}$

39. $4\sqrt{12} - \sqrt{75} = 4\sqrt{4}\sqrt{3} - \sqrt{25}\sqrt{3} = 4(2\sqrt{3}) - 5\sqrt{3} = 8\sqrt{3} - 5\sqrt{3} = 3\sqrt{3}$

43. $3\sqrt{72} - 5\sqrt{32} = 3(\sqrt{36}\sqrt{2}) - 5(\sqrt{16}\sqrt{2}) = 3(6\sqrt{2}) - 5(4\sqrt{2})$
$$= 18\sqrt{2} - 20\sqrt{2} = -2\sqrt{2}$$

45. $5\sqrt{36} + 4\sqrt{30} = 5 \cdot 6 + 4\sqrt{30} = 30 + 4\sqrt{30}$

49. $\sqrt{12w} + \sqrt{27w} = \sqrt{4}\sqrt{3w} + \sqrt{9}\sqrt{3w} = 2\sqrt{3w} + 3\sqrt{3w} = 5\sqrt{3w}$

53. $\sqrt{20y^3} - \sqrt{45y^3} = \sqrt{4y^2}\sqrt{5y} - \sqrt{9y^2}\sqrt{5y} = 2y\sqrt{5y} - 3y\sqrt{5y} = -y\sqrt{5y}$

55. $x\sqrt{28xy^3} + y\sqrt{63x^3y} = x\sqrt{4y^2}\sqrt{7xy} + y\sqrt{9x^2}\sqrt{7xy}$
$$= x(2y)\sqrt{7xy} + y(3x)\sqrt{7xy}$$
$$= 2xy\sqrt{7xy} + 3xy\sqrt{7xy}$$
$$= 5xy\sqrt{7xy}$$

57. $\dfrac{\sqrt{32x^3y^2}}{2xy} - \sqrt{8x} = \dfrac{\sqrt{16x^2y^2}\sqrt{2x}}{2xy} - \sqrt{4}\sqrt{2x} = \dfrac{\overset{2}{\cancel{4xy}}\sqrt{2x}}{\cancel{2xy}} - 2\sqrt{2x}$
$$= 2\sqrt{2x} - 2\sqrt{2x} = 0$$

61. $\sqrt{27} + \dfrac{4}{\sqrt{3}} = \sqrt{9}\sqrt{3} + \dfrac{4 \cdot \sqrt{3}}{\sqrt{3} \cdot \sqrt{3}} = 3\sqrt{3} + \dfrac{4}{3}\sqrt{3} = \left(3 + \dfrac{4}{3}\right)\sqrt{3} = \dfrac{13}{3}\sqrt{3}$

65. $\sqrt{\dfrac{2}{7}} + \sqrt{\dfrac{7}{2}} = \dfrac{\sqrt{2}}{\sqrt{7}} + \dfrac{\sqrt{7}}{\sqrt{2}} = \dfrac{\sqrt{2} \cdot \sqrt{7}}{\sqrt{7} \cdot \sqrt{7}} + \dfrac{\sqrt{7} \cdot \sqrt{2}}{\sqrt{2} \cdot \sqrt{2}} = \dfrac{\sqrt{14}}{7} + \dfrac{\sqrt{14}}{2}$
$$= \dfrac{1}{7}\sqrt{14} + \dfrac{1}{2}\sqrt{14} = \left(\dfrac{1}{7} + \dfrac{1}{2}\right)\sqrt{14} = \dfrac{9}{14}\sqrt{14}$$

67. $\sqrt{80} = \sqrt{16 \cdot 5} = \sqrt{16}\sqrt{5} = 4\sqrt{5}$

   $\sqrt{80} = 8.9442719$

   $4\sqrt{5} = 4(2.2360679) = 8.9442716$

   The two results are the same, to 6 places. These results should be equal, and only appear to differ because of rounding off.

68. $\sqrt{150} = \sqrt{25 \cdot 6} = \sqrt{25}\sqrt{6} = 5\sqrt{6}$

   $\sqrt{150} = 12.247448$

   $5\sqrt{6} = 5(2.4494897) = 12.247448$

Exercises 9.4

3. $\sqrt{3}\sqrt{5}\sqrt{13} = \sqrt{3 \cdot 5 \cdot 13} = \sqrt{195}$

7. $\sqrt{6}\sqrt{24} = \sqrt{6}(\sqrt{4}\sqrt{6}) = \sqrt{6}(2\sqrt{6}) = 2(\sqrt{6}\sqrt{6}) = 2 \cdot 6 = 12$

11. $\sqrt{3}(\sqrt{5} + \sqrt{6}) = \sqrt{3}\sqrt{5} + \sqrt{3}\sqrt{6} = \sqrt{15} + \sqrt{18} = \sqrt{15} + \sqrt{9}\sqrt{2} = \sqrt{15} + 3\sqrt{2}$

15. $\sqrt{3}(2\sqrt{3} - 3\sqrt{2}) = \sqrt{3}(2\sqrt{3}) - \sqrt{3}(3\sqrt{2}) = 2(\sqrt{3}\sqrt{3}) - 3(\sqrt{3}\sqrt{2})$
$$= 2 \cdot 3 - 3\sqrt{6} = 6 - 3\sqrt{6}$$

19. $3\sqrt{2}(\sqrt{2} - 4) + \sqrt{2}(5 - \sqrt{2}) = 3\sqrt{2}(\sqrt{2}) - 3\sqrt{2}(4) + \sqrt{2}(5) - \sqrt{2}\sqrt{2}$
$$= 3(\sqrt{2}\sqrt{2}) - 3 \cdot 4\sqrt{2} + 5\sqrt{2} - 2$$
$$= 3 \cdot 2 - 12\sqrt{2} + 5\sqrt{2} - 2$$
$$= 6 - 12\sqrt{2} + 5\sqrt{2} - 2$$
$$= 4 - 7\sqrt{2}$$

21. $4\sqrt{x}(\sqrt{x} - \sqrt{2}) - \sqrt{x}(3\sqrt{x} - 2\sqrt{2}) = 4\sqrt{x}\sqrt{x} - 4\sqrt{x}\sqrt{2} - 3\sqrt{x}\sqrt{x} + 2\sqrt{x}\sqrt{2}$
$$= 4x - 4\sqrt{2x} - 3x + 2\sqrt{2x}$$
$$= x - 2\sqrt{2x}$$

25. $(\sqrt{x} + \sqrt{3})^2 = (\sqrt{x} + \sqrt{3})(\sqrt{x} + \sqrt{3}) = \sqrt{x}\sqrt{x} + \sqrt{x}\sqrt{3} + \sqrt{3}\sqrt{x} + \sqrt{3}\sqrt{3}$
$$= x + \sqrt{3x} + \sqrt{3x} + 3$$
$$= x + 2\sqrt{3x} + 3$$

27. $(\sqrt{x} + \sqrt{3})(\sqrt{x} - \sqrt{3}) = \sqrt{x}\sqrt{x} - \sqrt{x}\sqrt{3} + \sqrt{3}\sqrt{x} - \sqrt{3}\sqrt{3}$
$$= x - \sqrt{3x} + \sqrt{3x} - 3 = x - 3$$

29. $(3\sqrt{2} - 2\sqrt{5})^2 = (3\sqrt{2} - 2\sqrt{5})(3\sqrt{2} - 2\sqrt{5})$
$$= (3\sqrt{2})(3\sqrt{2}) - (3\sqrt{2})(2\sqrt{5}) - (2\sqrt{5})(3\sqrt{2}) + (2\sqrt{5})(2\sqrt{5})$$
$$= 3 \cdot 3\sqrt{2}\sqrt{2} - 3 \cdot 2\sqrt{2}\sqrt{5} - 2 \cdot 3\sqrt{5}\sqrt{2} + 2 \cdot 2\sqrt{5}\sqrt{5}$$
$$= 9 \cdot 2 - 6\sqrt{10} - 6\sqrt{10} + 4 \cdot 5$$
$$= 18 - 6\sqrt{10} - 6\sqrt{10} + 20$$
$$= 38 - 12\sqrt{10}$$

35. $(\sqrt{28} - \sqrt{24})(\sqrt{7} - \sqrt{6}) = (\sqrt{4}\sqrt{7} - \sqrt{4}\sqrt{6})(\sqrt{7} - \sqrt{6})$
$$= (2\sqrt{7} - 2\sqrt{6})(\sqrt{7} - \sqrt{6})$$
$$= 2\sqrt{7}\sqrt{7} - 2\sqrt{7}\sqrt{6} - 2\sqrt{6}\sqrt{7} + 2\sqrt{6}\sqrt{6}$$
$$= 2 \cdot 7 - 2\sqrt{42} - 2\sqrt{42} + 2 \cdot 6$$
$$= 14 - 2\sqrt{42} - 2\sqrt{42} + 12$$
$$= 26 - 4\sqrt{42}$$

39. $(\sqrt{x} + 2)^2 - (\sqrt{x + 2})^2 = (\sqrt{x} + 2)(\sqrt{x} + 2) - (x + 2)$

$\qquad\qquad\qquad\qquad\quad = \sqrt{x}\sqrt{x} + 2\sqrt{x} + 2\sqrt{x} + 4 - (x + 2)$

$\qquad\qquad\qquad\qquad\quad = x + 2\sqrt{x} + 2\sqrt{x} + 4 - x - 2$

$\qquad\qquad\qquad\qquad\quad = 4\sqrt{x} + 2$

43. $\dfrac{\sqrt{54}}{\sqrt{3}} = \sqrt{\dfrac{54}{3}} = \sqrt{18} = \sqrt{9}\sqrt{2} = 3\sqrt{2}$

47. $\dfrac{\sqrt{a^2b^5}}{\sqrt{ab^8}} = \sqrt{\dfrac{a^2b^5}{ab^8}} = \sqrt{\dfrac{a}{b^3}} = \dfrac{\sqrt{a}}{\sqrt{b^3}} = \dfrac{\sqrt{a}}{\sqrt{b^2}\sqrt{b}} = \dfrac{\sqrt{a}}{b\sqrt{b}} = \dfrac{\sqrt{a} \cdot \sqrt{b}}{b\sqrt{b} \cdot \sqrt{b}} = \dfrac{\sqrt{ab}}{b \cdot b} = \dfrac{\sqrt{ab}}{b}$

49. $\dfrac{10}{4 - \sqrt{11}} = \dfrac{10(4 + \sqrt{11})}{(4 - \sqrt{11})(4 + \sqrt{11})} = \dfrac{10(4 + \sqrt{11})}{16 - 11} = \dfrac{\overset{2}{\cancel{10}}(4 + \sqrt{11})}{\cancel{5}}$

$\qquad\qquad\qquad\qquad\qquad\qquad\qquad\quad = 2(4 + \sqrt{11})$

53. $\dfrac{\sqrt{3}}{2 + \sqrt{3}} = \dfrac{\sqrt{3}(2 - \sqrt{3})}{(2 + \sqrt{3})(2 - \sqrt{3})} = \dfrac{2\sqrt{3} - \sqrt{3}\sqrt{3}}{4 - 3} = \dfrac{2\sqrt{3} - 3}{1} = 2\sqrt{3} - 3$

55. $\dfrac{\sqrt{5} + \sqrt{3}}{\sqrt{5} - \sqrt{3}} = \dfrac{(\sqrt{5} + \sqrt{3})(\sqrt{5} + \sqrt{3})}{(\sqrt{5} - \sqrt{3})(\sqrt{5} + \sqrt{3})} = \dfrac{\sqrt{5}\sqrt{5} + \sqrt{5}\sqrt{3} + \sqrt{3}\sqrt{5} + \sqrt{3}\sqrt{3}}{5 - 3}$

$\qquad\qquad\quad = \dfrac{5 + \sqrt{15} + \sqrt{15} + 3}{5 - 3} = \dfrac{8 + 2\sqrt{15}}{2} = \dfrac{\cancel{2}(4 + \sqrt{15})}{\cancel{2}_1} = 4 + \sqrt{15}$

59. $\dfrac{6}{3 - \sqrt{7}} - \dfrac{21}{\sqrt{7}} = \dfrac{6(3 + \sqrt{7})}{(3 - \sqrt{7})(3 + \sqrt{7})} - \dfrac{21\sqrt{7}}{\sqrt{7}\sqrt{7}} = \dfrac{18 + 6\sqrt{7}}{9 - 7} - \dfrac{21\sqrt{7}}{7}$

$\qquad\qquad\qquad = \dfrac{\overset{3}{\cancel{6}}(3 + \sqrt{7})}{\cancel{2}_1} - \dfrac{\overset{3}{\cancel{21}}\sqrt{7}}{\cancel{7}_1} = 9 + 3\sqrt{7} - 3\sqrt{7} = 9$

61. $(3 + \sqrt{5})^2 + \dfrac{8}{3 - \sqrt{5}} = (3 + \sqrt{5})(3 + \sqrt{5}) + \dfrac{8(3 + \sqrt{5})}{(3 - \sqrt{5})(3 + \sqrt{5})}$

$\qquad\qquad\qquad\qquad = 9 + 3\sqrt{5} + 3\sqrt{5} + 5 + \dfrac{24 + 8\sqrt{5}}{9 - 5}$

$\qquad\qquad\qquad\qquad = 14 + 6\sqrt{5} + \dfrac{\overset{2}{\cancel{8}}(3 + \sqrt{5})}{\cancel{4}_1}$

$\qquad\qquad\qquad\qquad = 14 + 6\sqrt{5} + 6 + 2\sqrt{5}$

$\qquad\qquad\qquad\qquad = 20 + 8\sqrt{5}$

65. $\dfrac{12 - \sqrt{20}}{10} = \dfrac{12 - \sqrt{4}\sqrt{5}}{10} = \dfrac{12 - 2\sqrt{5}}{10} = \dfrac{2(6 - \sqrt{5})}{\cancel{10}\,5} = \dfrac{6 - \sqrt{5}}{5}$

67. $(2 + \sqrt{10})^2 - 4(2 + \sqrt{10}) - 6 = (2 + \sqrt{10})(2 + \sqrt{10}) - 4(2 + \sqrt{10}) - 6$

$\qquad\qquad\qquad\qquad\qquad\quad = 4 + 2\sqrt{10} + 2\sqrt{10} + 10 - 8 - 4\sqrt{10} - 6$

$\qquad\qquad\qquad\qquad\qquad\quad = 0$

69. (a) The "2" in the numerator is under the square root and is thus $\sqrt{2}$. This cannot be cancelled with the "2" in the denominator.

   (b) The cancellation is not valid since 2 is not a common factor of the numerator. Remember that terms cannot be cancelled.

Chapter 9 Review Exercises

1. $\sqrt{49} = 7$

3. $\sqrt{-16}$ does not exist

5. $\sqrt{96} = \sqrt{16 \cdot 6} = \sqrt{16}\sqrt{6} = 4\sqrt{6}$

7. $\sqrt{9x^9} = \sqrt{9x^8}\sqrt{x} = \sqrt{9}\sqrt{x^8}\sqrt{x} = 3x^4\sqrt{x}$

9. $\sqrt{\dfrac{4}{9}} = \dfrac{\sqrt{4}}{\sqrt{9}} = \dfrac{2}{3}$

11. $\sqrt{\dfrac{3}{5}} = \dfrac{\sqrt{3}}{\sqrt{5}} = \dfrac{\sqrt{3}\sqrt{5}}{\sqrt{5}\sqrt{5}} = \dfrac{\sqrt{15}}{5}$

13. $8\sqrt{7} - 5\sqrt{7} - \sqrt{7} = (8 - 5 - 1)\sqrt{7} = 2\sqrt{7}$

15. $\sqrt{45} - \sqrt{20} = \sqrt{9}\sqrt{5} - \sqrt{4}\sqrt{5} = 3\sqrt{5} - 2\sqrt{5} = \sqrt{5}$

17. $\sqrt{75x} + \sqrt{12x} = \sqrt{25}\sqrt{3x} + \sqrt{4}\sqrt{3x} = 5\sqrt{3x} + 2\sqrt{3x} = 7\sqrt{3x}$

19. $\dfrac{\sqrt{12x^3y^2}}{xy} + \sqrt{27x} = \dfrac{\sqrt{4x^2y^2}\sqrt{3x}}{xy} + \sqrt{9}\sqrt{3x} = \dfrac{2\cancel{xy}\sqrt{3x}}{\cancel{xy}\,1} + 3\sqrt{3x}$

$\qquad\qquad\qquad = 2\sqrt{3x} + 3\sqrt{3x} = 5\sqrt{3x}$

21. $\sqrt{5}(3\sqrt{5} + \sqrt{2}) = 3\sqrt{5}\sqrt{5} + \sqrt{5}\sqrt{2} = 3 \cdot 5 + \sqrt{10} = 15 + \sqrt{10}$

23. $(3\sqrt{7} - 2\sqrt{3})(2\sqrt{7} + 5\sqrt{3}) = (3\sqrt{7})(2\sqrt{7}) + (3\sqrt{7})(5\sqrt{3})$

$- (2\sqrt{3})(2\sqrt{7}) - (2\sqrt{3})(5\sqrt{3})$

$= 3 \cdot 2\sqrt{7}\sqrt{7} + 3 \cdot 5\sqrt{7}\sqrt{3} - 2 \cdot 2\sqrt{3}\sqrt{7}$

$- 2 \cdot 5\sqrt{3}\sqrt{3}$

$= 6 \cdot 7 + 15\sqrt{21} - 4\sqrt{21} - 10 \cdot 3$

$= 42 + 15\sqrt{21} - 4\sqrt{21} - 30$

$= 12 + 11\sqrt{21}$

25. $(\sqrt{x} - 3)^2 = (\sqrt{x} - 3)(\sqrt{x} - 3) = \sqrt{x}\sqrt{x} - 3\sqrt{x} - 3\sqrt{x} + 9$

$= x - 6\sqrt{x} + 9$

27. $\dfrac{7}{\sqrt{3}} = \dfrac{7\sqrt{3}}{\sqrt{3}\sqrt{3}} = \dfrac{7\sqrt{3}}{3}$

29. $\dfrac{x^2}{\sqrt{x}} = \dfrac{x^2\sqrt{x}}{\sqrt{x}\sqrt{x}} = \dfrac{x^{2}\!\!\!\!\diagup\,\sqrt{x}}{\diagup\!\!\!\!x} = x\sqrt{x}$

31. $\dfrac{18}{\sqrt{12}} = \dfrac{18}{\sqrt{4}\sqrt{3}} = \dfrac{\overset{9}{\cancel{18}}}{\cancel{2}\sqrt{3}} = \dfrac{9}{\sqrt{3}} = \dfrac{9\sqrt{3}}{\sqrt{3}\sqrt{3}} = \dfrac{\overset{3}{\cancel{9}}\sqrt{3}}{\cancel{3}_{1}} = 3\sqrt{3}$

33. $\dfrac{14}{3 - \sqrt{2}} = \dfrac{14(3 + \sqrt{2})}{(3 - \sqrt{2})(3 + \sqrt{2})} = \dfrac{14(3 + \sqrt{2})}{9 - 2} = \dfrac{\overset{2}{\cancel{14}}(3 + \sqrt{2})}{\cancel{7}_{1}} = 2(3 + \sqrt{2})$

35. $\dfrac{2 + \sqrt{5}}{6 + \sqrt{5}} = \dfrac{(2 + \sqrt{5})(6 - \sqrt{5})}{(6 + \sqrt{5})(6 - \sqrt{5})} = \dfrac{12 - 2\sqrt{5} + 6\sqrt{5} - 5}{36 - 5} = \dfrac{7 + 4\sqrt{5}}{31}$

37. $(\sqrt{x + 7})^2 - (\sqrt{x} + \sqrt{7})^2 = x + 7 - (\sqrt{x} + \sqrt{7})(\sqrt{x} + \sqrt{7})$

$= x + 7 - (x + \sqrt{x}\sqrt{7} + \sqrt{7}\sqrt{x} + 7)$

$= x + 7 - (x + \sqrt{7x} + \sqrt{7x} + 7)$

$= x + 7 - x - \sqrt{7x} - \sqrt{7x} - 7$

$= -2\sqrt{7x}$

Chapter 9 Practice Test

1. $\sqrt{25x^{16}y^6} = \sqrt{25}\sqrt{x^{16}}\sqrt{y^6} = 5x^8y^3$

3. $\sqrt{50x} - x\sqrt{32x} = \sqrt{25x^2}\sqrt{2x} - x(\sqrt{16}\sqrt{2x}) = 5x\sqrt{2x} - x(4\sqrt{2x})$

$= 5x\sqrt{2x} - 4x\sqrt{2x} = x\sqrt{2x}$

5. $\sqrt{20x^8y^9} + 3x^4y^4\sqrt{5y} = \sqrt{4x^8y^8}\sqrt{5y} + 3x^4y^4\sqrt{5y}$

$= 2x^4y^4\sqrt{5y} + 3x^4y^4\sqrt{5y} = 5x^4y^4\sqrt{5y}$

7. $(2\sqrt{x} - \sqrt{5})(\sqrt{x} + 3\sqrt{5}) = 2\sqrt{x}\sqrt{x} + (2\sqrt{x})(3\sqrt{5}) - \sqrt{5}\sqrt{x} - 3\sqrt{5}\sqrt{5}$

$$= 2x + 6\sqrt{5x} - \sqrt{5x} - 3 \cdot 5$$

$$= 2x + 5\sqrt{5x} - 15$$

9. $(\sqrt{x} - 4)^2 - (\sqrt{x - 4})^2 = (\sqrt{x} - 4)(\sqrt{x} - 4) - (x - 4)$

$$= \sqrt{x}\sqrt{x} - 4\sqrt{x} - 4\sqrt{x} + 16 - x + 4$$

$$= x - 8\sqrt{x} + 16 - x + 4$$

$$= -8\sqrt{x} + 20$$

11. $x^2 - 2x = 1$

$(1 - \sqrt{2})^2 - 2(1 - \sqrt{2}) \overset{?}{=} 1$

$(1 - \sqrt{2})(1 - \sqrt{2}) - 2(1 - \sqrt{2}) \overset{?}{=} 1$

$1 - \sqrt{2} - \sqrt{2} + 2 - 2 + 2\sqrt{2} \overset{?}{=} 1$

$$1 \overset{\checkmark}{=} 1$$

So $1 - \sqrt{2}$ is a solution to the equation.

Cumulative Review: Chapters 7-9

1. $\sqrt{36x^{16}y^{12}} = \sqrt{36}\sqrt{x^{16}}\sqrt{y^{12}} = 6x^8y^6$

3. $\dfrac{t^2 - 5t + 6}{t^2 - 6t + 9} = \dfrac{(t - 2)(t - 3)}{(t - 3)(t - 3)} = \dfrac{t - 2}{t - 3}$

5. $\dfrac{7}{\sqrt{6}} = \dfrac{7\sqrt{6}}{\sqrt{6}\sqrt{6}} = \dfrac{7\sqrt{6}}{6}$

7. $\dfrac{20}{3 - \sqrt{5}} = \dfrac{20(3 + \sqrt{5})}{(3 - \sqrt{5})(3 + \sqrt{5})} = \dfrac{20(3 + \sqrt{5})}{9 - 5} = \dfrac{\overset{5}{\cancel{20}}(3 + \sqrt{5})}{\underset{1}{\cancel{4}}} = 5(3 + \sqrt{5})$

9. $\sqrt{120} = \sqrt{4}\sqrt{30} = 2\sqrt{30}$

11. $\dfrac{3}{4x} + \dfrac{5}{x + 4} = \dfrac{3(x + 4)}{4x(x + 4)} + \dfrac{5(4x)}{(x + 4)(4x)} = \dfrac{3x + 12}{4x(x + 4)} + \dfrac{20x}{4x(x + 4)}$

$$= \dfrac{3x + 12 + 20x}{4x(x + 4)} = \dfrac{23x + 12}{4x(x + 4)}$$

13. $\dfrac{5}{6xy^3} - \dfrac{7}{4x^2} = \dfrac{5(2x)}{6xy^3(2x)} - \dfrac{7(3y^3)}{4x^2(3y^3)} = \dfrac{10x}{12x^2y^3} - \dfrac{21y^3}{12x^2y^3} = \dfrac{10x - 21y^3}{12x^2y^3}$

15. $\sqrt{\dfrac{3}{7}} + \sqrt{21} = \dfrac{\sqrt{3}}{\sqrt{7}} + \sqrt{21} = \dfrac{\sqrt{3}\sqrt{7}}{\sqrt{7}\sqrt{7}} + \sqrt{21} = \dfrac{\sqrt{21}}{7} + \sqrt{21} = (\dfrac{1}{7} + 1)\sqrt{21} = \dfrac{8}{7}\sqrt{21}$

17. $(2\sqrt{x} - 3)(\sqrt{x} + 5) = 2\sqrt{x}\sqrt{x} + 5(2\sqrt{x}) - 3\sqrt{x} - 15$

$= 2x + 10\sqrt{x} - 3\sqrt{x} - 15$

$= 2x + 7\sqrt{x} - 15$

19. $\dfrac{6}{x^2 + 2x} - \dfrac{4}{x^2 - 2x} = \dfrac{6}{x(x + 2)} - \dfrac{4}{x(x - 2)}$

$= \dfrac{6(x - 2)}{x(x + 2)(x - 2)} - \dfrac{4(x + 2)}{x(x - 2)(x + 2)}$

$= \dfrac{6x - 12}{x(x + 2)(x - 2)} - \dfrac{4x + 8}{x(x + 2)(x - 2)}$

$= \dfrac{6x - 12 - (4x + 8)}{x(x + 2)(x - 2)}$

$= \dfrac{6x - 12 - 4x - 8}{x(x + 2)(x - 2)}$

$= \dfrac{2x - 20}{x(x + 2)(x - 2)} = \dfrac{2(x - 10)}{x(x + 2)(x - 2)}$

21. $\dfrac{6}{\sqrt{5}} + \dfrac{3}{\sqrt{20}} = \dfrac{6}{\sqrt{5}} + \dfrac{3}{\sqrt{4}\sqrt{5}} = \dfrac{6}{\sqrt{5}} + \dfrac{3}{2\sqrt{5}} = \dfrac{6\sqrt{5}}{\sqrt{5}\sqrt{5}} + \dfrac{3\sqrt{5}}{2\sqrt{5}\sqrt{5}}$

$= \dfrac{6\sqrt{5}}{5} + \dfrac{3\sqrt{5}}{10} = \dfrac{(6\sqrt{5})(2)}{5(2)} + \dfrac{3\sqrt{5}}{10} = \dfrac{12\sqrt{5}}{10} + \dfrac{3\sqrt{5}}{10}$

$= \dfrac{12\sqrt{5} + 3\sqrt{5}}{10} = \dfrac{\overset{3}{\cancel{15}}\sqrt{5}}{\underset{2}{\cancel{10}}} = \dfrac{3\sqrt{5}}{2}$

23. $(3\sqrt{2} - 4\sqrt{5})(4\sqrt{2} - 2\sqrt{5}) = (3\sqrt{2})(4\sqrt{2}) - (3\sqrt{2})(2\sqrt{5})$

$- (4\sqrt{5})(4\sqrt{2}) + (4\sqrt{5})(2\sqrt{5})$

$= 3 \cdot 4\sqrt{2}\sqrt{2} - 3 \cdot 2\sqrt{2}\sqrt{5} - 4 \cdot 4\sqrt{5}\sqrt{2}$

$+ 4 \cdot 2\sqrt{5}\sqrt{5}$

$= 12 \cdot 2 - 6\sqrt{10} - 16\sqrt{10} + 8 \cdot 5$

$= 24 - 6\sqrt{10} - 16\sqrt{10} + 40$

$= 64 - 22\sqrt{10}$

25. $8 \cdot \dfrac{t}{t + 2} - \dfrac{5}{3t^2 + 6t} \cdot (6t^2 + 18t) = \dfrac{8}{1} \cdot \dfrac{t}{t + 2} - \dfrac{5}{\cancel{3t}(t + 2)} \cdot \dfrac{\overset{2}{\cancel{6t}}(t + 3)}{1}$

$= \dfrac{8t}{t + 2} - \dfrac{10(t + 3)}{t + 2}$

$= \dfrac{8t}{t + 2} - \dfrac{10t + 30}{t + 2} = \dfrac{8t - (10t + 30)}{t + 2}$

$= \dfrac{8t - 10t - 30}{t + 2} = \dfrac{-2t - 30}{t + 2} = \dfrac{-2(t + 15)}{t + 2}$

27. $\dfrac{15}{\sqrt{7} - \sqrt{2}} - \dfrac{10}{\sqrt{2}} = \dfrac{15(\sqrt{7} + \sqrt{2})}{(\sqrt{7} - \sqrt{2})(\sqrt{7} + \sqrt{2})} - \dfrac{10\sqrt{2}}{\sqrt{2}\sqrt{2}}$

$= \dfrac{15(\sqrt{7} + \sqrt{2})}{7 - 2} - \dfrac{\overset{5}{\cancel{10\sqrt{2}}}}{\cancel{2}_1}$

$= \dfrac{\overset{3}{\cancel{15}}(\sqrt{7} + \sqrt{2})}{\cancel{5}_1} - 5\sqrt{2}$

$= 3(\sqrt{7} + \sqrt{2}) - 5\sqrt{2} = 3\sqrt{7} + 3\sqrt{2} - 5\sqrt{2}$

$= 3\sqrt{7} - 2\sqrt{2}$

29. $\dfrac{11}{x} - \dfrac{2}{3} = \dfrac{25}{3x}$

$3x\left(\dfrac{11}{x} - \dfrac{2}{3}\right) = 3x\left(\dfrac{25}{3x}\right)$

$\dfrac{3\cancel{x}}{1} \cdot \dfrac{11}{\cancel{x}_1} - \dfrac{\cancel{3}x}{1} \cdot \dfrac{2}{\cancel{3}_1} = \dfrac{\cancel{3x}}{1} \cdot \dfrac{25}{\cancel{3x}_1}$

$33 - 2x = 25$

$-2x = -8$

$x = 4$

31. $5x - 7t = 9x - 4t + 12$

$\dfrac{+ 4t \qquad\qquad + 4t}{5x - 3t = 9x \qquad + 12}$

$\dfrac{-5x \qquad\qquad -5x}{\qquad -3t = 4x + 12}$

$\dfrac{-3t}{-3} = \dfrac{4x + 12}{-3}$

$t = -\dfrac{4x + 12}{3}$

33. $\dfrac{8}{z - 2} + 5 = \dfrac{4z}{z - 2}$

$(z - 2)\left(\dfrac{8}{z - 2} + 5\right) = (z - 2)\left(\dfrac{4z}{z - 2}\right)$

$\dfrac{\cancel{z - 2}^1}{1} \cdot \dfrac{8}{\cancel{z - 2}_1} + \dfrac{z - 2}{1} \cdot \dfrac{5}{1} = \dfrac{\cancel{z - 2}^1}{1} \cdot \dfrac{4z}{\cancel{z - 2}_1}$

$8 + 5(z - 2) = 4z$

$8 + 5z - 10 = 4z$

$5z - 2 = 4z$

$-2 = -z$

$2 = z$

This proposed solution does not check in the original equation, since it leads to fractions with zero denominators. Thus, the equation has no solution.

35. $\frac{3}{4}(x - 6) + \frac{2}{5}(x - 7) = 1 - (x + 4)$

$20(\frac{3}{4}(x - 6) + \frac{2}{5}(x - 7)) = 20(1 - (x + 4))$

$\frac{\cancel{20}^{5}}{1} \cdot \frac{3}{\cancel{4}_{1}}(x - 6) + \frac{\cancel{20}^{4}}{1} \cdot \frac{2}{\cancel{5}_{1}}(x - 7) = 20(-x - 3)$

$15(x - 6) + 8(x - 7) = 20(-x - 3)$

$15x - 90 + 8x - 56 = -20x - 60$

$23x - 146 = -20x - 60$

$43x - 146 = -60$

$43x = 86$

$x = 2$

37. $y = 2x - 6$

x-intercept: y-intercept: check point: choose x = 2

  $0 = 2x - 6$ $y = 2(0) - 6$ $y = 2(2) - 6$

  $6 = 2x$ $y = 0 - 6$ $y = 4 - 6$

  $3 = x$ $y = -6$ $y = -2$

 Plot (3,0)   Plot (0,-6)   Plot (2, -2)

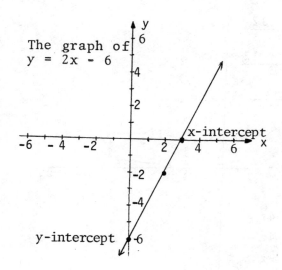

The graph of
$y = 2x - 6$

39. 3y - 6x = 12

    x-intercept: y-intercept: check point: choose y = 2

      3(0) - 6x = 12   3y - 6(0) = 12   3(2) - 6x = 12
        0 - 6x = 12   3y - 0 = 12   6 - 6x = 12
           -6x = 12   3y = 12   -6x = 6
             x = -2   y = 4   x = -1

    Plot (-2,0)   Plot (0,4)   Plot (-1,2)

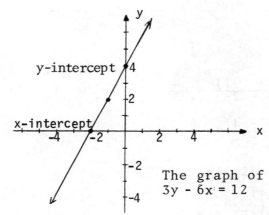

The graph of
3y - 6x = 12

41. x - 2 = 0

    Add 2 to both sides of this
    equation to get the equivalent
    equation x = 2. The graph of
    this equation is a line
    parallel to the y-axis and
    2 units to right of it.

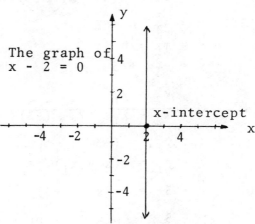

The graph of
x - 2 = 0

43. y = 5x

    x-intercept: second point: choose   check point: choose
                        x = 1   x = -1

       0 = 5x   y = 5(1)   y = 5(-1)
       0 = x   y = 5   y = -5

    Plot (0,0)   Plot (1,5)   Plot (-1,-5)
    (This implies
    that y-intercept
    is 0.)

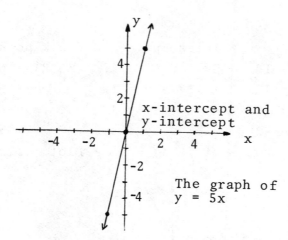

x-intercept and
y-intercept

The graph of
y = 5x

45. $m = \dfrac{y_2 - y_1}{x_2 - x_1} = \dfrac{4 - (-1)}{-3 - 2} = \dfrac{4 + 1}{-3 - 2} = \dfrac{5}{-5} = -1$

47. $m = \dfrac{y_2 - y_1}{x_2 - x_1} = \dfrac{4 - 4}{-1 - 2} = \dfrac{0}{-3} = 0$

49. $m = 4,\ (x_1, y_1) = (2, 3)$

$y - y_1 = m(x - x_1)$

$y - 3\ \ = 4(x - 2)$ or $y = 4x - 5$

51. $m = -\dfrac{3}{4},\ b = 3$

$y = mx + b$

$y = -\dfrac{3}{4}x + 3$

53. $m = \dfrac{y_2 - y_1}{x_2 - x_1} = \dfrac{-2 - 5}{2 - (-3)} = \dfrac{-2 - 5}{2 + 3} = \dfrac{-7}{5} = -\dfrac{7}{5}$

$(x_1, y_1) = (-3, 5)$

$y - y_1 = m(x - x_1)$

$y - 5\ \ = -\dfrac{7}{5}(x - (-3))$

$y - 5\ \ = -\dfrac{7}{5}(x + 3)$ or $y = -\dfrac{7}{5}x + \dfrac{4}{5}$

55. $2x - y = 7$

To find x-intercept, set $y = 0$ and solve for x. We get $x = \dfrac{7}{2}$.

To find y-intercept, set $x = 0$ and solve for y. We get $y = -7$.

x + 2y = 6

To find x-intercept, set y = 0 and solve for x. We get x = 6.
To find y-intercept, set x = 0 and solve for y. We get y = 3.

The lines cross at the
point (4,1). Therefore,
the system $\{\begin{array}{l} 2x - y = 7 \\ x + 2y = 6 \end{array}$
is satisfied by the point
(4,1).

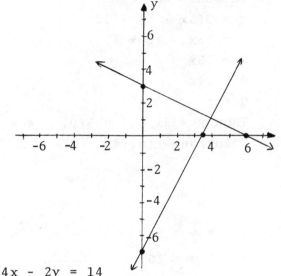

57. $\{\begin{array}{l} 2x - y = 7 \\ x + 2y = 6 \end{array}$ $\xrightarrow{\text{multiply by 2}}$ $\xrightarrow{\text{as is}}$ $\begin{array}{l} 4x - 2y = 14 \\ x + 2y = 6 \end{array}$

$$\text{Add: } 5x = 20$$
$$x = 4$$

$$2x - y = 7$$
$$2(4) - y = 7$$
$$8 - y = 7$$
$$-y = -1$$
$$y = 1$$

CHECK: x + 2y = 6
$$(4) + 2(1) \overset{?}{=} 6$$
$$4 + 2 \overset{?}{=} 6$$
$$6 \overset{\checkmark}{=} 6$$

Solution: (4,1)

59. $\{\begin{array}{l} 4x - 3y = 0 \\ 2x - y = \frac{1}{3} \end{array}$ $\xrightarrow{\text{as is}}$ $\xrightarrow{\text{multiply by -3}}$ $\begin{array}{l} 4x - 3y = 0 \\ -6x + 3y = -1 \end{array}$

$$\text{Add: } -2x = -1$$
$$x = \frac{1}{2}$$

$$4x - 3y = 0$$
$$4\left(\frac{1}{2}\right) - 3y = 0$$
$$2 - 3y = 0$$
$$2 = 3y$$
$$\frac{2}{3} = y$$

CHECK: $2x - y = \frac{1}{3}$
$$2\left(\frac{1}{2}\right) - \left(\frac{2}{3}\right) \overset{?}{=} \frac{1}{3}$$
$$1 - \frac{2}{3} \overset{?}{=} \frac{1}{3}$$
$$\frac{1}{3} \overset{\checkmark}{=} \frac{1}{3}$$

Solution: $\left(\frac{1}{2}, \frac{2}{3}\right)$

61. $\begin{cases} y = 5x - 4 \\ x = 3y + 12 \end{cases}$

    Substitute the value of y given in the first equation into the second. We get

    $x = 3(5x - 4) + 12$

    $x = 15x - 12 + 12$

    $x = 15x$

    $0 = 14x$

    $0 = x$

    Then $y = 5x - 4 = 5(0) - 4 = 0 - 4 = -4$.

    Solution: $(0,-4)$ CHECK: $x = 3y + 12$

    $(0) \overset{?}{=} 3(-4) + 12$

    $0 \overset{?}{=} -12 + 12$

    $0 \overset{\checkmark}{=} 0$

63. $\begin{cases} x + \dfrac{y}{2} = 5 \xrightarrow{\text{multiply by 2}} 2x + y = 10 \\ 2x + y = 10 \xrightarrow{\text{as is}} 2x + y = 10 \end{cases}$

    Subtract: $0 = 0$, an identity

    Therefore, the system has infinitely many solutions: $\{(x,y) \mid 2x + y = 10$

65. Let x = # of days Bob and Martha need if they work together.

    $\frac{1}{6}x + \frac{1}{4}x = 1$ CHECK: In $\frac{12}{5}$ days, Bob does

    $12(\frac{1}{6}x + \frac{1}{4}x) = 12 \cdot 1$ $\frac{1}{\cancel{6}}(\frac{\cancel{12}}{5})^2 = \frac{2}{5}$ of the job.

    $\frac{\cancel{12}^2}{1} \cdot \frac{1}{\cancel{6}}x + \frac{\cancel{12}^3}{1} \cdot \frac{1}{\cancel{4}}x = 12$ In $\frac{12}{5}$ days, Martha does

    $2x + 3x = 12$ $\frac{1}{\cancel{4}}(\frac{\cancel{12}}{5})^3 = \frac{3}{5}$ of the job.

    $5x = 12$ $\frac{2}{5} + \frac{3}{5} = 1$ (the entire job)

    $x = \frac{12}{5} = 2\frac{2}{5}$

    Thus, it takes Bob and Martha $2\frac{2}{5}$ days if they work together.

67. Let d = original denominator.

    d - 4 = original numerator.

    $\dfrac{(d - 4) + 3}{d + 1} = \dfrac{1}{2}$

    $\dfrac{d - 1}{d + 1} = \dfrac{1}{2}$ CHECK: $\dfrac{-1 + 3}{3 + 1} = \dfrac{2}{4} = \dfrac{1}{2}$

$$\frac{2(d + 1)}{1} \cdot \frac{d - 1}{1 \, d + 1} = \frac{2(d + 1)}{1} \cdot \frac{1}{2 \, 1}$$

$$2(d - 1) = d + 1$$
$$2d - 2 = d + 1$$
$$d - 2 = 1$$
$$d = 3$$

Then $d - 4 = 3 - 4 = -1$. Thus, the original fraction is $\frac{-1}{3}$.

Cumulative Practice Test: Chapters 7-9

1. $\sqrt{64x^{16}} = \sqrt{64}\sqrt{x^{16}} = 8x^8$

3. $\sqrt{40x^7y^{10}} = \sqrt{4x^6y^{10}}\sqrt{10x} = \sqrt{4}\sqrt{x^6}\sqrt{y^{10}}\sqrt{10x} = 2x^3y^5\sqrt{10x}$

5. $\dfrac{t^2 - t - 6}{t^2 + t - 6} = \dfrac{(t - 3)(t + 2)}{(t + 3)(t - 2)}$ cannot be reduced

7. $\dfrac{5}{x + 5} - \dfrac{4}{x + 4} = \dfrac{5(x + 4)}{(x + 5)(x + 4)} - \dfrac{4(x + 5)}{(x + 4)(x + 5)}$

$$= \dfrac{5x + 20}{(x + 5)(x + 4)} - \dfrac{4x + 20}{(x + 5)(x + 4)}$$

$$= \dfrac{5x + 20 - (4x + 20)}{(x + 5)(x + 4)}$$

$$= \dfrac{5x + 20 - 4x - 20}{(x + 5)(x + 4)}$$

$$= \dfrac{x}{(x + 5)(x + 4)}$$

9. $(\sqrt{x} + \sqrt{y})^2 = (\sqrt{x} + \sqrt{y})(\sqrt{x} + \sqrt{y}) = \sqrt{x}\sqrt{x} + \sqrt{x}\sqrt{y} + \sqrt{x}\sqrt{y} + \sqrt{y}\sqrt{y}$

$$= x + \sqrt{xy} + \sqrt{xy} + y = x + 2\sqrt{xy} + y$$

11. $\dfrac{6}{a^2 + 3a} - \dfrac{3}{a^2 - 3a} = \dfrac{6}{a(a + 3)} - \dfrac{3}{a(a - 3)}$

$$= \dfrac{6(a - 3)}{a(a + 3)(a - 3)} - \dfrac{3(a + 3)}{a(a - 3)(a + 3)}$$

$$= \dfrac{6a - 18}{a(a + 3)(a - 3)} - \dfrac{3a + 9}{a(a + 3)(a - 3)}$$

$$= \dfrac{6a - 18 - (3a + 9)}{a(a + 3)(a - 3)} = \dfrac{6a - 18 - 3a - 9}{a(a + 3)(a - 3)}$$

$$= \dfrac{3a - 27}{a(a + 3)(a - 3)} = \dfrac{3(a - 9)}{a(a + 3)(a - 3)}$$

13. $(2\sqrt{z} - 3\sqrt{7})(3\sqrt{z} + \sqrt{7}) = (2\sqrt{z})(3\sqrt{z}) + 2\sqrt{z}\sqrt{7} - (3\sqrt{7})(3\sqrt{z})$

$$- 3\sqrt{7}\sqrt{7}$$

$$= 6z + 2\sqrt{7z} - 9\sqrt{7z} - 3 \cdot 7$$

$$= 6z - 7\sqrt{7z} - 21$$

15. $\dfrac{2 + \dfrac{1}{x}}{4 - \dfrac{1}{x^2}} = \dfrac{x^2(2 + \dfrac{1}{x})}{x^2(4 - \dfrac{1}{x^2})} = \dfrac{2x^2 + \dfrac{\cancel{x}^{2x}}{1} \cdot \dfrac{1}{\cancel{x}1}}{4x^2 - \dfrac{\cancel{x}^2}{1} \cdot \dfrac{1}{\cancel{x^2}1}} = \dfrac{2x^2 + x}{4x^2 - 1}$

$$= \dfrac{x\cancel{(2x + 1)}}{(2x - 1)\cancel{(2x + 1)}} = \dfrac{x}{2x - 1}$$

17. $\dfrac{9}{4t - 12} - \dfrac{2}{3} = \dfrac{11}{12t - 36}$

$\dfrac{9}{4(t - 3)} - \dfrac{2}{3} = \dfrac{11}{12(t - 3)}$

$12(t - 3)(\dfrac{9}{4(t - 3)} - \dfrac{2}{3}) = 12(t - 3)(\dfrac{11}{12(t - 3)})$

$\dfrac{\cancel{12(t - 3)}^3}{1} \cdot \dfrac{9}{\cancel{4(t - 3)}_1} - \dfrac{\cancel{12(t - 3)}^4}{1} \cdot \dfrac{2}{\cancel{3}_1} = \dfrac{\cancel{12(t - 3)}^1}{1} \cdot \dfrac{11}{\cancel{12(t - 3)}_1}$

$27 - 8(t - 3) = 11$

$27 - 8t + 24 = 11$

$-8t + 51 = 11$

$-8t = -40$

$t = 5$

19. $\dfrac{10}{x + 4} + \dfrac{3}{5} = \dfrac{6 - x}{x + 4}$

$5(x + 4)(\dfrac{10}{x + 4} + \dfrac{3}{5}) = 5(x + 4)(\dfrac{6 - x}{x + 4})$

$\dfrac{\cancel{5(x + 4)}}{1} \cdot \dfrac{10}{\cancel{x + 4}_1} + \dfrac{\cancel{5}(x + 4)}{1} \cdot \dfrac{3}{\cancel{5}_1} = \dfrac{\cancel{5(x + 4)}}{1} \cdot \dfrac{6 - x}{\cancel{x + 4}_1}$

$50 + 3(x + 4) = 5(6 - x)$

$50 + 3x + 12 = 30 - 5x$

$3x + 62 = 30 - 5x$

$8x + 62 = 30$

$8x = -32$

$x = -4$

When this value of x is checked in the original equation, it produces fractions with zero denominators. Therefore, the equation has no solution.

21. x - 3y = 6

    x-intercept: y-intercept: check point: choose x = 3

      x - 3(0) = 6   0 - 3y = 6   3 - 3y = 6

         x - 0 = 6   -3y = 6   -3y = 3

            x = 6   y = -2   y = -1

    Plot (6,0)   Plot (0,-2)   Plot (3,-1)

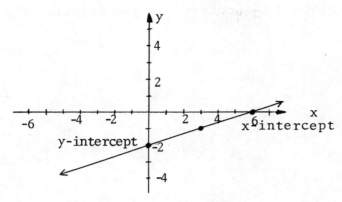

The graph of x - 3y = 6

23. $m = \dfrac{y_2 - y_1}{x_2 - x_1} = \dfrac{6 - 2}{3 - (-2)} = \dfrac{4}{5}$

25. $\begin{cases} 3x - 2y = 7 \\ 4x + y = -9 \end{cases}$ $\xrightarrow{\text{as is}}$ $3x - 2y = 7$

                             $\xrightarrow{\text{multiply by 2}}$ $\underline{8x + 2y = -18}$

                                       Add: 11x = -11

                                           x = -1

                             3x - 2y = 7

                         3(-1) - 2y = 7

                           -3 - 2y = 7

                             -2y = 10

                               y = -5

    Solution: (-1,-5)   CHECK: 4x + y = -9

                            4(-1) + (-5) $\overset{?}{=}$ -9

                                 -4 - 5 $\overset{?}{=}$ -9

                                    -9 $\overset{\checkmark}{=}$ -9

27. Let x = # of hours Susan needs to finish painting the house.

    $\dfrac{5}{12} + \dfrac{x}{9} = 1$

    $36\left(\dfrac{5}{12} + \dfrac{x}{9}\right) = 36 \cdot 1$

$$\frac{\cancel{36}^{3}}{1} \cdot \frac{5}{\cancel{12}_{1}} + \frac{\cancel{36}^{4}}{1} \cdot \frac{x}{\cancel{9}_{1}} = 36$$

$$15 + 4x = 36$$

$$4x = 21$$

$$x = \frac{21}{4} = 5\frac{1}{4}$$

CHECK: In 5 hours, Jim completes
$5(\frac{1}{12}) = \frac{5}{12}$ of the job. In
$\frac{21}{4}$ hours, Susan completes
$\frac{^{7}\cancel{21}}{4}(\frac{1}{\cancel{9}})_{3} = \frac{7}{12}$ of the job.
$\frac{5}{12} + \frac{7}{12} \overset{\checkmark}{=} 1$ (the entire job)

Thus, Susan needs $5\frac{1}{4}$ hours to finish painting the house.

Chapter 10

QUADRATIC EQUATIONS

<u>Exercises 10.1</u>

1. $(x - 2)(x + 3) = 0$
    $x - 2 = 0$ or $x + 3 = 0$
    $x = 2$ or $x = -3$

3. $(x - 2)(x + 3) = 6$
    $x^2 + x - 6 = 6$
    $x^2 + x - 12 = 0$
    $(x + 4)(x - 3) = 0$
    $x + 4 = 0$ or $x - 3 = 0$
    $x = -4$ or $x = 3$

    CHECK:

    $x = -4$: $(x - 2)(x + 3) = 6$
    $(-4 - 2)(-4 + 3) \overset{?}{=} 6$
    $(-6)(-1) \overset{?}{=} 6$
    $6 \overset{\checkmark}{=} 6$

    $x = 3$: $(x - 2)(x + 3) = 6$
    $(3 - 2)(3 + 3) \overset{?}{=} 6$
    $(1)(6) \overset{?}{=} 6$
    $6 \overset{\checkmark}{=} 6$

9. $x^2 - x - 6 = 0$
    $(x - 3)(x + 2) = 0$
    $x - 3 = 0$ or $x + 2 = 0$
    $x = 3$ or $x = -2$

    CHECK:

    $x = 3$: $x^2 - x - 6 = 0$
    $(3)^2 - (3) - 6 \overset{?}{=} 0$
    $9 - 3 - 6 \overset{?}{=} 0$
    $0 \overset{\checkmark}{=} 0$

    $x = -2$: $x^2 - x - 6 = 0$
    $(-2)^2 - (-2) - 6 \overset{?}{=} 0$
    $4 + 2 - 6 \overset{?}{=} 0$
    $0 \overset{\checkmark}{=} 0$

11. $x^2 - 3x = 10$

   $x^2 - 3x - 10 = 0$

   $(x - 5)(x + 2) = 0$

   $x - 5 = 0$ or $x + 2 = 0$

   $x = 5$ or $x = -2$

CHECK:

$x = 5$: $x^2 - 3x = 10$

   $(5)^2 - 3(5) \overset{?}{=} 10$

   $25 - 15 \overset{?}{=} 10$

   $10 \overset{\checkmark}{=} 10$

$x = -2$: $x^2 - 3x = 10$

   $(-2)^2 - 3(-2) \overset{?}{=} 10$

   $4 + 6 \overset{?}{=} 10$

   $10 \overset{\checkmark}{=} 10$

15. $-m^2 = 8 - 9m$

   $-m^2 + 9m - 8 = 0$

   $m^2 - 9m + 8 = 0$

   $(m - 1)(m - 8) = 0$

   $m - 1 = 0$ or $m - 8 = 0$

   $m = 1$ or $m = 8$

CHECK:

$m = 1$: $-m^2 = 8 - 9m$

   $-(1)^2 \overset{?}{=} 8 - 9(1)$

   $-1 \overset{?}{=} 8 - 9$

   $-1 \overset{\checkmark}{=} -1$

$m = 8$: $-m^2 = 8 - 9m$

   $-(8)^2 \overset{?}{=} 8 - 9(8)$

   $-64 \overset{?}{=} 8 - 72$

   $-64 \overset{\checkmark}{=} -64$

17. $p^2 + 3p = p(p + 4)$

   $p^2 + 3p = p^2 + 4p$

   $3p = 4p$

   $0 = p$

CHECK:

$p = 0$: $p^2 + 3p = p(p + 4)$

   $(0)^2 + 3(0) \overset{?}{=} 0(0 + 4)$

   $0 + 0 \overset{?}{=} 0(4)$

   $0 \overset{\checkmark}{=} 0$

23. $2a(a + 3) = 20$

   $2a^2 + 6a = 20$

   $2a^2 + 6a - 20 = 0$

   $2(a^2 + 3a - 10) = 0$

   $a^2 + 3a - 10 = 0$

   $(a + 5)(a - 2) = 0$

   $a + 5 = 0$ or $a - 2 = 0$

   $a = -5$ or $a = 2$

CHECK:

$a = -5$: $2a(a + 3) = 20$

   $2(-5)(-5 + 3) \overset{?}{=} 20$

   $2(-5)(-2) \overset{?}{=} 20$

   $20 \overset{\checkmark}{=} 20$

$a = 2$: $2a(a + 3) = 20$

   $2(2)(2 + 3) \overset{?}{=} 20$

   $2(2)(5) \overset{?}{=} 20$

   $20 \overset{\checkmark}{=} 20$

27. $a^2 - 4a - 2 = 2a^2 - 9a - 16$ CHECK:

    $-4a - 2 = a^2 - 9a - 16$ $a = 7$: $a^2 - 4a - 2 = 2a^2 - 9a - 16$

    $-2 = a^2 - 5a - 16$ $(7)^2 - 4(7) - 2 \overset{?}{=} 2(7)^2 - 9(7) - 16$

    $0 = a^2 - 5a - 14$ $49 - 28 - 2 \overset{?}{=} 98 - 63 - 16$

    $0 = (a - 7)(a + 2)$ $19 \overset{\checkmark}{=} 19$

    $0 = a - 7$ or $0 = a + 2$ $a = -2$: $a^2 - 4a - 2 = 2a^2 - 9a - 16$

    $7 = a$ or $-2 = a$ $(-2)^2 - 4(-2) - 2 \overset{?}{=} 2(-2)^2 - 9(-2) - 16$

    $4 + 8 - 2 \overset{?}{=} 8 + 18 - 16$

    $10 \overset{\checkmark}{=} 10$

31. $(x + 3)^2 = 3x^2 - 10$

    $x^2 + 6x + 9 = 3x^2 - 10$

    $6x + 9 = 2x^2 - 10$

    $9 = 2x^2 - 6x - 10$

    $0 = 2x^2 - 6x - 19$

The quadratic expression $2x^2 - 6x - 19$ cannot be factored.

35. $(x + 2)^2 = 25$ CHECK:

    $(x + 2)(x + 2) = 25$ $x = -7$: $(x + 2)^2 = 25$

    $x^2 + 4x + 4 = 25$ $(-7 + 2)^2 \overset{?}{=} 25$

    $x^2 + 4x - 21 = 0$ $(-5)^2 \overset{?}{=} 25$

    $(x + 7)(x - 3) = 0$ $25 \overset{\checkmark}{=} 25$

    $x + 7 = 0$ or $x - 3 = 0$ $x = 3$: $(x + 2)^2 = 25$

    $x = -7$ or $x = 3$ $(3 + 2)^2 \overset{?}{=} 25$

    $5^2 \overset{?}{=} 25$

    $25 \overset{\checkmark}{=} 25$

39. $(2x - 4)(x + 1) = (x - 3)(x - 2)$ CHECK:

    $2x^2 - 2x - 4 = x^2 - 5x + 6$ $x = -5$: $(2x - 4)(x + 1) = (x - 3)(x - 2)$

    $x^2 - 2x - 4 = -5x + 6$ $(2(-5) - 4)(-5 + 1) \overset{?}{=} (-5 - 3)(-5 - 2)$

    $x^2 + 3x - 4 = 6$ $(-14)(-4) \overset{?}{=} (-8)(-7)$

    $x^2 + 3x - 10 = 0$ $56 \overset{\checkmark}{=} 56$

    $(x + 5)(x - 2) = 0$ $x = 2$: $(2x - 4)(x + 1) = (x - 3)(x - 2)$

    $x + 5 = 0$ or $x - 2 = 0$ $(2(2) - 4)(2 + 1) \overset{?}{=} (2 - 3)(2 - 2)$

    $x = -5$ or $x = 2$ $(0)(3) \overset{?}{=} (-1)(0)$

    $0 \overset{\checkmark}{=} 0$

41. $x + \dfrac{1}{x} = 2$

$x(x + \dfrac{1}{x}) = x(2)$

$x \cdot x + \dfrac{\cancel{x}^{1}}{1} \cdot \dfrac{1}{\cancel{x}_{1}} = 2x$

$x^2 + 1 = 2x$

$x^2 - 2x + 1 = 0$

$(x - 1)(x - 1) = 0$

$x - 1 = 0$ or $x - 1 = 0$

$x = 1$ or $x = 1$

So $x = 1$

CHECK:

$x = 1:$ $x + \dfrac{1}{x} = 2$

$(1) + \dfrac{1}{(1)} \overset{?}{=} 2$

$1 + 1 \overset{?}{=} 2$

$2 \overset{\checkmark}{=} 2$

45. $\dfrac{2x}{x + 2} + 1 = x$

$(x + 2)(\dfrac{2x}{x + 2} + 1) = (x + 2)x$

$\dfrac{\cancel{x + 2}^{1}}{1} \cdot \dfrac{2x}{\cancel{x + 2}_{1}} + (x + 2) \cdot 1 = (x + 2)x$

$2x + x + 2 = x^2 + 2x$

$3x + 2 = x^2 + 2x$

$2 = x^2 - x$

$0 = x^2 - x - 2$

$0 = (x - 2)(x + 1)$

$0 = x - 2$ or $0 = x + 1$

$2 = x$ or $-1 = x$

CHECK: $x = 2:$ $\dfrac{2x}{x + 2} + 1 = x$

$\dfrac{2(2)}{(2) + 2} + 1 \overset{?}{=} 2$

$\dfrac{4}{4} + 1 \overset{?}{=} 2$

$1 + 1 \overset{?}{=} 2$

$2 \overset{\checkmark}{=} 2$

$x = -1:$ $\dfrac{2x}{x + 2} + 1 = x$

$\dfrac{2(-1)}{(-1) + 2} + 1 \overset{?}{=} -1$

$\dfrac{-2}{1} + 1 \overset{?}{=} -1$

$-2 + 1 \overset{?}{=} -1$

$-1 \overset{\checkmark}{=} -1$

47. $a - \dfrac{5a}{a + 1} = \dfrac{5}{a + 1}$

$(a + 1)(a - \dfrac{5a}{a + 1}) = (a + 1)(\dfrac{5}{a + 1})$

$(a + 1)a - \dfrac{\cancel{a + 1}^{1}}{1} \cdot \dfrac{5a}{\cancel{a + 1}_{1}} = \dfrac{\cancel{a + 1}^{1}}{1} \cdot \dfrac{5}{\cancel{a + 1}_{1}}$

$(a + 1)a - 5a = 5$

$a^2 + a - 5a = 5$

$a^2 - 4a = 5$

$a^2 - 4a - 5 = 0$

$(a - 5)(a + 1) = 0$

$a - 5 = 0$ or $a + 1 = 0$

$a = 5$ or $a = -1$

CHECK:

$a = 5:$ $a - \dfrac{5a}{a + 1} = \dfrac{5}{a + 1}$

$5 - \dfrac{5(5)}{5 + 1} \overset{?}{=} \dfrac{5}{5 + 1}$

$5 - \dfrac{25}{6} \overset{?}{=} \dfrac{5}{6}$

$\dfrac{30}{6} - \dfrac{25}{6} \overset{?}{=} \dfrac{5}{6}$

$\dfrac{5}{6} \overset{\checkmark}{=} \dfrac{5}{6}$

$$a = -1: \quad a - \frac{5a}{a+1} = \frac{5}{a+1}$$

$$1 - \frac{5(-1)}{-1+1} \stackrel{?}{=} \frac{5}{-1+1}$$

$$-1 + \frac{5}{0} \stackrel{?}{=} \frac{5}{0}$$

$$-1 + \frac{5}{0} \neq \frac{5}{0}$$

since we cannot divide by 0.

Therefore, we have only one solution: $a = 5$.

49. $\dfrac{3}{x-2} + \dfrac{7}{x+2} = \dfrac{x+1}{x-2}$

$$(x-2)(x+2)(\frac{3}{x-2} + \frac{7}{x+2}) = (x-2)(x+2)(\frac{x+1}{x-2})$$

$$\frac{\overset{1}{\cancel{(x-2)}}(x+2)}{1} \cdot \frac{3}{\underset{1}{\cancel{x-2}}} + \frac{(x-2)\overset{1}{\cancel{(x+2)}}}{1} \cdot \frac{7}{\cancel{x+2}}$$

$$= \frac{\overset{1}{\cancel{(x-2)}}(x+2)}{1} \cdot \frac{x+1}{\underset{1}{\cancel{x-2}}}$$

$3(x+2)+(7(x-2) = (x+2)(x+1)$

$3x + 6 + 7x - 14 = x^2 + 3x + 2$

$10x - 8 = x^2 + 3x + 2$

$-8 = x^2 - 7x + 2$

$0 = x^2 - 7x + 10$

$0 = (x-2)(x-5)$

$0 = x - 2$ or $0 = x - 5$

$2 = x$ or $5 = x$

CHECK:

$x = 2: \quad \dfrac{3}{x-2} + \dfrac{7}{x+2} = \dfrac{x+1}{x-2}$

$\dfrac{3}{2-2} + \dfrac{7}{2+2} \stackrel{?}{=} \dfrac{2+1}{2-2}$

$\dfrac{3}{0} + \dfrac{7}{4} \stackrel{?}{=} \dfrac{3}{0}$

$\dfrac{3}{0} + \dfrac{7}{4} \neq \dfrac{3}{0}$

since we cannot divide by 0.

$x = 5: \quad \dfrac{3}{x-2} + \dfrac{7}{x+2} = \dfrac{x+1}{x-2}$

$\dfrac{3}{5-2} + \dfrac{7}{5+2} \stackrel{?}{=} \dfrac{5+1}{5-2}$

$\dfrac{3}{3} + \dfrac{7}{7} \stackrel{?}{=} \dfrac{6}{3}$

$1 + 1 \stackrel{?}{=} 2$

$2 \stackrel{\checkmark}{=} 2$

Therefore, we have only one solution: $x = 5$.

51. (a) We cannot set each of the factors equal to 7. The zero-factor property requires that the product of the factors be equal to 0.

(b) $x = 3$ is not a possible solution. The first factor on the left side of the equation can never be equal to zero. We can either ignore its presence or divide both sides of the equation by it. (This logic is valid for constant factors of a zero product, but <u>not</u> for variable factors.)

52. Since the square of any real number must be non-negative, x^2 must be at least zero. Therefore, $x^2 + 4$ must be at least 4, which means that $x^2 + 4$ cannot ever equal 0. Thus, the equation $x^2 + 4 = 0$ cannot have any solution in the real number system.

<u>Exercises 10.2</u>

3. $b^2 - 16 = 0$

$\qquad b^2 = 16$

$\qquad b = \pm\sqrt{16} = \pm 4$

5. $9b^2 - 16 = 0$

$\qquad 9b^2 = 16$

$\qquad b^2 = \dfrac{16}{9}$

$\qquad b = \pm\sqrt{\dfrac{16}{9}} = \pm\dfrac{\sqrt{16}}{\sqrt{9}} = \pm\dfrac{4}{3}$

7. $b^2 + 16 = 0$

$\qquad b^2 = -16$

$\qquad b = \pm\sqrt{-16}$

Since $\sqrt{-16}$ is not a real number, the given equation has no real solutions.

11. $36x^2 - 15 = 0$

$\qquad 36x^2 = 15$

$\qquad x^2 = \dfrac{15}{36}$

$\qquad x = \pm\sqrt{\dfrac{15}{36}} = \pm\dfrac{\sqrt{15}}{\sqrt{36}} = \pm\dfrac{\sqrt{15}}{6}$

13. $3b^2 = 11$

$\qquad b^2 = \dfrac{11}{3}$

$\qquad b = \pm\sqrt{\dfrac{11}{3}} = \pm\dfrac{\sqrt{11}}{\sqrt{3}} = \pm\dfrac{\sqrt{11}\sqrt{3}}{\sqrt{3}\sqrt{3}} = \pm\dfrac{\sqrt{33}}{3}$

17. $9a^2 = 20$

$a^2 = \dfrac{20}{9}$

$a = \pm\sqrt{\dfrac{20}{9}} = \pm\dfrac{\sqrt{20}}{\sqrt{9}} = \pm\dfrac{\sqrt{20}}{3} = \pm\dfrac{\sqrt{4}\sqrt{5}}{3} = \pm\dfrac{2\sqrt{5}}{3}$

21. $7y^2 - 4 = 5y^2 + 6$

$2y^2 - 4 = 6$

$2y^2 = 10$

$y^2 = 5$

$y = \pm\sqrt{5}$

23. $5a^2 - 3a + 4 = 2a^2 - 3a + 13$

$3a^2 - 3a + 4 = -3a + 13$

$3a^2 + 4 = 13$

$3a^2 = 9$

$a^2 = 3$

$a = \pm\sqrt{3}$

27. $(y - 3)(y + 4) = y$

$y^2 + y - 12 = y$

$y^2 - 12 = 0$

$y^2 = 12$

$y = \pm\sqrt{12} = \pm\sqrt{4}\sqrt{3} = \pm 2\sqrt{3}$

31. $(x + 2)^2 = 4(x + 7)$

$x^2 + 4x + 4 = 4x + 28$

$x^2 + 4 = 28$

$x^2 = 24$

$x = \pm\sqrt{24} = \pm\sqrt{4}\sqrt{6} = \pm 2\sqrt{6}$

33. $(t - 2)^2 = 9$

$t - 2 = \pm\sqrt{9}$

$t - 2 = \pm 3$

$t - 2 = 3$ or $t - 2 = -3$

$t = 5$ or $t = -1$

35. $(a + 5)^2 = 7$

$a + 5 = \pm\sqrt{7}$

$a = -5 \pm \sqrt{7}$

39. $(m - \frac{2}{3})^2 = \frac{4}{9}$

$m - \frac{2}{3} = \pm\sqrt{\frac{4}{9}}$

$m - \frac{2}{3} = \pm\frac{\sqrt{4}}{\sqrt{9}}$

$m - \frac{2}{3} = \pm\frac{2}{3}$

$m - \frac{2}{3} = \frac{2}{3}$ or $m - \frac{2}{3} = -\frac{2}{3}$

$m = \frac{4}{3}$ or $m = 0$

41. $(x + \frac{2}{5})^2 = \frac{3}{25}$

$x + \frac{2}{5} = \pm\sqrt{\frac{3}{25}}$

$x + \frac{2}{5} = \pm\frac{\sqrt{3}}{\sqrt{25}}$

$x + \frac{2}{5} = \pm\frac{\sqrt{3}}{5}$

$x = -\frac{2}{5} \pm \frac{\sqrt{3}}{5} = \frac{-2 \pm \sqrt{3}}{5}$

45. $2x^2 + 7x - 5 = 3x^2 + 9x - 4$

$7x - 5 = x^2 + 9x - 4$

$-5 = x^2 + 2x - 4$

$0 = x^2 + 2x + 1$

$0 = (x + 1)(x + 1)$

$0 = x + 1$ or $0 = x + 1$

$-1 = x$ or $-1 = x$

So $x = -1$

47. $(y - 2)(y + 3) = y + 10$

$y^2 + y - 6 = y + 10$

$y^2 - 6 = 10$

$y^2 = 16$

$y = \pm\sqrt{16} = \pm 4$

49. $(y - 2)(y + 3) = (2y - 7)(y + 4)$

$y^2 + y - 6 = 2y^2 + y - 28$

$y - 6 = y^2 + y - 28$

$-6 = y^2 - 28$

$22 = y^2$

$\pm\sqrt{22} = y$

53. $4(x + 1) = \frac{9}{x + 1}$

$(x + 1)(4(x + 1)) = \frac{\cancel{x + 1}^{\,1}}{1} \cdot \frac{9}{\cancel{x + 1}_{\,1}}$

$4(x + 1)^2 = 9$

$(x + 1)^2 = \frac{9}{4}$

$x + 1 = \pm\sqrt{\frac{9}{4}}$

$x + 1 = \pm\frac{\sqrt{9}}{\sqrt{4}}$

$x + 1 = \pm\frac{3}{2}$

$x + 1 = \frac{3}{2}$ or $x + 1 = -\frac{3}{2}$

$x = \frac{1}{2}$ or $x = -\frac{5}{2}$

55. Step 1: We can add the same quantity, 7, to both sides of an equation to obtain an equivalent equation.

Step 2: We can add the same quantity, 4, to both sides of an equation to obtain an equivalent equation.

Step 3: $7 + 4 = 11$

Step 4: $x^2 + 4x + 4$ factors as the square of the sum $x + 2$.

Step 5: $u^2 = d$ implies that $u = \pm\sqrt{d}$.

Step 6: We can subtract the same quantity, 2, from both sides of an equation to obtain an equivalent equation.

56. $$(2 + \sqrt{3})^2 - 4(2 + \sqrt{3}) + 1 = (2 + \sqrt{3})(2 + \sqrt{3}) - 4(2 + \sqrt{3}) + 1$$
$$= 4 + 2\sqrt{3} + 2\sqrt{3} + 3 - 8 - 4\sqrt{3} + 1$$
$$= 0$$

So $2 + \sqrt{3}$ is a solution to the equation $x^2 - 4x + 1 = 0$.

$$(2 - \sqrt{3})^2 - 4(2 - \sqrt{3}) + 1 = (2 - \sqrt{3})(2 - \sqrt{3}) - 4(2 - \sqrt{3}) + 1$$
$$= 4 - 2\sqrt{3} - 2\sqrt{3} + 3 - 8 + 4\sqrt{3} + 1$$
$$= 0$$

So $2 - \sqrt{3}$ is also a solution to the equation $x^2 - 4x + 1 = 0$.   (This is no coincidence. In fact, whenever $a + \sqrt{b}$ satisfies an equation, it must be true that $a - \sqrt{b}$ also satisfies the equation.)

Exercises 10.3

1. $x^2 + 8x + 6 = 0$
    $x^2 + 8x = -6$
    $ +16 +16 \qquad [(\tfrac{8}{2}) = 4, \ 4^2 = 16]$
    $\overline{x^2 + 8x + 16 = 10}$
    $(x + 4)^2 = 10$
    $x + 4 = \pm\sqrt{10}$
    $x = -4 \pm \sqrt{10}$

5. $x^2 - 10x = 15$
    $ + 25 +25 \qquad [(\tfrac{-10}{2}) = -5, \ (-5)^2 = 25]$
    $\overline{x^2 - 10x + 25 = 40}$
    $(x - 5)^2 = 40$
    $x - 5 = \pm\sqrt{40}$
    $x - 5 = \pm 2\sqrt{10}$
    $x = 5 \pm 2\sqrt{10}$

7. $a^2 - 8a - 20 = 0$

    $a^2 - 8a \quad\quad = 20$

    $\underline{\quad\quad\quad + 16 \quad +16}$

    $a^2 - 8a + 16 = 36$ $[\,(\frac{-8}{2}) = -4, \ (-4)^2 = 16\,]$

    $\quad\quad (a - 4)^2 = 36$

    $\quad\quad\quad a - 4 = \pm\sqrt{36}$

    $\quad\quad\quad a - 4 = \pm 6$

    $a - 4 = 6$ or $a - 4 = -6$

    $a = 10$ or $a = -2$

11. $2z^2 - 12z + 4 = 0$

    $2z^2 - 12z \quad\quad = -4$

    $z^2 - 6z \quad\quad = -2$

    $\underline{\quad\quad\quad + 9 \quad +9}$

    $z^2 - 6z + 9 = 7$ $[\,(\frac{-6}{2}) = -3, \ (-3)^2 = 9\,]$

    $\quad\quad (z - 3)^2 = 7$

    $\quad\quad\quad z - 3 = \pm\sqrt{7}$

    $\quad\quad\quad\quad z = 3 \pm \sqrt{7}$

15. $u^2 + 5u - 2 = 0$

    $u^2 + 5u \quad\quad = 2$

    $\underline{\quad\quad\quad + \frac{25}{4} \quad +\frac{25}{4}}$

    $u^2 + 5u + \frac{25}{4} = 2 + \frac{25}{4}$ $[\,(\frac{5}{2})^2 = \frac{25}{4}\,]$

    $\quad (u + \frac{5}{2})^2 = \frac{8}{4} + \frac{25}{4}$

    $\quad (u + \frac{5}{2})^2 = \frac{33}{4}$

    $\quad\quad u + \frac{5}{2} = \pm\sqrt{\frac{33}{4}} = \pm\frac{\sqrt{33}}{2}$

    $\quad\quad\quad\quad u = -\frac{5}{2} \pm \frac{\sqrt{33}}{2}$

    $\quad\quad\quad\quad u = \frac{-5 \pm \sqrt{33}}{2}$

19.
$$w^2 - 3w = 2w^2 - 7w + 2$$
$$-w^2 - 3w = - 7w + 2$$
$$-w^2 + 4w = 2$$
$$w^2 - 4w = -2$$

$$\underline{ + 4 +4}$$

$$w^2 - 4w + 4 = 2 \qquad \left[\left(-\frac{4}{2}\right) = -2,\ (-2)^2 = 4\right]$$

$$(w - 2)^2 = 2$$
$$w - 2 = \pm\sqrt{2}$$
$$w = 2 \pm \sqrt{2}$$

23.
$$(x - 3)(x + 2) = 9x - 1$$
$$x^2 - x - 6 = 9x - 1$$
$$x^2 - 10x - 6 = - 1$$
$$x^2 - 10x = 5$$

$$\underline{ +25 +25}$$

$$x^2 - 10x + 25 = 30 \qquad \left[\left(\frac{-10}{2}\right) = -5,\ (-5)^2 = 25\right]$$

$$(x - 5)^2 = 30$$
$$x - 5 = \pm\sqrt{30}$$
$$x = 5 \pm \sqrt{30}$$

25.
$$(a - 2)(a + 1) = 6$$
$$a^2 - a - 2 = 6$$
$$a^2 - a = 8$$

$$\underline{ + \frac{1}{4} +\frac{1}{4}}$$

$$a^2 - a + \frac{1}{4} = 8 + \frac{1}{4} \qquad \left[\left(\frac{-1}{2}\right)^2 = \frac{1}{4}\right]$$

$$\left(a - \frac{1}{2}\right)^2 = \frac{32}{4} + \frac{1}{4}$$
$$\left(a - \frac{1}{2}\right)^2 = \frac{33}{4}$$
$$a - \frac{1}{2} = \pm\sqrt{\frac{33}{4}} = \pm\frac{\sqrt{33}}{2}$$
$$a = \frac{1}{2} \pm \frac{\sqrt{33}}{2}$$
$$a = \frac{1 \pm \sqrt{33}}{2}$$

29. $2x^2 + 3 \qquad = 6x$

$2x^2 - 6x + 3 = 0$

$2x^2 - 6x \qquad = -3$

$x^2 - 3x \qquad = -\dfrac{3}{2}$

$\qquad \qquad + \dfrac{9}{4} \quad +\dfrac{9}{4}$ $\qquad \qquad [\,(-\dfrac{3}{2})^2 = \dfrac{9}{4}\,]$

$x^2 - 3x + \dfrac{9}{4} = -\dfrac{3}{2} + \dfrac{9}{4}$

$(x - \dfrac{3}{2})^2 = -\dfrac{6}{4} + \dfrac{9}{4}$

$(x - \dfrac{3}{2})^2 = \dfrac{3}{4}$

$x - \dfrac{3}{2} = \pm\sqrt{\dfrac{3}{4}} = \pm\dfrac{\sqrt{3}}{2}$

$x = \dfrac{3}{2} \pm \dfrac{\sqrt{3}}{2}$

$x = \dfrac{3 \pm \sqrt{3}}{2}$

33. $4z^2 + 20z + 19 = 0$

$4z^2 + 20z \qquad = -19$

$z^2 + 5z \qquad = -\dfrac{19}{4}$

$\qquad \qquad + \dfrac{25}{4} \quad +\dfrac{25}{4}$ $\qquad \qquad [\,(\dfrac{5}{2})^2 = \dfrac{25}{2}\,]$

$z^2 + 5z + \dfrac{25}{4} = \dfrac{-19}{4} + \dfrac{25}{4}$

$(z + \dfrac{5}{2})^2 = \dfrac{6}{4}$

$z + \dfrac{5}{2} = \pm\sqrt{\dfrac{6}{4}} = \pm\dfrac{\sqrt{6}}{2}$

$z = -\dfrac{5}{2} \pm \dfrac{\sqrt{6}}{2}$

$z = \dfrac{-5 \pm \sqrt{6}}{2}$

35. $(x + 3)^2 = 6$

$x + 3 = \pm\sqrt{6}$

$x = -3 \pm \sqrt{6}$

37. $(x + 3)^2 = 6x$

$x^2 + 6x + 9 = 6x$

$x^2 + 9 = 0$

$x^2 = -9$

This has no real solution.

39. $x^2 + 8x - 9 = 0$

$(x + 9)(x - 1) = 0$

$x + 9 = 0$ or $x - 1 = 0$

$x = -9$ or $x = 1$

41. $3x^2 + 4 = 8x$

$3x^2 - 8x + 4 = 0$

$(3x - 2)(x - 2) = 0$

$3x - 2 = 0$ or $x - 2 = 0$

$x = \dfrac{2}{3}$ or $x = 2$

43. The constant of a perfect square is the square of one-half of the coefficient of the middle term.

44. $\dfrac{x}{x - 1} = \dfrac{2}{x - 2}$

$\dfrac{\cancel{(x - 1)}(x - 2)}{1} \cdot \dfrac{x}{\cancel{x - 1}_1} = \dfrac{(x - 1)\cancel{(x - 2)}}{1} \cdot \dfrac{2}{\cancel{x - 2}_1}$

$x(x - 2) = 2(x - 1)$

$x^2 - 2x = 2x - 2$

$x^2 - 4x = -2$

$\underline{\qquad +4 \qquad\qquad +4 \qquad}$

$x^2 - 4x + 4 = 2$

$(x - 2)^2 = 2$

$x - 2 = \pm\sqrt{2}$

$x = 2 \pm \sqrt{2}$

CHECK: $x = 2 + \sqrt{2}$

$\dfrac{x}{x - 1} = \dfrac{2}{x - 2}$

$\dfrac{2 + \sqrt{2}}{2 + \sqrt{2} - 1} \overset{?}{=} \dfrac{2}{2 + \sqrt{2} - 2}$

$\dfrac{2 + \sqrt{2}}{1 + \sqrt{2}} \overset{?}{=} \dfrac{2}{\sqrt{2}}$

$\dfrac{2 + \sqrt{2}}{1 + \sqrt{2}} = \dfrac{(2 + \sqrt{2})(1 - \sqrt{2})}{(1 + \sqrt{2})(1 - \sqrt{2})} = \dfrac{2 - 2\sqrt{2} + \sqrt{2} - 2}{1 - 2} = \dfrac{-\sqrt{2}}{-1} = \sqrt{2}$

$\dfrac{2}{\sqrt{2}} = \dfrac{2\sqrt{2}}{\sqrt{2}\sqrt{2}} = \dfrac{2\sqrt{2}}{2} = \sqrt{2}$ so $\dfrac{2 + \sqrt{2}}{1 + \sqrt{2}} \overset{\checkmark}{=} \dfrac{2}{\sqrt{2}}$

CHECK: $x = 2 - \sqrt{2}$

$$\frac{x}{x - 1} = \frac{2}{x - 2}$$

$$\frac{2 - \sqrt{2}}{2 - \sqrt{2} - 1} \overset{?}{=} \frac{2}{2 - \sqrt{2} - 2}$$

$$\frac{2 - \sqrt{2}}{1 - \sqrt{2}} \overset{?}{=} \frac{2}{-\sqrt{2}}$$

$$\frac{2 - \sqrt{2}}{1 - \sqrt{2}} = \frac{(2 - \sqrt{2})(1 + \sqrt{2})}{(1 - \sqrt{2})(1 + \sqrt{2})} = \frac{2 + 2\sqrt{2} - \sqrt{2} - 2}{1 - 2} = \frac{\sqrt{2}}{-1} = -\sqrt{2}$$

$$\frac{2}{-\sqrt{2}} = \frac{2\sqrt{2}}{-\sqrt{2}\sqrt{2}} = \frac{2\sqrt{2}}{-2} = -\sqrt{2} \quad \text{so} \quad \frac{2 - \sqrt{2}}{1 - \sqrt{2}} \overset{\checkmark}{=} \frac{2}{-\sqrt{2}}$$

Exercises 10.4

1. $x^2 + 3x - 5 = 0$ $a = 1, b = 3, c = -5$

5. $2u^2 = 8u$

$2u^2 - 8u = 0$ $a = 2, b = -8, c = 0$

9. $x^2 + 3x - 5 = 0$ $a = 1, b = 3, c = -5$

$$x = \frac{-b \pm \sqrt{b^2 - 4ac}}{2a}$$

$$x = \frac{-3 \pm \sqrt{(3)^2 - 4(1)(-5)}}{2(1)}$$

$$x = \frac{-3 \pm \sqrt{9 + 20}}{2}$$

$$x = \frac{-3 \pm \sqrt{29}}{2}$$

13. $u^2 - 2u + 3 = 0$ $a = 1, b = -2, c = 3$

$$u = \frac{-b \pm \sqrt{b^2 - 4ac}}{2a}$$

$$u = \frac{-(-2) \pm \sqrt{(-2)^2 - 4(1)(3)}}{2(1)}$$

$$u = \frac{2 \pm \sqrt{4 - 12}}{2}$$

$$u = \frac{2 \pm \sqrt{-8}}{2}$$

No real solutions, since the answer involves the square root of a negative number.

17. $2x^2 - 3x - 1 = 0$ \qquad\qquad $a = 2, b = -3, c = -1$

$$x = \frac{-b \pm \sqrt{b^2 - 4ac}}{2a}$$

$$x = \frac{-(-3) \pm \sqrt{(-3)^2 - 4(2)(-1)}}{2(2)}$$

$$x = \frac{3 \pm \sqrt{9 + 8}}{4}$$

$$x = \frac{3 \pm \sqrt{17}}{4}$$

19. $5x^2 - x = 2$

$5x^2 - x - 2 = 0$ \qquad\qquad $a = 5, b = -1, c = -2$

$$x = \frac{-b \pm \sqrt{b^2 - 4ac}}{2a}$$

$$x = \frac{-(-1) \pm \sqrt{(-1)^2 - 4(5)(-2)}}{2(5)}$$

$$x = \frac{1 \pm \sqrt{1 + 40}}{10}$$

$$x = \frac{1 \pm \sqrt{41}}{10}$$

21. $t^2 - 3t + 4 = 2t^2 + 4t - 3$

$\qquad -3t + 4 = t^2 + 4t - 3$

$\qquad\qquad 4 = t^2 + 7t - 3$

$\qquad\qquad 0 = t^2 + 7t - 7$ \qquad\qquad $a = 1, b = 7, c = -7$

$$t = \frac{-b \pm \sqrt{b^2 - 4ac}}{2a}$$

$$t = \frac{-7 \pm \sqrt{(7)^2 - 4(1)(-7)}}{2(1)}$$

$$t = \frac{-7 \pm \sqrt{49 + 28}}{2}$$

$$t = \frac{-7 \pm \sqrt{77}}{2}$$

23. $(5w + 2)(w - 1) = 3w + 1$

$\qquad 5w^2 - 3w - 2 = 3w + 1$

$\qquad 5w^2 - 6w - 2 = 1$

$\qquad 5w^2 - 6w - 3 = 0$ \qquad\qquad $a = 5, b = -6, c = -3$

$$w = \frac{-b \pm \sqrt{b^2 - 4ac}}{2a}$$

$$w = \frac{-(-6) \pm \sqrt{(-6)^2 - 4(5)(-3)}}{2(5)}$$

$$w = \frac{6 \pm \sqrt{36 + 60}}{10}$$

$$w = \frac{6 \pm \sqrt{96}}{10}$$

$$w = \frac{6 \pm 4\sqrt{6}}{10} = \frac{2(3 \pm 2\sqrt{6})}{\cancel{10}\,5}$$

$$w = \frac{3 \pm 2\sqrt{6}}{5}$$

27. $3x^2 - 5x + 7 = 2x(x - 5) + 9x + 5$

   $3x^2 - 5x + 7 = 2x^2 - 10x + 9x + 5$

   $3x^2 - 5x + 7 = 2x^2 - x + 5$

   $x^2 - 5x + 7 = -x + 5$

   $x^2 - 4x + 7 = 5$

   $x^2 - 4x + 2 = 0$ $a = 1, \ b = -4, \ c = 2$

   $x = \dfrac{-b \pm \sqrt{b^2 - 4ac}}{2a}$

   $x = \dfrac{-(-4) \pm \sqrt{(-4)^2 - 4(1)(2)}}{2(1)}$

   $x = \dfrac{4 \pm \sqrt{16 - 8}}{2}$

   $x = \dfrac{4 \pm \sqrt{8}}{2}$

   $x = \dfrac{4 \pm 2\sqrt{2}}{2} = \dfrac{\cancel{2}(2 \pm \sqrt{2})}{\cancel{2}} = 2 \pm \sqrt{2}$

31. $x^2(x - 1) = (x - 1)^3$

   $x^3 - x^2 = x^3 - 3x^2 + 3x - 1$

   $-x^2 = -3x^2 + 3x - 1$

   $0 = -2x^2 + 3x - 1$

   $0 = 2x^2 - 3x + 1$ $a = 2, \ b = -3, \ c = 1$

   $x = \dfrac{-b \pm \sqrt{b^2 - 4ac}}{2a}$

   $x = \dfrac{-(-3) \pm \sqrt{(-3)^2 - 4(2)(1)}}{2(2)}$

   $x = \dfrac{3 \pm \sqrt{9 - 8}}{4}$

$$x = \frac{3 \pm \sqrt{1}}{4} = \frac{3 \pm 1}{4}$$

$$x = \frac{3 + 1}{4} = \frac{4}{4} = 1 \text{ or } x = \frac{3 - 1}{4} = \frac{2}{4} = \frac{1}{2}$$

33. $4x = 9x^2$

$0 = 9x^2 - 4x$ $a = 9, b = -4, c = 0$

$$x = \frac{-b \pm \sqrt{b^2 - 4ac}}{2a}$$

$$x = \frac{-(-4) \pm \sqrt{(-4)^2 - 4(9)(0)}}{2(9)}$$

$$x = \frac{4 \pm \sqrt{16 - 0}}{18}$$

$$x = \frac{4 \pm \sqrt{16}}{18}$$

$$x = \frac{4 \pm 4}{18}$$

$$x = \frac{4 + 4}{18} = \frac{8}{18} = \frac{4}{9} \text{ or } x = \frac{4 - 4}{18} = \frac{0}{18} = 0$$

37. $\frac{w}{2} = \frac{3}{w + 2}$

$$\frac{2(w + 2)}{1} \cdot \frac{w}{2}_1 = \frac{2(w + 2)}{1} \cdot \frac{3}{w + 2}_1$$

$w(w + 2) = 6$

$w^2 + 2w = 6$

$w^2 + 2w - 6 = 0$ $a = 1, b = 2, c = -6$

$$w = \frac{-b \pm \sqrt{b^2 - 4ac}}{2a}$$

$$w = \frac{-2 \pm \sqrt{2^2 - 4(1)(-6)}}{2(1)}$$

$$w = \frac{-2 \pm \sqrt{4 + 24}}{2}$$

$$w = \frac{-2 \pm \sqrt{28}}{2}$$

$$w = \frac{-2 \pm 2\sqrt{7}}{2} = \frac{2(-1 \pm \sqrt{7})}{2} = -1 \pm \sqrt{7}$$

41. $2x^2 + 7x + 4 = 0$ $a = 2, \ b = 7, \ c = 4$

$$x = \frac{-b \pm \sqrt{b^2 - 4ac}}{2a}$$

$$x = \frac{-7 \pm \sqrt{7^2 - 4(2)(4)}}{2(2)}$$

$$x = \frac{-7 \pm \sqrt{49 - 32}}{4}$$

$$x = \frac{-7 \pm \sqrt{17}}{4}$$

Using the quadratic formula is easier than the method of completing the square.

42. The factoring method, when it works, is usually the easiest method to use. However, it does not always work. Completing the square and the quadratic formula work for any quadratic equation. Generally, completing the square is the more complicated of these two methods.

43. (a) Since $b = -3$ and $c = -1$, $x = \dfrac{-(-3) \pm \sqrt{9 - 4(-1)}}{2} = \dfrac{3 \pm \sqrt{9 + 4}}{2}$

   $= \dfrac{3 \pm \sqrt{13}}{2}$.

   (b) The minus sign under the square root should be a plus sign.

   (c) The "5" should be divided by 2 as well. That is,

   $x = \dfrac{5 \pm \sqrt{25 - 12}}{2} = \dfrac{5 \pm \sqrt{13}}{2}$.

   (d) This is correct up until the last step. Then $\dfrac{6 \pm 4\sqrt{3}}{2}$

   $= \dfrac{2(3 \pm 2\sqrt{3})}{2} = 3 \pm 2\sqrt{3}$, not $6 \pm 2\sqrt{3}$.

Exercises 10.5

1. $x^2 + 6x + 5 = 0$ $x^2 + 6x \qquad = -5$

   $(x + 1)(x + 5) = 0$ $\underline{\qquad \quad + 9 \quad +9}$

   $x + 1 = 0$ or $x + 5 = 0$ $x^2 + 6x + 9 = \quad 4$

   $x = -1$ or $x = -5$ $(x + 3)^2 = \quad 4$

   $\qquad\qquad\qquad\qquad\qquad\qquad x + 3 = \pm\sqrt{4} = \pm 2$

   $\qquad\qquad\qquad\qquad x + 3 = 2$ or $x + 3 = -2$

   $\qquad\qquad\qquad\qquad\qquad x = -1$ or $x = -5$

5. $2r^2 + 1 = 3r$

  $2r^2 - 3r + 1 = 0$

  $(2r - 1)(r - 1) = 0$

  $2r - 1 = 0$ or $r - 1 = 0$

  $2r = 1$

  $r = \frac{1}{2}$ or $r = 1$

$a = 2, b = -3, c = 1$

$r = \dfrac{-b \pm \sqrt{b^2 - 4ac}}{2a}$

$r = \dfrac{-(-3) \pm \sqrt{(-3)^2 - 4(2)(1)}}{2(2)}$

$r = \dfrac{3 \pm \sqrt{9 - 8}}{4}$

$r = \dfrac{3 \pm \sqrt{1}}{4} = \dfrac{3 \pm 1}{4}$

$r = \dfrac{3 + 1}{4} = \dfrac{4}{4} = 1$ or $r = \dfrac{3 - 1}{4} = \dfrac{2}{4} = \dfrac{1}{2}$

7. $w^2 = 4w + 5$

  $w^2 - 4w = 5$

  $w^2 - 4w - 5 = 0$

  $(w - 5)(w + 1) = 0$

  $w - 5 = 0$ or $w + 1 = 0$

  $w = 5$ or $w = -1$

$w^2 \qquad = 4w + 5$

$w^2 - 4w \qquad = 5$

$\underline{\qquad +4 \qquad\quad +4\qquad}$

$w^2 - 4w + 4 = 9$

$\quad (w - 2)^2 = 9$

$\qquad w - 2 = \pm\sqrt{9} = \pm 3$

$w - 2 = 3$ or $w - 2 = -3$

$w = 5$ or $w = -1$

13. $4x^2 = 16x - 28$

  $4x^2 - 16x = -28$

  $x^2 - 4x \quad = -7$

  $\underline{\qquad +4 \qquad +4\qquad}$

  $x^2 - 4x + 4 = -3$

  $\quad (x - 2)^2 = -3$

  $\qquad x - 2 = \pm\sqrt{-3}$

Thus, there are no real solutions, since square roots of negative numbers are not real.

$4x^2 = 16x - 28$

$4x^2 - 16x = -28$

$4x^2 - 16x + 28 = 0$

$x^2 - 4x + 7 = 0$

$a = 1, b = -4, c = 7$

$x = \dfrac{-b \pm \sqrt{b^2 - 4ac}}{2a}$

$x = \dfrac{-(-4) \pm \sqrt{(-4)^2 - 4(1)(7)}}{2(1)}$

$x = \dfrac{4 \pm \sqrt{16 - 28}}{2}$

$x = \dfrac{4 \pm \sqrt{-12}}{2},$

which leads to the same conclusion for the same reason.

15. $(x - 1)^2 = 5$

$x - 1 = \pm\sqrt{5}$

$x = 1 \pm \sqrt{5}$

$(x - 1)^2 = 5$

$x^2 - 2x + 1 = 5$

$x^2 - 2x - 4 = 0$

$a = 1, \ b = -2, \ c = -4$

$x = \dfrac{-b \pm \sqrt{b^2 - 4ac}}{2a}$

$x = \dfrac{-(-2) \pm \sqrt{(-2)^2 - 4(1)(-4)}}{2(1)}$

$x = \dfrac{2 \pm \sqrt{4 + 16}}{2}$

$x = \dfrac{2 \pm \sqrt{20}}{2}$

$x = \dfrac{2 \pm 2\sqrt{5}}{2}$

$x = \dfrac{2(1 \pm \sqrt{5})}{2}$

$x = 1 \pm \sqrt{5}$

17. $(x - 1)^2 = 5x$

$x^2 - 2x + 1 = 5x$

$x^2 - 7x + 1 = 0$

$a = 1, \ b = -7, \ c = 1$

$x = \dfrac{-b \pm \sqrt{b^2 - 4ac}}{2a}$

$x = \dfrac{-(-7) \pm \sqrt{(-7)^2 - 4(1)(1)}}{2(1)}$

$x = \dfrac{7 \pm \sqrt{49 - 4}}{2}$

$x = \dfrac{7 \pm \sqrt{45}}{2}$

$x = \dfrac{7 \pm 3\sqrt{5}}{2}$

$(x - 1)^2 = 5x$

$x^2 - 2x + 1 = 5x$

$x^2 - 7x + 1 = 0$

$x^2 - 7x \qquad = -1$

$\qquad + \dfrac{49}{4} \quad +\dfrac{49}{4}$

$x^2 - 7x + \dfrac{49}{4} = -1 + \dfrac{49}{4}$

$\left(x - \dfrac{7}{2}\right)^2 = \dfrac{-4}{4} + \dfrac{49}{4}$

$\left(x - \dfrac{7}{2}\right)^2 = \dfrac{45}{4}$

$x - \dfrac{7}{2} = \pm\sqrt{\dfrac{45}{4}} = \pm\dfrac{\sqrt{45}}{2}$

$x - \dfrac{7}{2} = \pm\dfrac{3\sqrt{5}}{2}$

$x = \dfrac{7}{2} \pm \dfrac{3\sqrt{5}}{2}$

$x = \dfrac{7 \pm 3\sqrt{5}}{2}$

21. $y^2 - 4y + 10 = 5(y + 2)$
     $y^2 - 4y + 10 = 5y + 10$
     $y^2 - 9y + 10 = 10$
     $y^2 - 9y = 0$
     $y(y - 9) = 0$
     $y = 0$ or $y - 9 = 0$
     $y = 0$ or $y = 9$

$y^2 - 9y = 0$
$a = 1, b = -9, c = 0$
$$y = \frac{-b \pm \sqrt{b^2 - 4ac}}{2a}$$
$$y = \frac{-(-9) \pm \sqrt{(-9)^2 - 4(1)(0)}}{2(1)}$$
$$y = \frac{9 \pm \sqrt{81 - 0}}{2}$$
$$y = \frac{9 \pm \sqrt{81}}{2}$$
$$y = \frac{9 \pm 9}{2}$$
$$y = \frac{9 + 9}{2} = \frac{18}{2} = 9 \text{ or}$$
$$y = \frac{9 - 9}{2} = \frac{0}{2} = 0$$

23. $(t + 4)(t - 8) = 13$
     $t^2 - 4t - 32 = 13$
     $t^2 - 4t - 45 = 0$
     $(t - 9)(t + 5) = 0$
     $t - 9 = 0$ or $t + 5 = 0$
     $t = 9$ or $t = -5$

$(t + 4)(t - 8) = 13$
$t^2 - 4t - 32 = 13$
$t^2 - 4t \qquad = 45$
$\underline{\qquad + 4 \qquad +4 \qquad}$
$t^2 - 4t + 4 = 49$
$(t - 2)^2 = 49$
$t - 2 = \pm\sqrt{49} = \pm7$
$t - 2 = 7$ or $t - 2 = -7$
$t = 9$ or $t = -5$

27. $z^2 - 3z \qquad = 3z - 9$
     $z^2 - 6z \qquad = -9$
     $z^2 - 6z + 9 = 0$
     $(z - 3)^2 = 0$
     $z - 3 = 0$
     $z = 3$

$z^2 - 3z \qquad = 3z - 9$
$z^2 - 6z \qquad = -9$
$z^2 - 6z + 9 = 0$
$a = 1, b = -6, c = 9$
$$z = \frac{-b \pm \sqrt{b^2 - 4ac}}{2a}$$
$$z = \frac{-(-6) \pm \sqrt{(-6)^2 - 4(1)(9)}}{2(1)}$$
$$z = \frac{6 \pm \sqrt{36 - 36}}{2}$$
$$z = \frac{6 \pm \sqrt{0}}{2}$$
$$z = \frac{6 \pm 0}{2}$$

$$z = \frac{6 + 0}{2} = \frac{6}{2} = 3 \text{ or}$$

$$z = \frac{6 - 0}{2} = \frac{6}{2} = 3, \text{ so } z = 3.$$

33. $x^2 + 1 = \frac{5}{2}x$

$2(x^2 + 1) = 2(\frac{5}{2}x)$

$2x^2 + 2 = \frac{\cancel{2}}{1} \cdot \frac{5}{\cancel{2}}x$

$2x^2 + 2 = 5x$

$2x^2 - 5x + 2 = 0$

$(2x - 1)(x - 2) = 0$

$2x - 1 = 0$ or $x - 2 = 0$

$2x = 1$

$x = \frac{1}{2}$ or $x = 2$

$2x^2 - 5x + 2 = 0$

$a = 2, \ b = -5, \ c = 2$

$x = \frac{-b \pm \sqrt{b^2 - 4ac}}{2a}$

$x = \frac{-(-5) \pm \sqrt{(-5)^2 - 4(2)(2)}}{2(2)}$

$x = \frac{5 \pm \sqrt{25 - 16}}{4}$

$x = \frac{5 \pm \sqrt{9}}{4} = \frac{5 \pm 3}{4}$

$x = \frac{5 + 3}{4} = \frac{8}{4} = 2$ or

$x = \frac{5 - 3}{4} = \frac{2}{4} = \frac{1}{2}$

35. $\frac{x}{x + 1} = \frac{4}{x + 4}$

$\frac{\cancel{(x + 1)}(x + 4)}{1} \cdot \frac{x}{\cancel{x + 1}_1} = \frac{(x + 1)\cancel{(x + 4)}}{1} \cdot \frac{4}{\cancel{x + 4}_1}$

$x(x + 4) = 4(x + 1)$ $x^2 = 4$

$x^2 + 4x = 4x + 4$ $x^2 - 4 = 0$

$x^2 = 4$ $(x - 2)(x + 2) = 0$

$x = \pm\sqrt{4}$ $x - 2 = 0$ or $x + 2 = 0$

$x = \pm 2$ $x = 2$ or $x = -2$

39. $\frac{3x}{x + 1} + \frac{2}{x - 1} = 4$

$(x + 1)(x - 1)(\frac{3x}{x + 1} + \frac{2}{x - 1}) = (x + 1)(x - 1)(4)$

$\frac{\cancel{(x + 1)}(x - 1)}{1} \cdot \frac{3x}{\cancel{x + 1}_1} + \frac{(x + 1)\cancel{(x - 1)}}{1} \cdot \frac{2}{\cancel{x - 1}_1} = 4(x + 1)(x - 1)$

$3x(x - 1) + 2(x + 1) = 4(x + 1)(x - 1)$

$3x^2 - 3x + 2x + 2 = 4(x^2 - 1)$

$3x^2 - x + 2 = 4x^2 - 4$

$-x + 2 = x^2 - 4$

$2 = x^2 + x - 4$

$0 = x^2 + x - 6$

$$0 = (x + 3)(x - 2)$$

$$0 = x + 3 \text{ or } 0 = x - 2$$

$$-3 = x \text{ or } 2 = x$$

$$x^2 + x - 6 = 0$$

$$a = 1, \; b = 1, \; c = -6$$

$$x = \frac{-b \pm \sqrt{b^2 - 4ac}}{2a}$$

$$x = \frac{-1 \pm \sqrt{1^2 - 4(1)(-6)}}{2(1)}$$

$$x = \frac{-1 \pm \sqrt{1 + 24}}{2}$$

$$x = \frac{-1 \pm \sqrt{25}}{2}$$

$$x = \frac{-1 \pm 5}{2}$$

$$x = \frac{-1 + 5}{2} = \frac{4}{2} = 2 \text{ or}$$

$$x = \frac{-1 - 5}{2} = \frac{-6}{2} = -3$$

41. $2x^2 + 3x = 20$

Method 1 - factoring:

$$2x^2 + 3x - 20 = 0$$

$$(2x - 5)(x + 4) = 0$$

$$2x - 5 = 0 \text{ or } x + 4 = 0$$

$$2x = 5$$

$$x = \frac{5}{2} \text{ or } x = -4$$

Method 2 - completing the square:

$$2x^2 + 3x \qquad = 20$$

$$x^2 + \frac{3}{2}x \qquad = 10$$

$$+ \frac{9}{16} \quad + \frac{9}{16}$$

$$\overline{x^2 + \frac{3}{2}x + \frac{9}{16} = 10 + \frac{9}{16}}$$

$$\left(x + \frac{3}{4}\right)^2 = \frac{160}{16} + \frac{9}{16}$$

$$\left(x + \frac{3}{4}\right)^2 = \frac{169}{16}$$

$$x + \frac{3}{4} = \pm\sqrt{\frac{169}{16}} = \pm\frac{\sqrt{169}}{\sqrt{16}}$$

$$x + \frac{3}{4} = \pm\frac{13}{4}$$

$$x = -\frac{3}{4} \pm \frac{13}{4}$$

$$x = \frac{-3 \pm 13}{4}$$

$$x = \frac{-3 + 13}{4} = \frac{10}{4} = \frac{5}{2} \text{ or}$$

$$x = \frac{-3 - 13}{4} = \frac{-16}{4} = -4$$

Method 3 - quadratic formula:

$$2x^2 + 3x - 20 = 0$$

$$a = 2, \ b = 3, \ c = -20$$

$$x = \frac{-b \pm \sqrt{b^2 - 4ac}}{2a}$$

$$x = \frac{-3 \pm \sqrt{3^2 - 4(2)(-20)}}{2(2)}$$

$$x = \frac{-3 \pm \sqrt{9 + 160}}{4}$$

$$x = \frac{-3 \pm \sqrt{169}}{4} = \frac{-3 \pm 13}{4}$$

$$x = \frac{-3 + 13}{4} = \frac{10}{4} = \frac{5}{2} \text{ or}$$

$$x = \frac{-3 - 13}{4} = \frac{-16}{4} = -4$$

The easiest of these methods is the first, while the second one appears to be the most difficult.

42. $3x^2 - 5x - 1 = 0$ $a = 3, \ b = -5, \ c = -1$

$$x = \frac{-b \pm \sqrt{b^2 - 4ac}}{2a}$$

$$x = \frac{-(-5) \pm \sqrt{(-5)^2 - 4(3)(-1)}}{2(3)}$$

$$x = \frac{5 \pm \sqrt{25 + 12}}{6} = \frac{5 \pm \sqrt{37}}{6}$$

CHECK: $x = \dfrac{5 + \sqrt{37}}{6}$

$$3x^2 - 5x - 1 = 0$$

$$3\left(\frac{5 + \sqrt{37}}{6}\right)^2 - 5\left(\frac{5 + \sqrt{37}}{6}\right) - 1 \overset{?}{=} 0$$

$$3\left(\frac{5 + \sqrt{37}}{6}\right)\left(\frac{5 + \sqrt{37}}{6}\right) - 5\left(\frac{5 + \sqrt{37}}{6}\right) - 1 \overset{?}{=} 0$$

$$\frac{\cancel{3}}{1}\left(\frac{25 + 10\sqrt{37} + 37}{\underset{12}{\cancel{36}}}\right) - \frac{5}{1}\left(\frac{5 + \sqrt{37}}{6}\right) - 1 \overset{?}{=} 0$$

$$\frac{62 + 10\sqrt{37}}{12} - \frac{25 + 5\sqrt{37}}{6} - 1 \overset{?}{=} 0$$

$$\frac{\cancel{2}(31 + 5\sqrt{37})}{\underset{6}{\cancel{12}}} - \frac{25 + 5\sqrt{37}}{6} - 1 \overset{?}{=} 0$$

$$\frac{31 + 5\sqrt{37} - (25 + 5\sqrt{37})}{6} - 1 \overset{?}{=} 0$$

$$\frac{6}{6} - 1 \overset{?}{=} 0$$

$$1 - 1 \overset{?}{=} 0$$

$$0 \overset{\checkmark}{=} 0$$

$$3x^2 - 5x - 1 = 0$$

$$\underline{\qquad\qquad + 1 \quad +1}$$

$$3x^2 - 5x \qquad = 1$$

$$x^2 - \frac{5}{3}x \qquad = \frac{1}{3}$$

$$\underline{\qquad\qquad +\frac{25}{36} \quad +\frac{25}{36}}$$

$$x^2 - \frac{5}{3}x + \frac{25}{36} = \frac{1}{3} + \frac{25}{36}$$

$$(x - \frac{5}{6})^2 = \frac{12}{36} + \frac{25}{36}$$

$$(x - \frac{5}{6})^2 = \frac{37}{36}$$

$$x - \frac{5}{6} = \pm\sqrt{\frac{37}{36}} = \pm\frac{\sqrt{37}}{\sqrt{36}}$$

$$x - \frac{5}{6} = \pm\frac{\sqrt{37}}{6}$$

$$x = \frac{5}{6} \pm \frac{\sqrt{37}}{6} = \frac{5 \pm \sqrt{37}}{6}$$

The second method of checking was by far easier in this example. The first check was more complicated than the actual solution. If the first check happened to fail, we really would not know whether an error was made in the solution to the problem or in the check of that solution. Further, the first check only verified that $x = \dfrac{5 + \sqrt{37}}{6}$ is a valid solution. We would still have to examine $x = \dfrac{5 - \sqrt{37}}{6}$ and verify that it satisfied the equation as well.

Exercises 10.6

3. Let x = one of the numbers
    20 - x = the other number

    $x(20 - x) = 96$

    $20x - x^2 = 96$ CHECK: $8 + 12 \overset{\checkmark}{=} 20$

    $x^2 - 20x + 96 = 0$ $8(12) \overset{\checkmark}{=} 96$

    $(x - 8)(x - 12) = 0$

    $x - 8 = 0$ or $x - 12 = 0$

    $x = 8$ or $x = 12$

    If x = 8, then 20 - x = 20 - 8 = 12. If x = 12, then 20 - x = 20 - 12 = 8. In both cases, we conclude that the numbers are 8 and 12.

5. Let W = width of the rectangle
    2W + 3 = length of the rectangle

    $W(2W + 3) = 90$

    $2W^2 + 3W = 90$ CHECK: 15 is 3 more than twice

    $2W^2 + 3W - 90 = 0$ 6, and 15(6) = 90.

    $(2W + 15)(W - 6) = 0$

    $2W + 15 = 0$ or $W - 6 = 0$

    $W = -\dfrac{15}{2}$ or $W = 6$
        ↑
    Reject this, since width
    cannot be negative.

    So W = 6. Then 2W + 3 = 2(6) + 3 = 15. Thus, the rectangle
    has a width of 6 meters and a length of 15 meters.

9. Let d = length of the diagonal. From the Pythagorean Theorem,
    we get

    $8^2 + 8^2 = d^2$ CHECK: $8^2 + 8^2 \overset{?}{=} (8\sqrt{2})^2$

    $64 + 64 = d^2$ $64 + 64 \overset{?}{=} 64 \cdot 2$

    $128 = d^2$ $128 \overset{\checkmark}{=} 128$

    $\pm\sqrt{128} = d$

    $\pm 8\sqrt{2} = d$

    Reject d = $-8\sqrt{2}$, since we cannot have a negative length. So
    d = $8\sqrt{2}$. Thus, the length of the diagonal is $8\sqrt{2}$ inches.

13. Let x = length of the shortest side
    x + 1 = length of the middle side
    x + 2 = length of the longest side

    Using the Pythagorean Theorem, it follows that

    $x^2 + (x + 1)^2 = (x + 2)^2$

    $x^2 + x^2 + 2x + 1 = x^2 + 4x + 4$

    $2x^2 + 2x + 1 = x^2 + 4x + 4$

    $x^2 - 2x - 3 = 0$

    $(x - 3)(x + 1) = 0$

    $x - 3 = 0$ or $x + 1 = 0$

    $x = 3$ or $x = -1$

    Reject x = -1, since the side of a triangle cannot have
    negative length. So x = 3. Then x + 1 = 3 + 1 = 4 and
    x + 2 = 3 + 2 = 5. Thus, the sides of the triangle have
    lengths of 3, 4, and 5.   CHECK: 3, 4, and 5 are three
    consecutive integers and $3^2 + 4^2 = 9 + 16 = 25 = 5^2$.

15. Let n = numerator of the original fraction
    n + 1 = denominator of the original fraction

$$\frac{n + 3}{n + 1} = \frac{n}{n + 1} + 1$$

$$(n + 1)(\frac{n + 3}{n + 1}) = (n + 1)(\frac{n}{n + 1} + 1)$$

$$\frac{\cancel{n + 1}^{1}}{1} \cdot \frac{n + 3}{\cancel{n + 1}_{1}} = \frac{\cancel{n + 1}^{1}}{1} \cdot \frac{n}{\cancel{n + 1}_{1}} + (n + 1) \cdot 1$$

n + 3 = n + n + 1   CHECK: $\frac{2 + 3}{3} = \frac{5}{3}$, which is
n + 3 = 2n + 1   one more than $\frac{2}{3}$.
    3 = n + 1
    2 = n

Then n + 1 = 2 + 1 = 3. Thus, the original fraction is $\frac{2}{3}$.

17. Let s = # of seats in each row
    s - 8 = # of rows of seats

s(s - 8) = 768   CHECK: 24 is eight less than
s^2 - 8s = 768   32, and 24 · 32 = 768.

s^2 - 8s - 768 = 0

(s - 32)(s + 24) = 0

s - 32 = 0 or s + 24 = 0

s = 32 or s = -24

Reject s = -24, since the number of seats in a row cannot be
negative. So s = 32. Then s - 8 = 32 - 8 = 24. Thus, there
are 24 rows of seats in the concert hall, and each row has
32 seats in it.

19. Let x = speed of the motorist for first part of trip
    x - 20 = speed of the motorist for second part of trip.

$$\frac{120}{x} + \frac{30}{x - 20} = 2$$

$$x(x - 20)(\frac{120}{x} + \frac{30}{x - 20}) = x(x - 20) \cdot 2$$

$$\frac{\cancel{x}(x - 20)}{1} \cdot \frac{120}{\cancel{x}_{1}} + \frac{x\cancel{(x - 20)}}{1} \cdot \frac{30}{\cancel{x - 20}_{1}} = 2x(x - 20)$$

120(x - 20) + 30x = 2x(x - 20)

120x - 2400 + 30x = $2x^2$ - 40x

150x - 2400 = $2x^2$ - 40x

0 = $2x^2$ - 190x + 2400

0 = x^2 - 95x + 1200

0 = (x - 15)(x - 80)

0 = x - 15 or 0 = x - 80

15 = x or 80 = x

We reject x = 15, since this would mean that x - 20 = 15 - 20 = -5, and a negative speed is impossible. So x = 80. Thus, the motorist's speed for the first part of the trip is 80 kph.

CHECK: At 80 kph, the motorist covers 120 kilometers in $\frac{120}{80}$ = $\frac{3}{2}$ hours. At (80 - 20) = 60 kph, the motorist covers the remaining 30 kilometers in $\frac{30}{60}$ = $\frac{1}{2}$ hour. Then $\frac{3}{2}$ + $\frac{1}{2}$ = $\frac{4}{2}$ = 2 hours, as required.

21. When x = 5, P = $1000(-(5)^2 + 15(5) - 35)$

$\qquad\qquad\qquad$ = $1000(-25 + 75 - 35)$

$\qquad\qquad\qquad$ = $1000(15)$ = \$15,000

When x = 4, P = $1000(-(4)^2 + 15(4) - 35)$

$\qquad\qquad\qquad$ = $1000(-16 + 60 - 35)$

$\qquad\qquad\qquad$ = $1000(9)$ = \$9,000.

23. (a) $\dfrac{1}{\ell}$ = $\dfrac{\ell}{1 + \ell}$

$\dfrac{\cancel{\ell}(1 + \ell)}{1} \cdot \dfrac{1}{\cancel{\ell}_1}$ = $\dfrac{\ell\cancel{(1 + \ell)}}{1} \cdot \dfrac{\ell}{\cancel{1 + \ell}_1}$

$1 + \ell = \ell^2$

$0 = \ell^2 - \ell - 1$

$a = 1,\ b = -1,\ c = -1$

$\ell = \dfrac{-b \pm \sqrt{b^2 - 4ac}}{2a}$

$\ell = \dfrac{-(-1) \pm \sqrt{(-1)^2 - 4(1)(-1)}}{2(1)}$

$\ell = \dfrac{1 \pm \sqrt{1 + 4}}{2}$ = $\dfrac{1 \pm \sqrt{5}}{2}$

So $\ell = \dfrac{1 + \sqrt{5}}{2}$ or $\ell = \dfrac{1 - \sqrt{5}}{2}$. Since $\sqrt{5}$ is greater than 1, $\dfrac{1 - \sqrt{5}}{2}$ is negative, and thus must be rejected. So $\ell = \dfrac{1 + \sqrt{5}}{2}$ inches.

(b) $\dfrac{w}{\ell}$ = $\dfrac{\ell}{w + \ell}$

$\dfrac{\cancel{\ell}(w + \ell)}{1} \cdot \dfrac{w}{\cancel{\ell}_1}$ = $\dfrac{\ell\cancel{(w + \ell)}}{1} \cdot \dfrac{\ell}{\cancel{w + \ell}_1}$

$$w(w + \ell) = \ell^2$$
$$w^2 + w\ell = \ell^2$$
$$0 = \ell^2 - w\ell - w^2$$
$$a = 1, \ b = -w, \ c = -w^2$$
$$\ell = \frac{-b \pm \sqrt{b^2 - 4ac}}{2a}$$
$$\ell = \frac{-(-w) \pm \sqrt{(-w)^2 - 4(1)(-w^2)}}{2(1)}$$
$$\ell = \frac{w \pm \sqrt{w^2 + 4w^2}}{2}$$
$$\ell = \frac{w \pm \sqrt{5w^2}}{2}$$
$$\ell = \frac{w \pm \sqrt{5}w}{2} = \frac{(1 \pm \sqrt{5})w}{2}$$

As in part (a), we reject $\frac{(1 - \sqrt{5})w}{2}$ because it is negative.
Thus, $\ell = \frac{(1 + \sqrt{5})w}{2}$. (If w = 1, we get the golden ratio
of part (a).)

24. $\dfrac{1}{x - 1} = \dfrac{x}{1}$

$\dfrac{x - 1}{1} \cdot \dfrac{1}{x - 1} = \dfrac{x - 1}{1} \cdot \dfrac{x}{1}$

$1 = x(x - 1)$
$1 = x^2 - x$
$0 = x^2 - x - 1$

Proceed with the quadratic formula to find that $x = \dfrac{1 + \sqrt{5}}{2}$.

(This quadratic equation is the same as the one encountered in
part (a) of exercise (23), except for the letter used to
represent the variable.)

25. Let x = length of the shortest side
x + 2 = length of the middle side
x + 4 = length of the longest side

Use the Pythagorean Theorem to find that
$$x^2 + (x + 2)^2 = (x + 4)^2$$

Then
$$x^2 + x^2 + 4x + 4 = x^2 + 8x + 16$$
$$2x^2 + 4x + 4 = x^2 + 8x + 16$$
$$x^2 - 4x - 12 = 0$$
$$(x - 6)(x + 2) = 0$$

$x - 6 = 0$ or $x + 2 = 0$

$x = 6$ or $x = -2$

Reject $x = 6$, since it is not odd. Reject $x = -2$, since we cannot have a negative length. Since both possible solutions to the problem have been rejected, we conclude that it is impossible to find three consecutive odd integers that are the sides of a right triangle.

Chapter 10 Review Exercises

1. $x^2 - 7x - 6 = 0$ $\qquad\qquad$ $a = 1$, $b = -7$, $c = -6$

$x = \dfrac{-b \pm \sqrt{b^2 - 4ac}}{2a}$

$x = \dfrac{-(-7) \pm \sqrt{(-7)^2 - 4(1)(-6)}}{2(1)}$

$x = \dfrac{7 \pm \sqrt{49 + 24}}{2} = \dfrac{7 \pm \sqrt{73}}{2}$

3. $x^2 + 5 = 4x$

$x^2 - 4x + 5 = 0$

$x^2 - 4x \qquad = -5$

$\underline{\qquad\quad + 4 \qquad +4}$

$x^2 - 4x + 4 = -1$

$(x - 2)^2 = -1$

$x - 2 = \pm\sqrt{-1}$

Therefore, there are no real solutions.

5. $(u - 6)^2 = 13$

$u - 6 = \pm\sqrt{13}$

$u = 6 \pm \sqrt{13}$

7. $2y^2 + 7y = 15$

$2y^2 + 7y - 15 = 0$

$(2y - 3)(y + 5) = 0$

$2y - 3 = 0$ or $y + 5 = 0$

$y = \dfrac{3}{2}$ or $y = -5$

9. $18x^2 - 24x + 6 = 0$

$3x^2 - 4x + 1 = 0$

$(3x - 1)(x - 1) = 0$

$3x - 1 = 0$ or $x - 1 = 0$

$x = \dfrac{1}{3}$ or $x = 1$

11. $(x - 6)^2 = (x + 3)(x - 5)$

$x^2 - 12x + 36 = x^2 - 2x - 15$

$-12x + 36 = -2x - 15$

$36 = 10x - 15$

$51 = 10x$

$\dfrac{51}{10} = x$

13. $u^2 + 1 = \dfrac{13u}{6}$

$6(u^2 + 1) = \dfrac{\cancel{6}}{1} \cdot \dfrac{13u}{\cancel{6}_1}$

$6u^2 + 6 = 13u$

$6u^2 - 13u + 6 = 0$

$(3u - 2)(2u - 3) = 0$

$3u - 2 = 0$ or $2u - 3 = 0$

$u = \dfrac{2}{3}$ or $u = \dfrac{3}{2}$

15. $3x(x - 2) = (x - 3)^2$

$3x^2 - 6x = x^2 - 6x + 9$

$2x^2 - 6x = -6x + 9$

$2x^2 = 9$

$x^2 = \dfrac{9}{2}$

$x = \pm\sqrt{\dfrac{9}{2}} = \pm\dfrac{\sqrt{9}}{\sqrt{2}} = \pm\dfrac{3}{\sqrt{2}} = \pm\dfrac{3\sqrt{2}}{\sqrt{2}\sqrt{2}}$

$x = \pm\dfrac{3\sqrt{2}}{2}$

17. $\dfrac{x + 3}{x + 6} = \dfrac{x + 2}{x + 4}$

$\dfrac{\cancel{(x + 6)}(x + 4)}{1} \cdot \dfrac{x + 3}{\cancel{x + 6}_1} = \dfrac{(x + 6)\cancel{(x + 4)}}{1} \cdot \dfrac{x + 2}{\cancel{x + 4}_1}$

$(x + 4)(x + 3) = (x + 6)(x + 2)$

$x^2 + 7x + 12 = x^2 + 8x + 12$

$7x + 12 = 8x + 12$

$7x = 8x$

$0 = x$

19. $x^2 - 7x + 3 = 0$

$x^2 - 7x \quad\;\;\, = -3$

$\qquad\quad +\dfrac{49}{4} \quad +\dfrac{49}{4}$

$x^2 - 7x + \dfrac{49}{4} = -3 + \dfrac{49}{4}$

$(x - \dfrac{7}{2})^2 = -\dfrac{12}{4} + \dfrac{49}{4}$

$(x - \dfrac{7}{2})^2 = \dfrac{37}{4}$

$x - \dfrac{7}{2} = \pm\sqrt{\dfrac{37}{4}} = \pm\dfrac{\sqrt{37}}{\sqrt{4}} = \pm\dfrac{\sqrt{37}}{2}$

$x = \dfrac{7}{2} \pm \dfrac{\sqrt{37}}{2} = \dfrac{7 \pm \sqrt{37}}{2}$

Chapter 10 Practice Test

1. $(x + 5)(x - 2) = 18$

$x^2 + 3x - 10 = 18$

$x^2 + 3x - 28 = 0$

$(x + 7)(x - 4) = 0$

$x + 7 = 0$ or $x - 4 = 0$

$x = -7$ or $x = 4$

3. $x^2 - x - 14 = 2x(x - 3)$

$x^2 - x - 14 = 2x^2 - 6x$

$0 = x^2 - 5x + 14$

$a = 1, \ b = -5, \ c = 14$

$x = \dfrac{-b \pm \sqrt{b^2 - 4ac}}{2a}$

$x = \dfrac{-(-5) \pm \sqrt{(-5)^2 - 4(1)(14)}}{2(1)}$

$x = \dfrac{5 \pm \sqrt{25 - 56}}{2}$

$x = \dfrac{5 \pm \sqrt{-31}}{2}$

Since a negative number appears under the square root, there are no real solutions.

5. $(x + 5)^2 = 10x$

$x^2 + 10x + 25 = 10x$

$x^2 + 25 = 0$

$x^2 = -25$

$x = \pm\sqrt{-25}$

Since square roots of negative numbers are not real, the equation has no real solutions.

7. $5x^2 + 15 = 30x$

$5x^2 - 30x + 15 = 0$

$5(x^2 - 6x + 3) = 0$

$x^2 - 6x + 3 = 0$

$a = 1, \ b = -6, \ c = 3$

$$x = \frac{-b \pm \sqrt{b^2 - 4ac}}{2a}$$

$$x = \frac{-(-6) \pm \sqrt{(-6)^2 - 4(1)(3)}}{2(1)}$$

$$x = \frac{6 \pm \sqrt{36 - 12}}{2}$$

$$x = \frac{6 \pm \sqrt{24}}{2}$$

$$x = \frac{6 \pm 2\sqrt{6}}{2}$$

$$x = \frac{\cancel{2}(3 \pm \sqrt{6})}{\cancel{2}} = 3 \pm \sqrt{6}$$

9.
$$3x^2 - 12x = 7$$
$$x^2 - 4x = \frac{7}{3}$$
$$\underline{\qquad\qquad +4 = +4}$$
$$x^2 - 4x + 4 = \frac{7}{3} + 4$$
$$(x - 2)^2 = \frac{19}{3}$$
$$x - 2 = \pm\sqrt{\frac{19}{3}}$$
$$x - 2 = \pm\frac{\sqrt{19}}{\sqrt{3}}$$
$$x - 2 = \pm\frac{\sqrt{19}\sqrt{3}}{\sqrt{3}\sqrt{3}}$$
$$x - 2 = \pm\frac{\sqrt{57}}{3}$$
$$x = 2 \pm \frac{\sqrt{57}}{3}$$
$$x = \frac{6 \pm \sqrt{57}}{3}$$

$$3x^2 - 12x = 7$$
$$3x^2 - 12x - 7 = 0$$
$$a = 3, \ b = -12, \ c = -7$$
$$x = \frac{-b \pm \sqrt{b^2 - 4ac}}{2a}$$
$$x = \frac{-(-12) \pm \sqrt{(-12)^2 - 4(3)(-7)}}{2(3)}$$
$$x = \frac{12 \pm \sqrt{144 + 84}}{6}$$
$$x = \frac{12 \pm \sqrt{228}}{6}$$
$$x = \frac{12 \pm 2\sqrt{57}}{6}$$
$$x = \frac{\cancel{2}(6 \pm \sqrt{57})}{\cancel{6}_3}$$
$$x = \frac{6 \pm \sqrt{57}}{3}$$

Appendix A Exercises

1.
```
   4.7
   3.5
+21.7
-----
 29.9
```

5.
```
 21.620
  4.100
+57.236
-------
 82.956
```

7.
```
 9.27
-7.85
-----
 1.42
```

11.
```
  13.05
x  2.63
-------
  3915
  7830
  2610
-------
34.3215
```

15.
```
       7.92
   5 )39.60
     35
     --
      46
      45
      --
       10
       10
       --
        0
```

19. $.16.\overline{)5.28.}$ becomes

$$16\overline{)\begin{array}{r}20.5\\ 328.0\end{array}}$$
$$\begin{array}{r}32\\ \hline 80\\ 80\\ \hline 0\end{array}$$

23. $.015.\overline{)5.900.}$ becomes

$$15\overline{)\begin{array}{r}260\\ 3900\end{array}}$$
$$\begin{array}{r}30\\ \hline 90\\ 90\\ \hline 00\\ 00\\ \hline 0\end{array}$$

25. $28\% = \dfrac{28}{100} = .28$ 27. $.67 = \dfrac{67}{100} = 67\%$

31. $137\% = \dfrac{137}{100} = 1.37$ 33. $.007 = \dfrac{.7}{100} = .7\%$

35. $62.4\% = \dfrac{62.4}{100} = .624$ 39. 30% of $70 = .30(70) = 21$

41. 7.2% of $35 = .072(35) = 2.52$

43. $.8\%$ of $5 = .008(5) = .04$

Chapter Tests, Cumulative Reviews and Cumulative Tests, Practice Final

Chapter 1 Test A

1. Let A = { 5, 10, 15, 20, ..., 40} and let
    B = { x| x is an even integer between 13 and 31}.
    Answer parts (a) through (d) "True" or "False":
    (a) 24 ∈ A   (b) 24 ∈ B
    (c) 12 ∈ B   (d) A has more elements than B
    (e) List the set C = { x| x ∈ A and x ∈ B}.

In each of the following problems, compute the given expression.

2. -8 + 1 - 2 - 4 + 5

3. |2 - 7| + |7 - 2|

4. 2 + (-5) - (-3) - 4

5. $\dfrac{(-2)(-5)(-3)}{-4 - 6}$

6. $\dfrac{(+1) - (-2)(-3)}{(+1)(-2) - (-3)}$

7. (3 + 2)(5 - 9)

8. 3 + 2 · 5 - 9

9. -9[3 + 2(5 - 9)]

10. 7 - 2[7 + 2(7 - 2)]

Chapter 1 Test B

1. Let $A = \{3, 6, 9, 12, \ldots, 27\}$ and let
    $B = \{x \mid x$ is a prime less than $27\}$.

    Answer parts (a) through (d) "True" or "False":

    (a) $21 \in A$ (b) $21 \in B$

    (c) $2 \in B$ (d) A has fewer elements than B

    (e) List the set $C = \{x \mid x \in A$ and $x \in B\}$

In each of the following problems, compute the given expression.

2. $6 - 3 - 7 + 1 - 2$

3. $|3 - 5| - |3 + 5|$

4. $-5 - (-1) + 6 + (-2)$

5. $\dfrac{(-4)(-3)(+2)}{5 - (-1)}$

6. $\dfrac{-1 - (-3)(-5)}{(-1)(-3) - (-5)}$

7. $(2 - 4 \cdot 3) - 6$

8. $2 - (4 \cdot 3 - 6)$

9. $5[(2 - 4)(3 - 6)]$

10. $1 + 3[1 - 3(1 + 3)]$

Chapter 2 Test A

In problems 1-4, evaluate each of the given expressions.

1. $(-2)^6$ 2. -2^6

3. $(-8 + 5 - (-2))^7$ 4. $3 - 5(3 - 5)^3$

In problems 5-8, evaluate the given expression for $x = -1$, $y = 4$, and $z = -2$.

5. $x + y - z$ 6. $x(y - z)$

7. $x^2y - xz^3$ 8. $|xy - z| + z$

In problems 9-13, perform the indicated operations and simplify as completely as possible.

9. $x^4 - 2xy^3 + x^3y - 3xy^3 + 4x^4 - 6x^3y$

10. $-5x^3y^2(-2xy)(xy^4)$

11. $x(xy - 3y^2) + 3y(xy + x) - xy(x + 1)$

12. $4x^2y^2(x + 2y^3) - 8xy^3(xy^2)$

13. $3 + [x - 2(x + 1)]$

14. If we let n stand for the "number," translate each of the following phrases:

(a) three less than four times a number

(b) seven more than three times a number is equal to one less than the number

15. Tin plates cost \$4 each and copper plates cost \$7 each. A customer bought a certain number of tin plates and one less than three times that many copper plates.

(a) How many tin plates did the customer buy?

(b) How much does a copper plate cost?

(c) How many copper plates did the customer buy?

(d) How much does a tin plate cost?

(e) How much did the customer spend on the copper plates?

(f) How much did the customer spend on the tin plates?

(g) How much did the customer spend altogether?

Chapter 2 Test B

In problems 1-4, evaluate each of the given expressions.

1. $(-4)^3$ 2. -4^3

3. $(5 - 8 - (-1))^4$ 4. $1 - 2(1 - 2)^7$

In problems 5-8, evaluate the given expression for $x = 2$, $y = -3$, and $z = -1$.

5. $2x - y + z$ 6. $2(x - y) + z$

7. $x^3 - xyz^2$ 8. $|x + y| + |xy|z$

In problems 9-13, perform the indicated operations and simplify as completely as possible.

9. $2x^2y^2 - xy - 3x^3 + 5xy - x^3 + 4x^2y^2$

10. $3xy^4(-x^3y^2)(-2xy^3)$

11. $y(x^3y + 2x) - x(xy + x^2y^2) - 2xy(1 - x)$

12. $5x^3y^3(y - 4x) + 2xy^2(10x^3y)$

13. $4 - [x + 3(x - 2)]$

14. If we let n stand for the "number," translate each of the following phrases:

(a) four times three less than a number

(b) six more than five times a number is equal to ten more than the number

15. Walnuts cost $5 a pound and cashews cost $6 a pound. Mrs. O'Brien bought a certain number of pounds of walnuts and one more than four times that many pounds of cashews.

(a) How much does a pound of cashews cost?

(b) How many pounds of walnuts did Mrs. O'Brien buy?

(c) How much does a pound of walnuts cost?

(d) How many pounds of cashews did Mrs. O'Brien buy?

(e) How much did Mrs. O'Brien spend on walnuts?

(f) How much did Mrs. O'Brien spend on cashews?

(g) How much did Mrs. O'Brien spend altogether?

Chapter 3 Test A

1. Determine whether the given equation is conditional, an identity, or a contradiction.

(a) $2x - 4(2x - 1) = -6x + 4$

(b) $2x - 4(2x - 1) = 6x + 4$

(c) $2x - 4(2x - 1) = -6x - 4$

2. Determine whether or not the given value is a solution to the equation or inequality.

(a) $x(x - 2) - (x + 1) = -2 - x$; $x = -1$

(b) $s(s + 5) + 2 = (s + 1)(s + 4) - 2$; $s = 2$

(c) $5 + 4(u + 3) > 9$; $u = -2$

3. Solve each of the following equations or inequalities.

(a) $4 + 2a = -2a + 16$

(b) $3(2z + 1) - (2 - z) = 4(z - 1) - 1$

(c) $t^2 - t(1 - t) = 2t(t - 2) + 12$

(d) Solve and sketch the solution set on a number line:
$5 - 3(x + 1) \leq -4$

(e) Solve and sketch the solution set on a number line:
$-7 < 1 - 4x < 13$.

4. One number is 7 more than 4 times another number. Find the numbers if their sum is 32.

5. A purse contains only dimes and quarters. If there are 16 coins altogether, and their total value is $2.50, how many of each type of coin are there in the purse?

6. A man leaves his home and travels at the rate of 40 mph. One hour later, his wife leaves and travels along the same road at the rate of 60 mph. How far from their home will she catch up to her husband?

Chapter 3 Test B

1. Determine whether the given equation is conditional, an identity, or a contradiction.

(a) $4x - 3(1 - x) = x - 3$

(b) $4x - 3(1 - x) = 7x + 3$

(c) $4x - 3(1 - x) = 7x - 3$

2. Determine whether or not the given value is a solution to the equation or inequality.

(a) $(x + 3)(x - 1) - (3 - x) = 2x$; $x = 2$

(b) $b(b - 4) + 3 = b^2 + 7b$; $b = -1$

(c) $-2 - 5(t - 1) \leq 13$; $t = -2$

3. Solve each of the following equations or inequalities.

(a) $-2 + 5n = -2n + 5$

(b) $3(3 - y) - 4(y + 4) = 2 - 4y$

(c) $4t^2 + 10 = 2t(2t + 1)$

(d) Solve and sketch the solution set on a number line:
$2 + 3(4 - x) < 2$

(e) Solve and sketch the solution set on a number line:
$-4 \leq 2 - 3x \leq -1$

4. Admission to a play costs $3 for a child's ticket and $5 for an adult's ticket. If 100 people attend the play and $380 is collected, how many children's tickets were sold?

5. Two sides of a triangle are equal in length. The third side is three less than the sum of the other two. If the perimeter of the triangle is 25 inches, find the lengths of its sides.

6. If 11 more than 3 times a number is 1 less than 5 times the number, what is the number?

Cumulative Review: Chapters 1-3

In exercises 1-24, perform the indicated operations and simplify as completely as possible.

1. $-2 - 3 - 4$ 2. $(-2)(-3)(-4)$

3. $(8 - 2 \cdot 3) - 1$ 4. $8 - (2 \cdot 3 - 1)$

5. $(-3)^4$ 6. -3^4

7. $a^2 a^4 a^6$ 8. $3bb^5 b^2 + 2b^3 b^4 b$

9. $3r^3 s^5 - 5r^5 s^3 + r^5 s^3 - r^3 s^5$

10. $6y^2 + 3y - 4 - 5y^2 - 6y + 2$

11. $3x^2(2y - 5z)$ 12. $3x^2(2y)(-5z)$

13. $-t^3(u^2)(-6t)$ 14. $-t^3(u^2 - 6t)$

15. $8(p + 2q) - 4(p - 4q)$ 16. $6(3c^5 - 2d^4) + 4(3d^4 - 2c^5)$

17. $v^2 w^3(5vw + 6v^3 w^2) - v^3 w^2(4w^2 - 3v^2 w^3)$

18. $2xz^3(3yz - x^2 y) + 3yz^2(x^3 z - 2xz^2)$

19. $5a^2 b^2 - 3ab - (5ab - 3a^2 b^2)$

20. $r(s - 2t) - (rs - 2t)$

21. $h + 6\{h - 5(h + 4)\}$

22. $n - [n^2 - n(n^2 - n)]$

23. $u(u - 2v) + 2v(u - 2v) - (u^2 - 4v^2)$

24. $c^3 - c(c^2 - cd + d^2) - d(c^2 - cd + d^2)$

In exercises 25-32, evaluate the given expression for $x = 4$, $y = -2$, and $z = -3$.

25. $x - y^2$

26. $(x - y)^2$

27. $x^2 - y^2$

28. $xy + (x + y)z$

29. $|xy + z - x(y + z)|$

30. $|xy + z| - |x(y + z)|$

31. $(y + 1)^3 + (z + 1)^2$

32. $(x - 4)(4y^4)(3z^3)$.

In exercises 33-44, solve the equation or inequality. In the case of an inequality, sketch the solution set on a number line.

33. $4x + 1 = 9x - 9$

34. $8 - 3s = 3s - 10$

35. $3(b + 5) + 2(2b - 1) = -1$

36. $4(3a + 2) - 3(2a - 1) = 11$

37. $x(6x + 5) - 3x(2x - 1) = -40$

38. $y - 3(y - 3) > 3$

39. $3(2z - 5) + 2(3z + 5) \leq 7z$

40. $4(k + 2) + 2(k + 4) = 5(k + 1) - 3(k + 3)$

41. $-2 \leq 3(c - 2) + 4 < 7$

42. $1 < 1 + 3(4 - 2y) < 7$

43. $3\{x - 3(x - 3)\} = -x - 3$

44. $x - 3\{x - 2(x - 3)\} = 2$

Solve each of the following problems algebraically. Be sure to clearly label what the variable represents.

45. One number is 3 more than 2 times another. If their difference is 11, find the numbers.

46. The length of a rectangle is 2 less than 5 times its width. If the perimeter is 11 times the width, find the dimensions of the rectangle.

47. Sara and David live 51 miles apart. Sara can pedal her bicycle at the rate of 6 mph, while David can pedal his bicycle at the rate of 7 mph. If Sara leaves her house at 9:00 a.m. and David leaves his house two hours later, when will they meet?

48. A florist sells red geranium plants for $2 apiece and white geranium plants for $3 apiece. If he sells 50 plants and earns $113, how many white geranium plants did he sell?

Cumulative Test: Chapters 1-3

1. Evaluate each of the following:

   (a) $-2^3 + 3(-3)^2$

   (b) $(-3 + 5 - 6)^3$

2. Evaluate each of the following for a = 2, b = -3:

(a) $(b - a)^2 + ab^2$

(b) $|3a + 2b| + |2a + 3b|$

3. Perform the indicated operations and simplify as completely as possible.

(a) $3x^3 - 8x^2 + 5x - x^3 + 4x^2 + 2x$

(b) $3(2x + y) - 5(x - y)$

(c) $2ab(a^3 + ab) - 3a^2(a^2b - 2b^2)$

(d) $5(m - 2n) - 3(m - 4n) - 2(n + m)$

(e) $3u^2v^4(u^3 + v^2) - 3uv(2u^3v)(2uv^2)$

(f) $3 - 2b(3 - 2b(3 - 2b))$

4. Solve each of the following equations or inequalities.

(a) $4 - 5x = 10 - 7x$

(b) $3(z - 4) + 4(z - 3) = 11$

(c) $2 + 3(4 - c) > -10$

(d) $4(s + 1) - 3(s - 1) = 2(s + 2) - (s - 3)$

(e) $2(t - 3) + 3(t - 2) = 12 - t$

(f) $3t + 7(5 - t) = 4(8 - t)$

5. Solve the following inequalities and sketch the solution set on a number line.

(a) $5 - 2(1 + x) < -7$

(b) $-3 < 5x + 2 \leq 2$

6. Solve each of the following problems algebraically.

(a) One number is 6 more than 4 times another number. If their difference is 36, find the numbers.

(b) Cities A and B are 2200 miles apart. A train leaves city A at 10:00 a.m. and travels towards city B at the rate of 200 mph. A second train leaves city B at 11:00 a.m. and travels towards city A at the rate of 300 mph. At what time will the two trains pass one another?

(c) A charity car wash collects $156 by washing 40 cars. If it costs $3 to wash a compact car and $5 to wash a full-sized car, how many full-sized cars were washed?

Chapter 4 Test A

1. Reduce each of the following to lowest terms:

   (a) $\dfrac{12}{-21}$

   (b) $\dfrac{y^9}{y^4}$

   (c) $\dfrac{-12x^8}{-8x^7}$

   (d) $\dfrac{-28a^3b^4}{8a^6b}$

2. Perform the indicated operations and express your answer in lowest terms.

   (a) $\dfrac{3x^2y}{4xy^3} \cdot \dfrac{6x^2y^2}{xy}$

   (b) $\dfrac{3x^2y}{4xy^3} \div \dfrac{6x^2y^2}{xy}$

   (c) $\dfrac{5s^2t}{8s^3} \cdot \dfrac{-4st^3}{15t^2} \cdot \dfrac{-6}{t^2}$

   (d) $\dfrac{3a^4b^3}{7a^5} \div 6b^2$

   (e) $\dfrac{c}{4} + \dfrac{c}{4}$

   (f) $\dfrac{c}{4} \cdot \dfrac{c}{4}$

   (g) $\dfrac{5}{3x^2} + \dfrac{1}{3x^2}$

   (h) $\dfrac{u}{2} - \dfrac{2u}{5}$

   (i) $\dfrac{3}{4y} + \dfrac{2}{3y}$

   (j) $\dfrac{2}{5xy^3} - \dfrac{5}{2x^2y^2}$

   (k) $\dfrac{x^2 - 3x + 4}{6x^2} - \dfrac{x^2 + 3x + 4}{6x^2}$

3. Solve each of the following equations or inequalities.

   (a) $\dfrac{5x}{6} - \dfrac{x}{4} = 7$

   (b) $\dfrac{2x - 1}{3} + \dfrac{x + 1}{8} \leq -1$

   (c) $\dfrac{5 - y}{5} - \dfrac{4 - y}{4} = \dfrac{1}{10}$

   (d) $.01z + .1z = 1.32$

Solve each of the following problems algebraically.

4. If there are 39.37 inches in a meter, how many meters are there in 100 inches?

5. When $\dfrac{3}{5}$ of a number is subtracted from 5 more than the number, the result is one less than the number. Find the number.

6. A bank contains pennies, nickels, and dimes. There are 15 more pennies than nickels, and 3 times as many dimes as pennies. If the value of the coins is $6.45, how many of each type of coin are in the bank?

7. An amount of money is invested at 7% and $1000 more than that amount is invested at 10%. If the total interest on the two investments is $950, how much was invested at each rate?

8. The length of a rectangle is 15 cm more than $\frac{5}{6}$ of its width. If the perimeter is 10 cm less than 7 times the width, find the dimensions of the rectangle.

9. How many liters of a 24% salt solution must be mixed with 40 liters of a 30% salt solution in order to produce a 26% salt solution?

Chapter 4 Test B

1. Reduce each of the following to lowest terms:

   (a) $\dfrac{-15}{-40}$

   (b) $\dfrac{z^{11}}{z^3}$

   (c) $\dfrac{15x^9}{-9x^6}$

   (d) $\dfrac{-30p^5q^2}{12p^4q^3}$

2. Perform the indicated operations and express your answer in lowest terms.

   (a) $\dfrac{2xy^3}{3x^2y^2} \cdot \dfrac{x^3y^2}{12xy}$

   (b) $\dfrac{2xy^3}{3x^2y^2} \div \dfrac{x^3y^2}{12xy}$

   (c) $\dfrac{3u^3v}{-7uv^3} \cdot \dfrac{14v}{15u} \cdot \dfrac{-5v^2}{2uv}$

   (d) $\dfrac{5c^2d^4}{6d^3} \div 10c^3$

   (e) $\dfrac{m}{6} + \dfrac{m}{6}$

   (f) $\dfrac{m}{6} \cdot \dfrac{m}{6}$

   (g) $\dfrac{13}{5x^3} - \dfrac{3}{5x^3}$

   (h) $\dfrac{v}{6} + \dfrac{4v}{9}$

   (i) $\dfrac{4}{5r} - \dfrac{1}{4r}$

   (j) $\dfrac{3}{4a^2b} + \dfrac{5}{3ab^3}$

   (k) $\dfrac{x^2 + 8x - 7}{2x^3} + \dfrac{7 - 4x - x^2}{2x^3}$

3. Solve each of the following equations or inequalities.

   (a) $\dfrac{3x}{8} + \dfrac{x}{6} = 13$

   (b) $\dfrac{x-3}{4} - \dfrac{3x+1}{5} > -2$

   (c) $\dfrac{6-y}{6} + \dfrac{5-y}{5} = \dfrac{8}{15}$

   (d) $.2t + .04t = 14.4$

Solve each of the following problems algebraically.

4. If there are 35.31 cubic feet in a cubic meter, how many cubic meters are there in 200 cubic feet?

5. When two times a number is added to $\frac{2}{3}$ of one more than the number, the result is one less than three times the number. Find the number.

6. A man has 60 coins in his pocket, consisting of nickels, dimes, and quarters. He has three times as many dimes as quarters and the total value of his coins is $6.50. How many of each type of coin are in the man's pocket?

7. Two people leave from the same point and travel in opposite directions. One leaves at 1:00 p.m. and drives at the rate of 50 kph. The other leaves 15 minutes later and drives at the rate of 60 kph. At what time will they be 205 kilometers apart?

8. A woman invests a sum of money at 8% and twice as much money at 9%. If her annual interest from the two investments is $390, how much was invested at each rate?

9. A chemist forms 20 gallons of a 35% hydrochloric acid solution by mixing a 25% solution and a 50% solution together. How many gallons of each are used to form the mixture?

Chapter 5 Test A

1. Evaluate $2^{-3} - 3^{-2}4^0$.

In problems 2-5, simplify as completely as possible. Express final answers with positive exponents only.

2. $x^{-2}x^{-3}$

3. $(x^{-2})^{-3}$

4. $\dfrac{(x^2y)^3(xy^2)^2}{x^4y^8}$

5. $\dfrac{(-2x^{-2}y^{-3})^3}{2(x^{-1}y^{-2})^5}$

6. Given the polynomial $3x^6 + 5x^3 - x^2 + 7x + 1$:

    (a) How many terms are there?

    (b) What is the coefficient of the second degree term? the first degree term?

    (c) What is the degree of the polynomial?

In problems 7-13, perform the indicated operations and simplify as completely as possible.

7. $2x^3y^2(5xy)(-3x^2y^3)$

8. $2x^3y^2(5xy - 3x^2y^3)$

9. $3y^2(x - y) - xy(3y + 2x) + y(2x^2 + 5y^2)$

10. $(2x + 1)(5x^2 - 3x + 4)$

11.   Add $x^3 + 8x^2 - 6x + 1$ and $2x - 5x^2 + 3$

12.   Subtract $x^2 - 8x + 9$ from $x^2 + 8x - 9$

13. $(z - 2)^2 - (z - 3)^2$

14.   Write in scientific notation:

(a) 258,000   (b) .0258

15.   Compute using scientific notation:

$$\frac{(.0032)(600,000)}{.08}$$

Chapter 5 Test B

1.   Evaluate $3^0 4^{-1} + 5^{-2}$.

In problems 2-5, simplify as completely as possible.   Express final answers with positive integers only.

2. $x^{-1}x^{-5}$

3. $(x^{-1})^{-5}$

4. $\dfrac{(xy^3)^3(x^3y^2)^2}{x^{10}y^{11}}$

5. $\dfrac{(-3x^{-3}y^{-4})^2}{-3(x^{-2}y^{-1})^4}$

6.   Given the polynomial $4x^7 + 3x^4 - 5x^3 - x + 2$:

(a) How many terms are there?

(b) What is the coefficient of the fourth degree term?   the third degree term?

(c) What is the degree of the polynomial?

In problems 7-13, perform the indicated operations and simplify as completely as possible.

7. $4x^2y^4(2x^3y)(-3xy^3)$

8. $4x^2y^4(2x^3y - 3xy^3)$

9. $2x^2y(1 - xy) - y(x^3 + 2x^2) + 2x^3(y + y^2)$

10. $(2x - 1)(3x^2 + 5x - 2)$

11. Add $2x^3 - 6x^2 + 5x - 3$ and $4 - 8x + 3x^2$

12. Subtract $x^2 - 6x - 4$ from $x^2 + 6x + 4$

13. $(1 - y)^2 - (2 - y)^2$

14. Write in scientific notation:
  (a) 7,950,000   (b) .000795

15. Compute using scientific notation:
  $$\frac{.00075}{(.03)(5,000,000)}$$

Chapter 6 Test A

In problems 1-11, factor as completely as possible. If not factorable, say so.

1. $2x^4 - 8x^3 + 6x^2$ 2. $3x^3y^2 + 12x^2y^3 - 9x^2y^2$

3. $x^2 + 13x + 36$ 4. $x^2 + xy - 12y^2$

5. $4x^5 - 16x^3$ 6. $7x^2 + 14x + 14$

7. $x^2 - 16x + 64$ 8. $2x^2 - 9x + 4$

9. $2x^2 - 4x + 9$ 10. $8x^2 + 13x - 6$

11. $x^2y^2 + 6xy + 9$

12. Divide: $\dfrac{40a^2b^3 + 30a^3b^4 - 24a^2b^2}{20a^3b^3}$

13. Divide: $\dfrac{3x^3 + 5x^2 - 7}{x + 2}$

Chapter 6 Test B

In problems 1-11, factor as completely as possible. If not factorable, say so.

1. $5x^4 + 15x^3 + 10x^2$ 2. $7x^3y^4 - 28x^4y^3 - 14x^3y^3$

3. $x^2 - 11x + 24$ 4. $x^2 - 7xy - 18y^2$

5. $3x^4 - 27x^2$

6. $4x^2 + 12x + 16$

7. $x^2 + 18x + 81$

8. $3x^2 + 4x - 15$

9. $3x^2 - 4x + 15$

10. $9x^2 - 14x - 8$

11. $x^2y^2 - 10xy + 25$

12. Divide: $\dfrac{54p^4q^3 - 24p^5q^4 + 27p^3q^3}{18p^4q^4}$

13. Divide: $\dfrac{2x^3 - 3x^2 + 1}{x - 3}$

Cumulative Review: Chapters 4-6

In exercises 1-4, reduce the fraction to lowest terms.

1. $\dfrac{56}{-35}$

2. $\dfrac{6x^3}{16x^8}$

3. $\dfrac{45a^3b^5}{25a^4b^4}$

4. $\dfrac{2c + 3c + 4c}{5c^2 + 6c^2 + 7c^2}$

In exercises 5-32, perform the indicated operations and simplify as completely as possible.

5. $\dfrac{8x^2}{27} \div \dfrac{x}{6}$

6. $\dfrac{8x^2}{27} \cdot \dfrac{x}{6}$

7. $\dfrac{8x^2}{27} - \dfrac{x}{6}$

8. $\dfrac{8}{3y^3} - \dfrac{2}{3y^3}$

9. $\dfrac{3u^2 + 1}{4u^2} + \dfrac{u^2 - 1}{4u^2}$

10. $\dfrac{2x + 5}{7x} + \dfrac{x - 3}{7x} - \dfrac{3x + 2}{7x}$

11. $(x + 2)(x - 7)$

12. $(x + 2)(x^2 + x - 7)$

13. $(x^2 + x + 2)(x^2 + x - 7)$

14. $5t(t + 1)(t - 4)$

15. $\dfrac{10a^4b^5}{21b^3c^2} \div \dfrac{15a^2c^4}{14b^4}$

16. $\dfrac{10a^4b^5}{21b^3c^2} \cdot \dfrac{15a^2c^4}{14b^4}$

17. $(6r - 5s)(3r + 2s)$

18. $3m(m - 2) + 2m(m - 3)$

19. $\dfrac{8}{5d} + \dfrac{5}{3d}$

20. $\dfrac{3}{4k} - \dfrac{5}{6\ell}$

21. $\dfrac{5}{8u^3v^2} + \dfrac{3}{10u^2v^3}$

22. $\dfrac{5}{8u^3v^2} \cdot \dfrac{3}{10u^2v^3}$

23. $(x + 4)(x + 16) - (x - 8)^2$ 24. $(2x + 1)(x - 8) + 2(x + 2)^2$

25. $(\frac{5}{2y} - \frac{1}{y}) \div \frac{4}{y}$ 26. $\frac{5}{2y} - (\frac{1}{y} \div \frac{4}{y})$

27. $(m + 3)(3m - 1)(3m + 1)$ 28. $(x - 2)(x + 5)(x + 2)(x - 5)$

29. $3x - \frac{2}{x} + \frac{4}{x^3}$ 30. $\frac{3}{2p^3q} + \frac{5}{4p^2q^2} - \frac{7}{6pq^3}$

31. Subtract $5z^2 + 4z - 8$ from $3z^2 + 6z - 1$

32. Add $y^2 - 8xy + 2x^2$ to the product of $x + 3y$ and $2x - y$

33. (a) What is the degree of the polynomial $7x^6 - 5x^4 + 3x^2 - 1$?

    (b) What is the coefficient of the fourth degree term?

34. Write the polynomial $2x - 3x^2 - 1 + 4x^4$ in complete standard form.

In exercises 35-40, divide the given polynomials. Use long division where necessary.

35. $\frac{2x^3 - 18x^4}{6x^2}$ 36. $\frac{18s^3t^2 + 24s^2t^2 - 12s^2t^3}{8s^3t^3}$

37. $\frac{a^2 - 4a + 7}{a + 3}$ 38. $\frac{3y^3 + y^2 - 12y - 4}{y + 2}$

39. $\frac{12t^3 + 10t^2 - 9}{2t - 1}$ 40. $\frac{b^4 + 3b + 2}{b - 1}$

In exercises 41-52, simplify the expression as completely as possible. Final answers should be expressed with positive exponents only.

41. $2^1 + 2^0 + 2^{-1}$ 42. $(3 - 1)^{-2} - (4 - 1)^{-2}$

43. $\frac{x^4 x^5}{(x^4)^5}$ 44. $\frac{y^{-10}}{y^{-5}}$

45. $\frac{(-3x^4)^3}{-9(x^7)^2}$ 46. $\frac{(a^{-1}b^{-2})^{-3}}{(b^{-3}a^{-2})^{-1}}$

47. $\frac{(2u^3v^{-3})^{-2}}{(3u^{-2}v^2)^{-3}}$ 48. $(\frac{4mn^{-2}}{3m^{-3}n})^{-1}$

49. Write in scientific notation: 123,000,000

50. Write in scientific notation: .00000975

51.   Evaluate: $\dfrac{(3 \times 10^{-5})(2.4 \times 10^{4})}{.6 \times 10^{2}}$

52.   Evaluate: $\dfrac{(.00015)(48,000,000)}{(.144)(80,000)}$

In exercises 53-60, solve the given equation.

53. $\dfrac{x}{4} + \dfrac{x}{6} = \dfrac{2x + 9}{12}$

54. $\dfrac{t + 1}{5} - \dfrac{2t}{15} = \dfrac{t - 1}{3}$

55. $\dfrac{w}{2} - \dfrac{w}{3} = \dfrac{w}{5}$

56. $\dfrac{z}{4} + \dfrac{z}{12} = \dfrac{z}{3}$

57. $\dfrac{1 - 3y}{4} + \dfrac{4 - 3y}{6} = \dfrac{9y + 7}{3}$

58. $\dfrac{x}{6} - \dfrac{1}{5} = \dfrac{x}{8}$

59. $.05(x + 1) + .5(x - 1) = .65$

60. $\dfrac{2}{3}(2u - 3) - \dfrac{3}{4}(3u + 2) = 2$

In exercises 61-80, factor the polynomial as completely as possible.
If the polynomial is not factorable, say so.

61. $x^{2} - 8x$

62. $x^{2} - 8x + 12$

63. $x^{2} - 8x - 9$

64. $x^{2} - 8x + 9$

65. $4a^{3}b^{2} - 6a^{2}b + 8ab^{3}$

66. $8r^{4}s^{6} - 2r^{6}s^{4}$

67. $18v^{2} - 32$

68. $18v^{2} + 32$

69. $t^{5} - 49t^{3}$

70. $3s^{2} - 7s - 10$

71. $6t^{2} - 13t + 6$

72. $6t^{2} - 37t + 6$

73. $6t^{2} - 12t + 6$

74. $6t^{2} - 13t - 6$

75. $56 - x - x^{2}$

76. $x^{2} - 29xy + 100y^{2}$

77. $x^{2} + 100y^{2}$

78. $x^{2} + ax + bx + ab$

79. $x^{2} + 3x - 2xy - 6y$

80. $81x^{4} - 16y^{4}$

81.   The sum of four consecutive odd numbers is 14 more than twice
the largest one. Find the four numbers.

82.   The ratio of married couples to single people in an apartment
house is 9 to 5. If there are 135 married couples living in
the apartment, how many single people live there?

83. A typist charges $1.50 more for typing a page of technical material than she does for typing a page of regular material. If a report contains 18 pages of regular material and 12 pages of technical material and if the total bill is $108, what is the charge for typing a page of regular material?

84. 100 liters of a 30% chlorine solution is to be formed by mixing a 20% chlorine solution, a 25% chlorine solution, and a 40% chlorine solution. If there is to be twice as much of the 25% solution in the mixture as the 20% solution, how many liters of each solution must be mixed?

85. A wallet contains only five and ten dollar bills. If there are 23 bills altogether and their total value is $200, how many of each type of bill are in the wallet?

Cumulative Test: Chapters 4-6

In problems 1-16, perform the indicated operations and simplify as completely as possible. Final answers should be reduced to lowest terms, and should be expressed with positive exponents only.

1. $(2x + 1)(x - 2) + (x - 3)(3x + 5)$

2. $\dfrac{12a^3 b^{-4}}{9a^{-2} b^{-1}}$

3. $(3s - 4t)(s^3 t + 2s^2 t^2 - 3st^3)$

4. $\dfrac{8p^4 q^3}{3r^2} \cdot \dfrac{9r}{4pq^3}$

5. $(2n - 1)^2 - 2(n - 1)^2$

6. $\dfrac{4y}{3ab} + \dfrac{7y}{3ab} - \dfrac{2y}{3ab}$

7. $\dfrac{2w + 5}{5w} - \dfrac{5 - 3w}{5w}$

8. $\dfrac{(4x^{-2})^{-2}}{(2x^{-3})^{-3}}$

9. $\dfrac{3}{4c^3 d} - \dfrac{5}{6cd^3}$

10. $\dfrac{16k^3 \ell^5 - 10k^5 \ell^3}{4k^4 \ell^4}$

11. Use long division to find the quotient and remainder:
$$\frac{x^3 + 3x^2 - x + 3}{x + 1}$$

12. Use long division to find the quotient and remainder:
$$\frac{18 - 11x^2 + x^4}{x + 3}$$

13. $\dfrac{12a^2b^3}{5c^5} \div 30a^3b^2c$

14. Write the following in scientific notation:
    (a) .000000531
    (b) 531,000,000

15. Compute using scientific notation:
$$\frac{(.00009)(1,600,000)}{(.0045)(320,000)}$$

16. Subtract $x^3 + 3x^2 - 4x + 1$ from the sum of $x^3 - 2x + 2$ and $5x^2 - x - 4$.

17. Solve for h: $\dfrac{h}{4} + \dfrac{h}{10} = 7$

18. Solve for v: $\dfrac{4v + 5}{2} - \dfrac{2v + 1}{6} = v + 1$

In problems 19-26, factor the given polynomial as completely as possible.

19. $x^2 - 5x + 6$

20. $x^2 - 5x - 6$

21. $2s^4t^6 - 8s^6t^4$

22. $10x^2 + 30x - 70$

23. $3y^2 - y - 14$

24. $12z^2 + 13z - 25$

25. $c(2c + 1) - 3(2c + 1)$

26. $x^3 + xy^2 - 2x^2 - 2y^2$

Solve each of the following problems algebraically. Be sure to clearly label what your variable represents.

27. If there are 5,280 feet in one mile, how many miles are there in 20,000 feet?

28. Two consecutive odd numbers have the property that the sum of $\frac{2}{5}$ of the smaller and $\frac{2}{3}$ of the larger is equal to one more than the larger. Find the numbers.

29. There are 200 orchestra seats and 120 balcony seats in a theater. If an orchestra seat costs $6 more than a balcony seat, and if a sold-out performance brings in $4080, find the cost of a balcony seat.

30. Bill invests some money at 8% and four times as much money at 13%. The total annual interest he receives on these investments is $100 more than he would have received if he had invested all of his money at 10%. How much did Bill invest at each rate?

Chapter 7 Test A

1. Reduce to lowest terms: $\dfrac{3x^2 + 9x}{x^2 - 9x}$

2. Reduce to lowest terms: $\dfrac{3x^2 + 9x}{x^2 - 9}$

In problems 3-7, perform the indicated operations and simplify as completely as possible.

3. $\dfrac{4}{x - 2} - \dfrac{2}{x - 4}$

4. $\dfrac{x^2}{4x^2 - 8x} \cdot \dfrac{2x^2 - 8}{(x + 2)^2}$

5. $\dfrac{6}{x^2 - 4x} + \dfrac{3}{2x}$

6. $\dfrac{x^2 - 3x - 4}{x^2 - x - 6} \div \dfrac{x^2 - 4x}{x^2 + 2x}$

7. $\dfrac{2x - 3}{x^2 - 2x - 3} + \dfrac{5x - 4}{x^2 - 2x - 3} - \dfrac{3x + 5}{x^2 - 2x - 3}$

8. Solve for x: $\dfrac{4}{x + 2} + \dfrac{2}{x} = \dfrac{14}{3x}$

9. Solve for y: $2xy + z = 1 - \dfrac{2y}{3}$

10. Solve for b: $\dfrac{2b + 8}{b + 3} + 3 = \dfrac{2}{b + 3}$

Solve each of the following problems algebraically.

11. What number must be added to the numerator and the denominator of the fraction $\dfrac{3}{5}$ so that the resulting fraction is equal to $\dfrac{5}{3}$?

12. George can build a bookcase in 6 hours. If he works together with his assistant Frank, the two men can build the bookcase in 4 hours. How long would it take Frank to build the bookcase if he works alone?

Chapter 7 Test B

1. Reduce to lowest terms: $\dfrac{x^2 - 16x}{2x^2 - 8x}$

2. Reduce to lowest terms: $\dfrac{x^2 - 16}{2x^2 - 8x}$

In problems 3-7, perform the indicated operations and simplify as completely as possible.

3. $\dfrac{2}{x + 5} + \dfrac{1}{x + 2}$

4. $\dfrac{3x^3 + 9x^2}{3x} \cdot \dfrac{(x - 3)^2}{3x^2 - 27}$

5. $\dfrac{6}{x^2 + 9x} - \dfrac{2}{3x}$

6. $\dfrac{x^2 + 4x - 5}{x^2 + x - 12} \div \dfrac{x^2 + 5x}{x^2 - 3x}$

7. $\dfrac{6x - 5}{x^2 - 5x + 4} - \dfrac{2x + 3}{x^2 - 5x + 4} - \dfrac{x + 4}{x^2 - 5x + 4}$

8. Solve for x: $\dfrac{1}{x} + \dfrac{3}{x - 3} = \dfrac{17}{2x}$

9. Solve for q: $3pq - 2r = 4 + \dfrac{1}{4}q$

10. Solve for a: $\dfrac{4a - 7}{4 - a} + 1 = \dfrac{5 + a}{4 - a}$

Solve each of the following problems algebraically.

11. The denominator of a fraction is one more than three times the numerator. If 2 is added to both the numerator and denominator, the resulting fraction is equal to 2/5. Find the original fraction.

12. Julia can run 4 times as fast as she can walk. If it takes her $3\dfrac{1}{4}$ hours to complete a trip in which she walks 5 miles and runs 6 miles, find her walking speed.

Chapter 8 Test A

1. Determine whether or not the point (2,-3) satisfies the equation $2x + 3y = 5(5y + 7x)$.

2. Find the missing coordinates for the ordered pair of the given equation.

   (a) $4x + y = 9$ (3,)

   (b) $x + 2y = 8$ (,-2)

   (c) $2x - 3y = 12$ (0,)

3. Sketch the graphs of each of the following in a rectangular coordinate system using the intercept method.

(a) $x + 3y = 6$ (b) $2x - 5y = 10$

(c) $3x + 4y = 0$ (d) $x = -1$

(e) $y = 5$

4. Find the slope of the line passing through the points $(4,-3)$ and $(-3,4)$.

5. Write an equation of the line with slope $= -\frac{2}{5}$ which passes through the point $(6,-1)$.

6. Write an equation of the line passing through the points $(4,-1)$ and $(0,7)$.

7. Write equations of the horizontal and vertical lines which pass through the point $(-2,3)$.

8. Solve the following system of equations by the graphical method:

$$\begin{cases} x + 3y = 6 \\ 2x - y = 5 \end{cases}$$

9. Solve each of the following systems by the elimination method:

(a) $\begin{cases} 2x + 3y = 5 \\ x - 2y = 6 \end{cases}$ (b) $\begin{cases} 4x - 5y = -10 \\ 5x + 6y = 12 \end{cases}$

(c) $\begin{cases} x + \frac{3}{4}y = 1 \\ \frac{4}{3}x + y = 2 \end{cases}$

Solve the following problem algebraically.

10. Five pounds of plums and four pounds of peaches cost $5.00. Two pounds of plums and three pounds of peaches cost $2.70. Find the cost of a pound of plums and a pound of peaches.

Chapter 8 Test B

1. Determine whether or not the point $(-3,1)$ satisfies the equation $3(x + 4y) = 3y + 2x$.

2. Find the missing coordinates for the ordered pair of the given equation.

(a) $5x - y = 7$ $(\quad ,3)$

(b) $x - 3y = -2$ $(-11,\quad)$

(c) $4x + 5y = 40$ $(\quad ,0)$

3. Sketch the graphs of each of the following in a rectangular coordinate system using the intercept method.

    (a) 3x + 2y = -6   (b) 4x - 3y = 12

    (c) x + 3y = 0   (d) x = 5

    (e) y = -1

4. Find the slope of the line passing through the points (-5,2) and (-2,5).

5. Write an equation of the line with slope $= -\frac{3}{4}$ which passes through the point (1,-4).

6. Write an equation of the line passing through the points (3,-2) and (0,10).

7. Write equations of the horizontal and vertical lines which pass through the point (4,-2).

8. Solve the following system of equations by the graphical method:
    $$\begin{cases} 3x - y = 3 \\ x + 2y = 8 \end{cases}$$

9. Solve each of the following systems by the elimination method:

    (a) $\begin{cases} 5x - 6y = -9 \\ 4x + 3y = -15 \end{cases}$ (b) $\begin{cases} 3x + 4y = 9 \\ 4x - 3y = 12 \end{cases}$

    (c) $\begin{cases} x - \frac{5}{2}y = 2 \\ \frac{2}{5}x - y = 1 \end{cases}$

Solve the following problem algebraically.

10. Three packages of veal and four packages of chicken cost $19. Five packages of veal and two packages of chicken cost $20. Find the cost of a package of veal and a package of chicken.

Chapter 9 Test A

Perform the indicated operations. Make sure your final answer is in simplest radical form. Assume all variables appearing under radical signs are non-negative.

1. $\sqrt{16x^{10}y^{12}}$

2. $\sqrt{32} + 4\sqrt{72} - \sqrt{200}$

3. $\sqrt{45x^5} - x^2\sqrt{20x}$

4. $\dfrac{\sqrt{180x^8y^7}}{\sqrt{12x^2y^3}}$

5. $\sqrt{48x^5y^{11}} - 2x^2y^3\sqrt{12xy^5}$

6. $\dfrac{6y^3}{\sqrt{8y}}$

7. $(\sqrt{x} + 2\sqrt{3})(\sqrt{4x} - \sqrt{27})$

8. $(\sqrt{a} + \sqrt{6})^2 - (\sqrt{a + 6})^2$

9. $\dfrac{7}{3 + \sqrt{2}}$

10. $\dfrac{2x - 8y}{\sqrt{x} - 2\sqrt{y}}$

11. Decide whether or not $1 + \sqrt{3}$ is a solution to the equation $x^2 - 2 = 2x$.

Chapter 9 Test B

Perform the indicated operations. Make sure your final answer is in simplest radical form. Assume all variables appearing under radical signs are non-negative.

1. $\sqrt{36x^{14}y^8}$

2. $\sqrt{50} - 3\sqrt{98} + \sqrt{128}$

3. $\sqrt{75x^5} - x\sqrt{27x^3}$

4. $\dfrac{\sqrt{120x^5y^{12}}}{\sqrt{12xy^4}}$

5. $\sqrt{72x^9y^5} - 2x^3y\sqrt{18x^3y^3}$

6. $\dfrac{8z^4}{\sqrt{12z}}$

7. $(\sqrt{x} - 3\sqrt{2})(\sqrt{9x} + \sqrt{8})$

8. $(\sqrt{b} + 7)^2 - (\sqrt{b} + \sqrt{7})^2$

9. $\dfrac{6}{4 - \sqrt{10}}$

10. $\dfrac{3x - 27y}{\sqrt{x} + 3\sqrt{y}}$

11. Decide whether or not $1 - \sqrt{3}$ is a solution to the equation $x^2 = 2x + 2$.

Cumulative Review: Chapters 7-9

In exercises 1-10, simplify the expression as completely as possible. Fractions should be reduced to lowest terms.

1. $\sqrt{4a^{20}b^{30}}$

2. $\dfrac{x^2 - 1}{x^2 - x}$

3. $\dfrac{4t^2 - 9}{4t^2 + 12t + 9}$

4. $\sqrt{\dfrac{12w^8z^{11}}{108wz^7}}$

5. $\dfrac{8}{\sqrt{11}}$

6. $\dfrac{8}{\sqrt{11} - 3}$

7. $\dfrac{12}{\sqrt{14} + \sqrt{10}}$

8. $\dfrac{21x}{\sqrt{7x}}$

9. $\sqrt{192}$

10. $\sqrt{84u^6v^7}$

In exercises 11-28, perform the indicated operations and simplify as completely as possible.

11. $\dfrac{2}{5x} - \dfrac{1}{3x + 2}$

12. $\sqrt{24rs} + \sqrt{54rs}$

13. $\dfrac{4}{3cd^2} + \dfrac{3}{4c^2d}$

14. $\sqrt{3}(4\sqrt{5} + \sqrt{10}) - 2\sqrt{3}(\sqrt{10} + \sqrt{20})$

15. $4\sqrt{\dfrac{5}{2}} - \sqrt{40}$

16. $\dfrac{x^2 - 1}{x - 1} \cdot \dfrac{x + 1}{x^2 + 1}$

17. $(3\sqrt{a} - \sqrt{4b})(\sqrt{4a} + 3\sqrt{b})$

18. $\dfrac{m^2n - mn^2}{m^2 - n^2} \div \dfrac{2mn}{m^2 + 2mn + n^2}$

19. $\dfrac{4}{x^2 + 4x + 3} - \dfrac{2}{x^2 + 3x + 2}$

20. $2\sqrt{50p^8q^5} - p^2q^2\sqrt{98p^4q}$

21. $\dfrac{5}{\sqrt{6}} + \dfrac{7}{\sqrt{96}}$

22. $\dfrac{1}{a - 2} - \dfrac{1}{2a} - \dfrac{2}{3a - 6}$

23. $(2\sqrt{6} + \sqrt{7})(2\sqrt{6} - \sqrt{7})$

24. $\dfrac{\dfrac{s}{3} - \dfrac{3}{s}}{\dfrac{s^2 + 6s + 9}{6s}}$

25. $\dfrac{3t}{t - 1} - \dfrac{t^2 + 2t}{t^2 - t}$

26. $(\sqrt{x + 5})^4$

27. $\left(\dfrac{8}{\sqrt{13} - 3} - \dfrac{26}{\sqrt{13}}\right)^2$

28. $\dfrac{5r + 4}{2r + 8} + \dfrac{3r + 7}{2r + 8} - \dfrac{8r + 3}{2r + 8}$

In exercises 29-36, solve the given equation. If it contains more than one variable, solve for the indicated variable.

29. $\dfrac{5}{x} - \dfrac{1}{4} = \dfrac{7}{2x}$

30. $\dfrac{2}{4a + 1} + \dfrac{5}{12a + 3} = \dfrac{1}{9}$

31. $3r + 2s = 8 - r - 2s$ for s

32. $\dfrac{3}{4}u - 8v + 2 = \dfrac{2}{3}u + v + 1$ for u

33. $\dfrac{3z - 2}{z + 5} - 2 = \dfrac{2z - 7}{z + 5}$

34. $\dfrac{1}{2}(x - 1) + \dfrac{1}{6}(x + 1) = \dfrac{1}{3}(x - 1) + \dfrac{1}{4}(x + 1)$

35. $\dfrac{6p + 1}{3p + 2} = \dfrac{2p - 3}{p}$

36. $\dfrac{6p + 1}{3p - 1} = \dfrac{2p + 1}{p}$

In exercises 37-44, sketch the graph of the given equation in a rectangular coordinate system.   Label the intercepts.

37. $y = -x + 4$

38. $2x - 7y = 14$

39. $5y + 4x = 10$

40. $6y - 9x = 18$

41. $y - 4 = 0$

42. $x + 4 = 0$

43. $y + 4x = 0$

44. $x - 4y = 0$

In exercises 45-48, find the slope of the line passing through the given pair of points.

45. $(5,-3)$ and $(3,-7)$

46. $(1,-8)$ and $(-5,7)$

47. $(3,11)$ and $(3,-11)$

48. $(3,11)$ and $(-3,11)$

In exercises 49-52, write an equation of the line with the given slope which passes through the given point.

49. $m = -5$, $(1,-4)$

50. $m = \dfrac{2}{3}$, $(0,-6)$

51. $m = 0$, $(-8,2)$

52. m is undefined, $(6,7)$

53. Write an equation of the line passing through the points $(4,-2)$ and $(-3,5)$.

54. Write an equation of the line whose x-intercept is 6 and whose y-intercept is 5.

In exercises 55-56, solve the given system of equations graphically.

55. $\begin{cases} 3x - 2y = 6 \\ 2x + y = -10 \end{cases}$

56. $\begin{cases} 3x + 2y = 10 \\ 2x + 3y = 10 \end{cases}$

In exercises 57-64, solve each system of equations algebraically.

57. $\begin{cases} 3x - 2y = 6 \\ 2x + y = -10 \end{cases}$

58. $\begin{cases} 3x + 2y = 10 \\ 2x + 3y = 10 \end{cases}$

59. $\begin{cases} 6x + 4y = 1 \\ 3x - 8y = 8 \end{cases}$

60. $\begin{cases} 8x + 3y = 19 \\ 9x - 8y = 10 \end{cases}$

61. $\begin{cases} 4x = 3 - y \\ 3y = -4 + x \end{cases}$

62. $\begin{cases} 5x - y = 5 \\ 4x + \dfrac{y}{5} = 1 \end{cases}$

63. $\begin{cases} 2x - 5y = 10 \\ 10y = 4x - 20 \end{cases}$

64. $\begin{cases} 3x - y = 9 \\ x - \frac{1}{3}y = 1 \end{cases}$

65. Tom can complete an assignment in 3 hours, Dick in 4 hours, and Harry in 12 hours. If the three work together, how long will it take for them to complete the assignment?

66. A man walks a distance of 4 kilometers at a certain rate and runs back to his starting point at three times his walking speed. If the round trip takes 2 hours, what is the man's running speed?

67. The denominator of a fraction is 5 more than twice its numerator. If 7 is subtracted from both the numerator and the denominator, the resulting fraction is equal to -1/2. Find the original fraction.

68. A car rental agency charges a certain rate for a weekly rental and another rate for a daily rental. One client rents a car for 2 weeks and 3 days and pays $250. A second client rents a car for 3 weeks and 5 days and pays $385. Find the agency's weekly and daily rates.

Cumulative Test: Chapters 7-9

In problems 1-6, simplify the expression as completely as possible. Reduce fractions to lowest terms and express radicals in simplest radical form.

1. $\sqrt{100a^{10}}$

2. $\dfrac{x^3 - 4x}{x^2 + 4x + 4}$

3. $\frac{1}{3}\sqrt{r^3 s^5 t^8}$

4. $\dfrac{2a^2 - 7a + 6}{a^2 - 5a + 6}$

5. $\dfrac{45}{\sqrt{10}}$

6. $\dfrac{45}{\sqrt{10} - 1}$

In problems 7-16, perform the indicated operations and simplify as completely as possible.

7. $\dfrac{6}{x + 3} + \dfrac{4}{x - 2}$

8. $5\sqrt{2}(\sqrt{3} + \sqrt{5}) - 5\sqrt{3}(\sqrt{2} - \sqrt{5})$

9. $\dfrac{3u^3 - 12u}{u^2 + 3u - 10} \cdot \dfrac{u^2 + 6u + 5}{6u^3 + 12u^2 + 6u}$

10. $\dfrac{3a}{a^2 - 3a - 4} - \dfrac{10}{a^2 - 3a - 4} - \dfrac{a - 2}{a^2 - 3a - 4}$

11. $\dfrac{9}{2x^2 + 5x + 2} + \dfrac{3}{2x^2 + x}$

12. $\dfrac{r^2 + 8r + 15}{r^2 + 8r + 16} \div \dfrac{r^2 + 6r + 9}{r^2 + 6r + 8}$

13. $5\sqrt{40b^3c^8} - 3bc^2\sqrt{90bc^4}$

14. $(\sqrt{16w} - \sqrt{24})(\sqrt{9w} + \sqrt{96})$

15. $\dfrac{\dfrac{1}{a} + \dfrac{1}{b}}{\dfrac{4}{a^2} - \dfrac{4}{b^2}}$

16. $\dfrac{\sqrt{11}}{\sqrt{7} - \sqrt{3}} - \dfrac{\sqrt{3}}{\sqrt{11} + \sqrt{7}}$

In problems 17-19, solve the given equation.

17. $\dfrac{8}{2t - 3} = \dfrac{5}{6t - 9} + \dfrac{19}{15}$

18. Solve for w: $\dfrac{3}{4}w + 5v = kw - \dfrac{1}{2}v + 4$

19. $\dfrac{2x + 3}{x + 7} - \dfrac{2}{3} = \dfrac{x - 4}{x + 7}$

In problems 20-21, sketch the graph of the equation in a rectangular coordinate system. Label the intercepts.

20. $3x - 4y = 12$ 21. $4x + 3y = 12$

Problems 22-24 refer to ℓ, the straight line that passes through the points (1,-3) and (-3,5).

22. Find the slope of ℓ.

23. Write an equation of ℓ.

24. Find the y-intercept of ℓ.

In problems 25-26, solve the system of equations algebraically.

25. $\begin{cases} 5x - 6y = 13 \\ 3x + 2y = -9 \end{cases}$ 26. $\begin{cases} x - \dfrac{5}{3}y = -3 \\ -6x + 10y = 15 \end{cases}$

27. An executive secretary can type a report in 3 hours, while a temporary secretary needs 5 hours to do the same job. If the temporary secretary begins typing at 9:00 a.m. and the executive secretary joins her an hour later, at what time will they complete the job?

28.   A collection of dimes and quarters is worth $2.40. If the number of dimes and the number of quarters are interchanged, the value of the coins increases to $2.85. How many dimes and how many quarters are in the collection?

Chapter 10 Test A

Solve each of the following equations. Choose any method you like.

1. $(x + 1)(x - 1) = 8$

2. $2x^2 - 4x - 1 = 0$

3. $3x^2 = 8x + 3$

4. $(2x - 1)^2 = 4$

5. $(2x - 1)^2 = 4x$

6. $3x^2 - 6x + 1 = -x^2 + 2x + 1$

7. $\dfrac{x + 3}{x} = \dfrac{x}{x - 1}$

8. $(x^2 + 1)(x + 1) = (x^2 - 2)(x - 2)$

9. $\dfrac{1}{x} + \dfrac{1}{x - 1} = \dfrac{3}{2}$

10.   Solve the following problem by completing the square, and check your answer by using the quadratic formula: $2x^2 - 16x = -5$.

Chapter 10 Test B

Solve each of the following equations. Choose any method you like.

1. $(x - 2)(x + 2) = 21$

2. $2x^2 + 4x + 1 = 0$

3. $5x^2 + 3x = 2$

4. $(3x + 1)^2 = 16$

5. $(3x + 1)^2 = 16x$

6. $2x^2 + 5x - 2 = x^2 - x + 1$

7. $\dfrac{2x - 3}{x} = \dfrac{4x}{2x + 1}$

8. $(x^2 + 2)(x - 1) = (x^2 - 2)(x + 1)$

9. $\dfrac{1}{x + 1} + \dfrac{1}{x} = \dfrac{3}{2}$

10.   Solve the following problem by completing the square, and check your answer by using the quadratic formula: $3x^2 + 18x = -2$.

Practice Final Exam

In problems 1-4, evaluate the given expression.

1. $\dfrac{(-1)(-2) - (-3)(-4)}{-5}$

2. $|1 - 2[3 - 4(5 - 6)]|$

3. $x^2 - xy - |x - y - z|$ when $x = -3$, $y = 3$, and $z = 2$

4. $(2^{-1} + 3^{-1})^{-1}$

In problems 5-12, perform the indicated operations and simplify as completely as possible. (Where applicable, express your answers with positive exponents only and in simplest radical form.)

5. $x^2(2x - 3y^2) + 2x(xy^2) - 3(x^3 - 2x(xy))$

6. Subtract the sum of $x - 1$ and $2x^2 - x + 2$ from the product of $x - 1$ and $2x^2 - x + 2$.

7. $\dfrac{1}{8y} - \dfrac{3x^2}{5y^2} \cdot \dfrac{y}{6x}$

8. $\dfrac{(x^3y^2)^{-1}(x^{-2}y^3)^{-2}}{(xy^{-2})^{-3}}$

9. $\dfrac{x^2 - 4x - 5}{x^2 - 5x + 4} \div \dfrac{x^2 + 5x + 4}{x^2 + 4x - 5}$

10. $\dfrac{1}{x^2 - x} + \dfrac{1}{x^2 + x}$

11. $4x\sqrt{24x} - \dfrac{2}{5}\sqrt{150x^3}$

12. $\dfrac{3}{3 - \sqrt{6}} - \dfrac{3}{\sqrt{6} + \sqrt{3}}$

In problems 13-14, solve the given inequality and sketch its solution set on a number line.

13. $-11 \le 2(4 - x) - 5(1 + x) < 24$

14. $\dfrac{x + 1}{2} - \dfrac{x + 2}{3} + \dfrac{x + 3}{4} > 1$

In problems 15-20, solve the given equation.

15. $3(p + 2) + p(p + 3) = p(p - 2) + 2(p - 3)$

16. $\dfrac{3x - 2}{4} + 2 = \dfrac{2x - 3}{5}$

17. $\dfrac{3}{2x + 1} + \dfrac{2}{3x} = \dfrac{2}{x}$

18. $(3a + 1)(a - 1) = (2a - 1)(a + 1)$

19. $y^2 - 1 = \frac{5}{6}y$

20. $5x^2 + 6x - 1 = 0$

21. Compute using scientific notation: $\dfrac{(7,200,000)(.0048)}{(64,000)(.000003)}$

In problems 22-23, factor as completely as possible.

22. $4x^4 + 18x^3 - 36x^2$ 23. $x^3 - xy^2 + 2x^2y - 2y^3$

24. Find the quotient and the remainder: $\dfrac{2x^3 - 1}{x + 1}$

25. Use the intercept method to sketch the graph of $5x - 6y = 15$.

26. Write an equation of the line whose x-intercept is 2 and whose y-intercept is -8.

27. Solve the following system algebraically:

$$\begin{cases} 7x + 12y = 3 \\ 5x - 3y = 6 \end{cases}$$

Solve each of the following problems algebraically.

28. My father's age is seven more than three times my age. If the sum of our ages is five less than five times my age, how old am I?

29. Red poker chips are worth 2¢, blue poker chips are worth 3¢, and white poker chips are worth 5¢. There are 150 chips in a pot, with twice the number of white chips as blue chips. If the total value of the pot is $5.80, how many red chips are contained in the pot?

30. Mrs. Brown invests some money at 6% and the rest at 9%, yielding her an annual interest of $306. If she had invested the same amounts in the opposite way, her annual interest would have increased to $324. How much money has Mrs. Brown invested in all?

31. Sam needs three more hours to plow a field than Hugo needs. Together, they can plow the field in two hours. How long would it take Hugo to plow the field if he works alone?

32. Find two numbers whose sum is 1 and whose product is $-\frac{3}{4}$.

ANSWERS TO STUDY GUIDE CHAPTER TESTS, CUMULATIVE REVIEWS AND TESTS, PRACTICE FINAL

Chapter 1 Test A

1. (a) F   (b) T
   (c) F   (d) F
   (e) {20, 30}

2. -8   3. 10

4. -4   5. 3

6. -5   7. -20

8. 4   9. 45

10. -27

Chapter 1 Test B

1. (a) T   (b) F
   (c) T   (d) F
   (e) {3}

2. -5   3. -6

4. 0   5. 4

6. -2   7. -16

8. -4   9. 30

10. -32

Chapter 2 Test A

1. 64

2. -64

3. -1

4. 43

5. 5

6. -6

7. -4

8. 0

9. $5x^4 - 5xy^3 - 5x^3y$

10. $10x^5y^7$

11. 2xy

12. $4x^3y^2$

13. -x + 1

14. (a) 4n - 3

(b) 3n + 7 = n - 1

15. (a) n

(b) 7 dollars

(c) 3n - 1

(d) 4 dollars

(e) 7(3n - 1) dollars

(f) 4n dollars

(g) 25n - 7 dollars

Chapter 2 Test B

1. -64

2. -64

3. 16

4. 3

5. 6

6. 9

7. 14

8. -5

9. $6x^2y^2 + 4xy - 4x^3$

10. $6x^5y^9$

11. x^2y

12. $5x^3y^4$

13. -4x + 10

14. (a) 4(n - 3)

(b) 5n + 6 = n + 10

15. (a) 6 dollars

(b) n

(c) 5 dollars

(d) 4n + 1

(e) 5n dollars

(f) 6(4n + 1) dollars

(g) 29n + 6 dollars

Chapter 3 Test A

1. (a) identity   (b) conditional
   (c) contradiction

2. (a) no   (b) yes
   (c) no

3. (a) 3   (b) -2
   (c) 4   (d) $x \geq 2$
   (e) $-3 < x < 2$

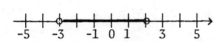   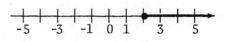

4. 5 and 27   5. 10 dimes and 6 quarters

6. 120 miles

Chapter 3 Test B

1. (a) conditional   (b) contradiction
   (c) identity

2. (a) yes   (b) no
   (c) yes

3. (a) 1   (b) -3
   (c) 5   (d) $x > 4$
   (e) $1 \leq x \leq 2$

4. 60 children's tickets   5. 7 inches, 7 inches, 11 inches

6. 6

Cumulative Review: Chapters 1-3

1. -9   2. -24

3. 1   4. 3

5. 81   6. -81

7. a^{12}

8. $5b^8$

9. $2r^3s^5 - 4r^5s^3$

10. $y^2 - 3y - 2$

11. $6x^2y - 15x^2z$

12. $-30x^2yz$

13. $6t^4u^2$

14. $-t^3u^2 + 6t^4$

15. $4p + 32q$

16. $10c^5$

17. $v^3w^4 + 9v^5w^5$

18. x^3yz^3

19. $8a^2b^2 - 8ab$

20. $-2rt + 2t$

21. $-23h - 120$

22. $n - 2n^2 + n^3$

23. 0

24. $-d^3$

25. 0

26. 36

27. 12

28. -14

29. 9

30. -9

31. 3

32. 0

33. 2

34. 3

35. -2

36. 0

37. -5

38. $y < 3$

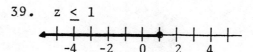

39. $z \le 1$

40. -5

41. $0 \le c < 3$

42. $1 < y < 2$

43. 6

44. 5

45. 8 and 19

46. width = 4, length = 18

47. 2 p.m.

48. 13 white geraniums

Cumulative Test: Chapters 1-3

1. (a) 19   (b) -64

2. (a) 7   (b) 5

3. (a) $2x^3 - 4x^2 + 7x$ (b) $x + 8y$

    (c) $-a^4b + 8a^2b^2$ (d) 0

    (e) $3u^2v^6 - 9u^5v^4$ (f) $3 - 6b + 12b^2 - 8b^3$

4. (a) 3   (b) 5

    (c) $c < 8$ (d) identity

    (e) 4   (f) contradiction

5. (a) $x > 5$ (b) $-1 < x \leq 0$

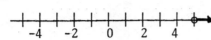   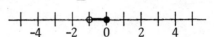

6. (a) 46 and 10   (b) 3 p.m.
    (c) 18 full-sized cars

Chapter 4 Test A

1. (a) $-\dfrac{4}{7}$ (b) y^5

    (c) $\dfrac{3x}{2}$ (d) $-\dfrac{7b^3}{a^3}$

2. (a) $\dfrac{9x^2}{2y}$ (b) $\dfrac{1}{8y^3}$

    (c) 1   (d) $\dfrac{b}{14a}$

    (e) $\dfrac{c}{2}$ (f) $\dfrac{c^2}{16}$

    (g) $\dfrac{2}{x^2}$ (h) $\dfrac{u}{10}$

    (i) $\dfrac{17}{12y}$ (j) $\dfrac{4x - 25y}{10x^2y^3}$

    (k) $-\dfrac{1}{x}$

3. (a) 12   (b) $x \le -1$
    (c) 2   (d) 12

4. 2.54 meters   5. 10

6. 5 nickels, 20 pennies, 60 dimes

7. $5000 at 7%, $6000 at 10%

8. width = 12 cm, length = 25 cm

9. 80 liters

Chapter 4 Test B

1. (a) $\frac{3}{8}$ (b) z^8

    (c) $-\frac{5x^3}{3}$ (d) $-\frac{5p}{2q}$

2. (a) $\frac{xy^2}{18}$ (b) $\frac{8}{x^3}$

    (c) 1   (d) $\frac{d}{12c}$

    (e) $\frac{m}{3}$ (f) $\frac{m^2}{36}$

    (g) $\frac{2}{x^3}$ (h) $\frac{11v}{18}$

    (i) $\frac{11}{20r}$ (j) $\frac{9b^2 + 20a}{12a^2b^3}$

    (k) $\frac{2}{x^2}$

3. (a) 24   (b) $x < 3$
    (c) 4   (d) 60

4. 5.66 cubic meters   5. 5

6. 10 quarters, 20 nickels, 30 dimes

7. 3 p.m.

8. $1500 at 8%, $3000 at 9%

9. 12 gallons of 25% solution, 8 gallons of 50% solution

Chapter 5 Test A

1. $\frac{1}{72}$

2. $\frac{1}{x^5}$

3. x^6

4. $\frac{x^4}{y}$

5. $-\frac{4y}{x}$

6. (a) 5

(b) -1; 7

(c) 6

7. $-30x^6y^6$

8. $10x^4y^3 - 6x^5y^5$

9. $2y^3$

10. $10x^3 - x^2 + 5x + 4$

11. $x^3 + 3x^2 - 4x + 4$

12. $16x - 18$

13. $2z - 5$

14. (a) 2.58×10^5

(b) 2.58×10^{-2}

15. 2.4×10^5

Chapter 5 Test B

1. $\frac{29}{100}$

2. $\frac{1}{x^6}$

3. x^5

4. $\frac{y^2}{x}$

5. $-\frac{3x^2}{y^4}$

6. (a) 5

(b) 3; -5

(c) 7

7. $-24x^6y^8$

8. $8x^5y^5 - 12x^3y^7$

9. x^3y

10. $6x^3 + 7x^2 - 9x + 2$

11. $2x^3 - 3x^2 - 3x + 1$

12. $12x + 8$

13. $2y - 3$

14. (a) 7.95×10^6

(b) 7.95×10^{-4}

15. 5×10^{-9}

Chapter 6 Test A

1. $2x^2(x - 1)(x - 3)$

2. $3x^2y^2(x + 4y - 3)$

3. $(x + 4)(x + 9)$

4. $(x - 3y)(x + 4y)$

5. $4x^3(x - 2)(x + 2)$

6. $7(x^2 + 2x + 2)$

7. $(x - 8)(x - 8)$

8. $(2x - 1)(x - 4)$

9. not factorable

10. $(8x - 3)(x + 2)$

11. $(xy + 3)(xy + 3)$

12. $\frac{2}{a} + \frac{3b}{2} - \frac{6}{5ab}$

13. quotient: $3x^2 - x + 2$; remainder: -11

Chapter 6 Test B

1. $5x^2(x + 1)(x + 2)$

2. $7x^3y^3(y - 4x - 2)$

3. $(x - 3)(x - 8)$

4. $(x - 9y)(x + 2y)$

5. $3x^2(x - 3)(x + 3)$

6. $4(x^2 + 3x + 4)$

7. $(x + 9)(x + 9)$

8. $(3x - 5)(x + 3)$

9. not factorable

10. $9x^2 - 14x - 8$

11. $(xy - 5)(xy - 5)$

12. $\frac{3}{q} - \frac{4p}{3} + \frac{3}{2pq}$

13. quotient: $2x^2 + 3x + 9$; remainder: 28

Cumulative Review: Chapters 4-6

1. $-\frac{8}{5}$

2. $\frac{3}{8x^5}$

3. $\frac{9b}{5a}$

4. $\frac{1}{2c}$

5. $\frac{16x}{9}$

6. $\frac{4x^3}{81}$

7. $\frac{16x^2 - 9x}{54}$

8. $\frac{2}{y^3}$

9. 1

10. 0

11. $x^2 - 5x - 14$

12. $x^3 + 3x^2 - 5x - 14$

13. $x^4 + 2x^3 - 4x^2 - 5x - 14$

14. $5t^3 - 15t^2 - 20t$

15. $\dfrac{4a^2b^6}{9c^6}$

16. $\dfrac{25a^6c^2}{49b^2}$

17. $18r^2 - 3rs - 10s^2$

18. $5m^2 - 12m$

19. $\dfrac{49}{15d}$

20. $\dfrac{9\ell - 10k}{12k\ell}$

21. $\dfrac{25v + 12u}{40u^3v^3}$

22. $\dfrac{3}{16u^5v^5}$

23. $36x$

24. $4x^2 - 7x$

25. $\dfrac{3}{8}$

26. $\dfrac{10 - y}{4y}$

27. $9m^3 + 27m^2 - m - 3$

28. $x^4 - 29x^2 + 100$

29. $\dfrac{3x^4 - 2x^2 + 4}{x^3}$

30. $\dfrac{18q^2 + 15pq - 14p^2}{12p^3q^3}$

31. $-2z^2 + 2z + 7$

32. $4x^2 - 3xy - 2y^2$

33. (a) 6

    (b) -5

34. $4x^4 + 0x^3 - 3x^2 + 2x - 1$

35. $\dfrac{x}{3} - 3x^2$

36. $\dfrac{9}{4t} + \dfrac{3}{st} - \dfrac{3}{2s}$

37. quotient: $a - 7$; remainder: 28

38. quotient: $3y^2 - 5y - 2$; remainder: 0

39. quotient: $6t^2 + 8t + 4$; remainder: -5

40. quotient: $b^3 + b^2 + b + 4$; remainder: 6

41. $\dfrac{7}{2}$

42. $\dfrac{5}{36}$

43. $\dfrac{1}{x^{11}}$

44. $\dfrac{1}{y^5}$

45. $\dfrac{3}{x^2}$

46. ab^3

47. $\dfrac{27v^{12}}{4u^{12}}$

48. $\dfrac{3n^3}{4m^4}$

49. 1.23×10^8

50. 9.75×10^{-6}

51. 1.2×10^{-2} or .012

52. 6.25×10^{-1} or .625

53. 3

54. 2

55. 0

56. identity

57. $-\frac{2}{3}$

58. $\frac{24}{5}$

59. 2

60. -6

61. $x(x - 8)$

62. $(x - 2)(x - 6)$

63. $(x - 9)(x + 1)$

64. not factorable

65. $2ab(2a^2b - 3a + 4b^2)$

66. $2r^4s^4(2s - r)(2s + r)$

67. $2(3v - 4)(3v + 4)$

68. $2(9v^2 + 16)$

69. $t^3(t - 7)(t + 7)$

70. $(3s - 10)(s + 1)$

71. $(2t - 3)(3t - 2)$

72. $(6t - 1)(t - 6)$

73. $6(t - 1)(t - 1)$

74. not factorable

75. $-(x + 8)(x - 7)$

76. $(x - 25y)(x - 4y)$

77. not factorable

78. $(x + a)(x + b)$

79. $(x - 2y)(x + 3)$

80. $(9x^2 + 4y^2)(3x + 2y)(3x - 2y)$

81. 7, 9, 11, 13

82. 75 single people

83. $3

84. 20 liters of 20% solution, 40 liters of 25% solution, 40 liters of 40% solution

85. 6 $5 bills, 17 $10 bills

Cumulative Test: Chapters 4-6

1. $5x^2 - 7x - 17$

2. $\frac{4a^5}{3b^3}$

3. $3s^4t + 2s^3t^2 - 17s^2t^3 + 12t^4$

4. $\frac{6p^3}{r}$

5. $2n^2 - 1$

6. $\frac{3y}{ab}$

7. 1

8. $\frac{1}{2x^5}$

9. $\frac{9d^2 - 10c^2}{12c^3d^3}$

10. $\dfrac{4\ell}{k} - \dfrac{5k}{2\ell}$

11. quotient: $x^2 + 2x - 3$; remainder: 6

12. quotient: $x^3 - 3x^2 - 2x + 6$; remainder: 0

13. $\dfrac{2b}{25ac^6}$

14. (a) 5.31×10^{-7} (b) 5.31×10^8

15. 1×10^{-1} or .1   16. $2x^2 + x - 3$

17. 20   18. -2

19. $(x - 2)(x - 3)$ 20. $(x - 6)(x + 1)$

21. $2s^4t^4(t - 2s)(t + 2s)$ 22. $10(x^2 + 3x - 7)$

23. $(3y - 7)(y + 2)$ 24. $(12z + 25)(z - 1)$

25. $(2c + 1)(c - 3)$ 26. $(x^2 + y^2)(x - 2)$

27. 3.79 miles   28. 25 and 27

29. \$9

30. \$1000 at 8%, \$4000 at 13%

Chapter 7 Test A

1. $\dfrac{3(x + 3)}{x - 9}$ 2. $\dfrac{3x}{x - 3}$

3. $\dfrac{2(x - 6)}{(x - 2)(x - 4)}$ 4. $\dfrac{x}{2(x + 2)}$

5. $\dfrac{3}{2(x - 4)}$ 6. $\dfrac{x + 1}{x - 3}$

7. $\dfrac{4}{x + 1}$ 8. 4

9. $y = \dfrac{3 - 3z}{6x + 2}$ 10. no solution

11. -8 12. 12 hours

Chapter 7 Test B

1. $\dfrac{x - 16}{2(x - 4)}$ 2. $\dfrac{x + 4}{2x}$

3. $\dfrac{3(x + 3)}{(x + 5)(x + 2)}$

4. $\dfrac{x(x - 3)}{3}$

5. $-\dfrac{2}{3(x + 9)}$

6. $\dfrac{x - 1}{x + 4}$

7. $\dfrac{3}{x - 1}$

8. 5

9. $q = \dfrac{8r + 16}{12p - 1}$

10. no solution

11. $\dfrac{4}{13}$

12. 2 mph

Chapter 8 Test A

1. yes

2. (a) -3   (b) 12
    (c) -4

3. (a)   (b)

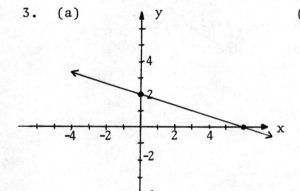
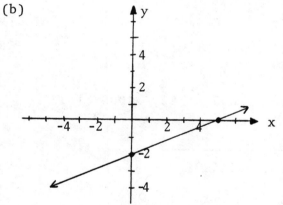

    (c)   (d)

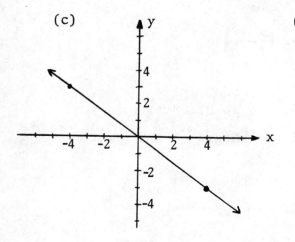
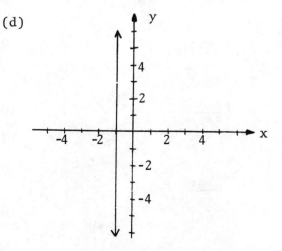

(e)

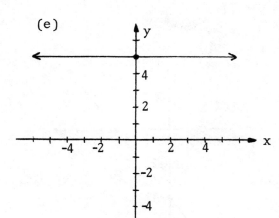

4.   -1

5. $y + 1 = -\frac{2}{5}(x - 6)$ or $y = -\frac{2}{5}x + \frac{7}{5}$

6. $y = -2x + 7$

7. $y = 3; x = -2$

8.

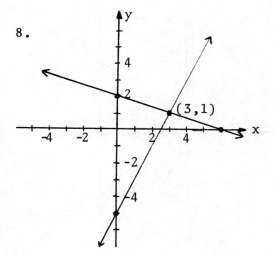

(3,1)

9.   (a) (4,-1)

    (b) (0,2)

    (c) no solution

10.   plums: 60¢/pound;
      peaches: 50¢/pound

Chapter 8 Test B

1.   no

2.   (a) 2   (b) -3

    (c) 10

3.   (a)

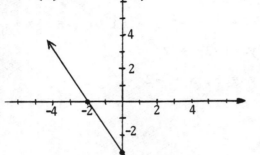

(b)

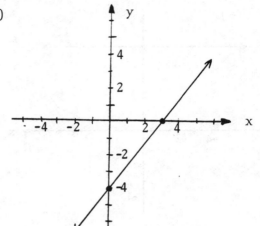

(c)

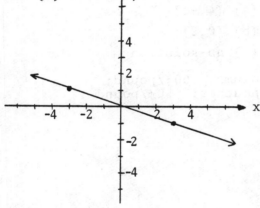

(d)

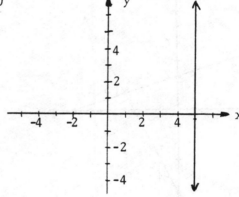

(e)

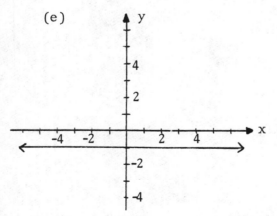

4.   1

5. $y + 4 = -\frac{3}{4}(x - 1)$ or $y = -\frac{3}{4}x - \frac{13}{4}$

6. $y = -4x + 10$

7. $y = -2;\ x = 4$

8.

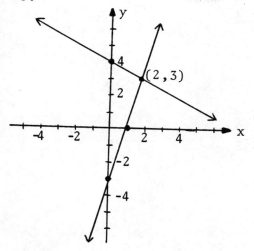

9. (a) $(-3,-1)$

    (b) $(3,0)$

    (c) no solution

10. veal: \$3/package;
     chicken: \$2.50/package

Chapter 9 Test A

1. $4x^5y^6$

2. $18\sqrt{2}$

3. $x^2\sqrt{5x}$

4. $\sqrt{15}x^3y^2$

5. 0

6. $\dfrac{3y^2\sqrt{2y}}{2}$

7. $2x + \sqrt{3x} - 18$

8. $2\sqrt{6a}$

9. $3 - \sqrt{2}$

10. $2(\sqrt{x} + 2\sqrt{y})$

11. yes

Chapter 9 Test B

1. $6x^7y^4$

2. $-8\sqrt{2}$

3. $2x^2\sqrt{3x}$

4. $\sqrt{10}x^2y^4$

5. 0

6. $\dfrac{4z^3\sqrt{3z}}{3}$

7. $3x - 7\sqrt{2x} - 12$

8. $-2\sqrt{7b}$

9. $4 + \sqrt{10}$

10. $3(\sqrt{x} - 3\sqrt{y})$

11. yes

Cumulative Review: Chapters 7-9

1. $2a^{10}b^{15}$

2. $\dfrac{x + 1}{x}$

3. $\dfrac{2t - 3}{2t + 3}$

4. $\dfrac{w^3 z^2}{3}\sqrt{w}$

5. $\dfrac{8\sqrt{11}}{11}$

6. $4(\sqrt{11} + 3)$

7. $3(\sqrt{14} - \sqrt{10})$

8. $3\sqrt{7x}$

9. $8\sqrt{3}$

10. $2u^3 v^3 \sqrt{21v}$

11. $\dfrac{x + 4}{5x(3x + 2)}$

12. $5\sqrt{6rs}$

13. $\dfrac{16c + 9d}{12c^2 d^2}$

14. $-\sqrt{30}$

15. 0

16. $\dfrac{x^2 + 2x + 1}{x^2 + 1}$

17. $6a + 5\sqrt{ab} - 6b$

18. $\dfrac{m + n}{2}$

19. $\dfrac{2}{(x + 2)(x + 3)}$

20. $3p^4 q^2 \sqrt{2q}$

21. $\dfrac{9\sqrt{6}}{8}$

22. $\dfrac{-a + 6}{6a(a - 2)}$

23. 17

24. $\dfrac{2(s - 3)}{s + 3}$

25. 2

26. $x^2 + 10x + 25$

27. 36

28. $\dfrac{4}{r + 4}$

29. 6

30. 8

31. $s = 2 - r$

32. $u = 12(9v - 1)$

33. no solution

34. 3

35. -1

36. no solution

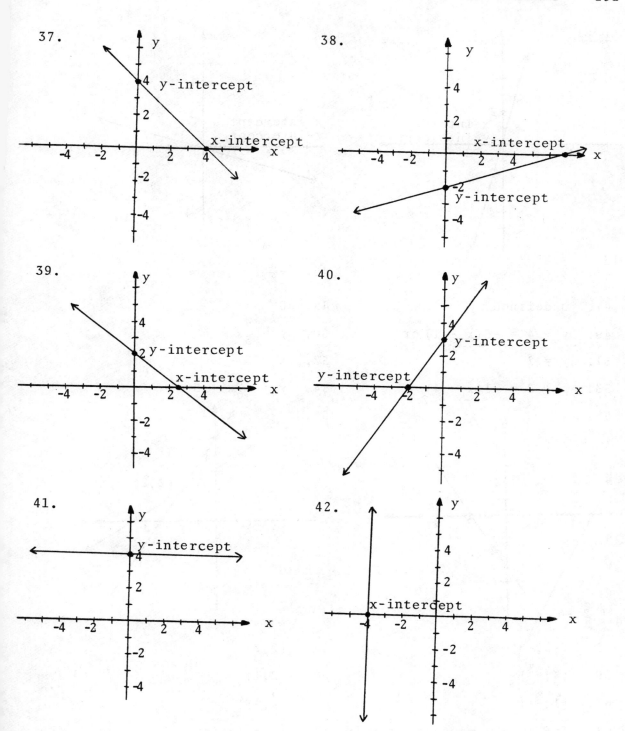

43.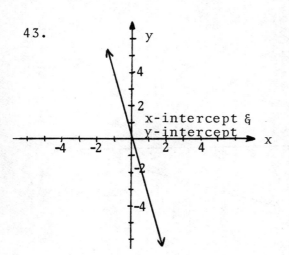

x-intercept &
y-intercept

44.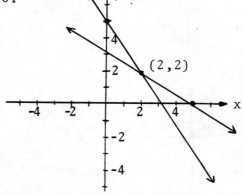

x-intercept &
y-intercept

45. 2

46. $-\frac{5}{2}$

47. undefined

48. 0

49. $y + 4 = -5(x - 1)$ or
      $y = -5x + 1$

50. $y = \frac{2}{3}x - 6$

51. $y = 2$

52. $x = 6$

53. $y + 2 = -1(x - 4)$ or
      $y = -x + 2$

54. $y = -\frac{5}{6}x + 5$

55.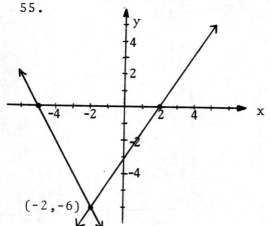

$(-2,-6)$

56.

$(2,2)$

57. $(-2,-6)$

58. $(2,2)$

59. $(\frac{2}{3},-\frac{3}{4})$

60. $(2,1)$

61. $(1,-1)$

62. $(\frac{2}{5},-3)$

63. infinitely many solutions:
      $\{(x,y) \mid 2x - 5y = 10\}$

64. no solution

65. $1\frac{1}{2}$ hours

66. 8 kph

67. $\frac{4}{13}$

68. weekly rate: $95;
     daily rate: $20

Cumulative Test: Chapters 7-9

1. $10a^5$

2. $\frac{x(x-2)}{x+2}$

3. $rs^2t^4\sqrt{6rs}$

4. $\frac{2a-3}{a-3}$

5. $\frac{9\sqrt{10}}{2}$

6. $5(\sqrt{10}+1)$

7. $\frac{10x}{(x+3)(x-2)}$

8. $5\sqrt{10}-5\sqrt{15}$

9. $\frac{u+2}{2(u+1)}$

10. $\frac{2}{a+1}$

11. $\frac{6}{x(x+2)}$

12. $\frac{(r+5)(r+2)}{(r+4)(r+3)}$

13. $bc^4\sqrt{10b}$

14. $12w+10\sqrt{6w}-48$

15. $\frac{ab}{4(b-a)}$

16. $\frac{\sqrt{7}(\sqrt{11}+\sqrt{3})}{4}$

17. 4

18. $w=\frac{22v-16}{4k-3}$

19. no solution

20.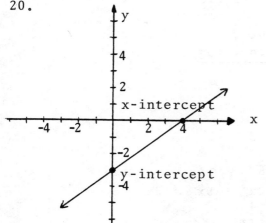

21.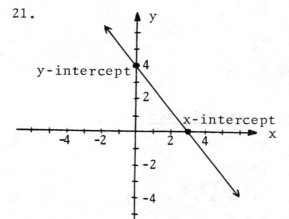

22. -2

23. $y - 5 = -2(x + 3)$ or $y = -2x - 1$

24. -1

25. $(-1,-3)$

26. no solution

27. 11:30 a.m.

28. 9 dimes, 6 quarters

Chapter 10 Test A

1. ± 3

2. $\dfrac{2 \pm \sqrt{6}}{2}$

3. $3, -\dfrac{1}{3}$

4. $\dfrac{3}{2}, -\dfrac{1}{2}$

5. $\dfrac{2 \pm \sqrt{3}}{2}$

6. $0, 2$

7. $\dfrac{3}{2}$

8. $\dfrac{-1 \pm \sqrt{5}}{2}$

9. $2, \dfrac{1}{3}$

10. $\dfrac{8 \pm 3\sqrt{6}}{2}$

Chapter 10 Test B

1. ± 5

2. $\dfrac{-2 \pm \sqrt{2}}{2}$

3. $\dfrac{2}{5}, -1$

4. $1, -\dfrac{5}{3}$

5. $\dfrac{1}{9}, 1$

6. $-3 \pm 2\sqrt{3}$

7. $-\dfrac{3}{4}$

8. $0, 2$

9. $1, -\dfrac{2}{3}$

10. $\dfrac{-9 \pm 5\sqrt{3}}{3}$

Practice Final Exam

1. 2

2. 13

3. 10

4. $\dfrac{6}{5}$

5. $-x^3 - x^2y^2 + 2x^2y$

6. $2x^3 - 5x^2 + 3x - 3$

7. $\dfrac{5 - 4x}{40y}$

8. $\dfrac{x^4}{y^{14}}$

9. $\dfrac{(x - 5)(x + 5)}{(x - 4)(x + 4)}$

10. $\dfrac{2}{x^2 - 1}$

11. $6x\sqrt{6x}$

12. $3 + \sqrt{3}$

13. $-3 < x \le 2$

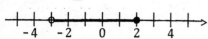

14. $x > 1$

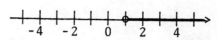

15. -2

16. -6

17. 4

18. $0, 3$

19. $-\dfrac{2}{3}, \dfrac{3}{2}$

20. $\dfrac{-3 \pm \sqrt{14}}{5}$

21. 1.8×10^5

22. $2x^2(2x - 3)(x + 6)$

23. $(x + 2y)(x - y)(x + y)$

24. quotient: $2x^2 - 2x + 2$; remainder: -3

25.

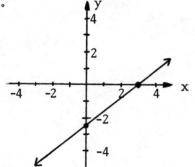

26. $y = 4x - 8$

27. $(1, -\dfrac{1}{3})$

28. 12 years old

29. 30 red chips

30. $4200

31. 3 hours

32. $-\dfrac{1}{2}$ and $\dfrac{3}{2}$